D1373101

ndamental Mathematical Structures | *Fundamental Mathematical Structures*

Fundamental Mathematical Structures

ALGEBRAIC SYSTEMS

Ralph Crouch

David Beckman

Scott, Foresman and Company

Glenview, Illinois; Atlanta; Dallas; Palo Alto; Oakland, N.J.

This is one of the books in the Fundamental Mathematical Structures series, which is a part of the Basic Mathematics Program, published by Scott, Foresman and Company.

The major authors of the Fundamental Mathematical Structures series, jointly responsible for the content of all the books and individually responsible for a particular book, are
Paul J. Kelly, Professor of Mathematics, University of California, Santa Barbara (Geometry);
Charles J. A. Halberg, Jr., Associate Professor of Mathematics, University of California, Riverside (Elementary Functions);
Ralph Crouch, Head, Department of Mathematics, Drexel Institute, Philadelphia (Linear Algebra and Algebraic Systems).

The advisory authors of the series, critical readers of all the manuscripts, are
Henry Van Engen, Professor of Education and Mathematics, University of Wisconsin;
Maurice L. Hartung, Professor of Education, University of Chicago;
Harold C. Trimble, Professor of Education, Ohio State University;
Michael Millar, Assistant Professor of Mathematics, State College of Iowa.

The specialists in mathematics education, serving as consultants to the authors, are
Emil J. Berger, Coördinator of Mathematics, St. Paul Public Schools, St. Paul, Minnesota;
Ray W. Cleveland, Associate Professor, Jersey City State College and Mathematics Consultant, Rahway Public Schools, Rahway, New Jersey;
A. B. Evenson, Assistant Superintendent of Secondary Education, Edmonton Public Schools, Edmonton, Alberta, Canada;
Ray Walch, Director of Mathematics, K-12, Public Schools, Westport, Connecticut.

The responsibility for assuring that the content of this book is appropriate for its intended audience is that of
David Beckman, Operations Research Analyst, Peat, Marwick, Caywood, Schiller, and Co., Chicago, and Former Head, Mathematics Department, Proviso East High School, Maywood, Illinois.

A critical mathematical review of the manuscript was prepared by
E. A. Walker, Professor of Mathematics, New Mexico State University.

This book was designed by William Nicoll and illustrated by Paul Hazelrigg.

Regional offices of Scott, Foresman and Company are located in Atlanta, Dallas, Glenview, Palo Alto, and Oakland, New Jersey.

Preface

This book is intended to serve as an introduction to the basic structure and elementary properties of the mathematical systems known as groups, rings, integral domains, and fields. These systems have been and continue to be studied in abstract algebra, which is one of the major branches of modern mathematics.

Some of the material in this book, particularly in Chapter 1, will be new to you only in the sense that it represents a new approach to old ideas from earlier courses. Even the totally new concepts are introduced and illustrated by familiar examples, such as the system of real numbers and its various subsystems or the set of all polynomials with rational coefficients.

It is the hope of the authors that from this course you will gain knowledge of new and important mathematical ideas, develop an understanding of and skill in the construction of proofs, and acquire an appreciation of the nature of an abstract mathematical system. The new concepts you will meet include the defining properties of various algebraic systems, special kinds of functions called isomorphisms and homomorphisms, and important examples of systems such as symmetric groups, cyclic groups, and polynomial rings. The proofs that you will be required to understand and construct include indirect proofs, inductive proofs, and proofs by counterexample. As you develop insight into abstract systems, you will see that if a theorem is proved for a general system, then it is unnecessary to prove it as it applies to a specific example of the system. Further, as your understanding and appreciation of an algebraic system increases, you will be able to distinguish between those properties of a system that automatically hold for a subsystem and those that do not.

Some of the early ideas of group theory grew out of geometric and physical situations. For instance, a particular subset of the set of all transformations of a square forms a group under the operation of composition, and the structures of certain kinds of molecules and crystals found in nature have the properties of a group. Today, abstract algebra has practical applications in physics and in the solution of engineering and industrial problems. However, it would have been necessary to introduce a great deal of specialized vocabulary in describing these problems, so no problems of this kind are included among the examples and exercises. Instead, it is our hope that the elementary ideas and skills introduced here will induce you to take more advanced courses in modern algebra and that, if you do so, these ideas and skills will provide a good foundation.

Ralph Crouch

David Beckman

Contents

Chapter 1 **Sets, relations, and functions**

1 *Set notation* 10
2 *Subsets of a set* 13
3 *Cartesian product* 18
4 *Relations* 22
5 *Domain and range of a relation* 27
6 *Functions* 31
7 *Binary operations* 36
8 *Union and intersection of sets* 39
9 *Composition of functions* 44
10 *Equivalence relations* 49
11 *The integers modulo* n 54

Chapter 2 **Groups**

12 *Closure of binary operations* 60
13 *The associative property of binary operations* 70
14 *Semi-groups and the existence of an identity* 77
15 *Semi-groups and the existence of inverses* 82
16 *Properties of groups* 86
17 *Symmetric groups and permutation groups* 96
18 *Commutative groups* 111
19 *Subgroups of a group* 117
20 *Intersection and union of subgroups* 124
21 *Cyclic groups* 131
22 *Classification of cyclic groups* 140
23* *The Cartesian product of groups* 151
[* *indicates optional sections.*]
24* *Construction of finite commutative groups* 160

Contents, continued

Chapter 3 **Rings and integral domains**

25 *Rings* 170
26 *Commutative rings with identity* 181
27 *Elementary properties of a ring* 189
28 *Subrings* 192
29* *Ideals* 198
30* *Homomorphisms* 202
31 *Polynomial rings* 208
32 *Integral domains* 217

Chapter 4 **Fields**

33 *The properties of a field* 227
34 *The characteristic of a field* 236
35 *Subfields* 244
36 *Simple field extensions* 251

Answers to selected exercises 261
Definitions and theorems 289
Index 300

Fundamental Mathematical Structures

ALGEBRAIC SYSTEMS

Chapter **1**

Sets, relations, and functions

1 *Set notation*

2 *Subsets of a set*

3 *Cartesian product*

4 *Relations*

5 *Domain and range of a relation*

6 *Functions*

7 *Binary operations*

8 *Union and intersection of sets*

9 *Composition of functions*

10 *Equivalence relations*

11 *The integers modulo* n

Introduction The main purpose of this chapter is to familiarize you with some fundamentals that are pertinent to a study of algebraic systems. The ideas, terminology, and notation presented in this chapter will be used throughout the book. The subsequent chapters will be concerned with a development of mathematical systems.

Much of the mathematics written recently, beginning with textbooks for the elementary grades and extending through high school and university level texts and research papers that give new mathematical results, is expressed in the language of sets. It seems appropriate, therefore, to begin this book with an elementary discussion of sets. This modest discussion is not to be interpreted as a course in set theory, which is a deep and somewhat difficult branch of mathematics. Rather, our concern is to see how the language of sets can be used to achieve precise expression of mathematical ideas.

Set notation 1/1

Most subject matters, including mathematics, have undefined terms and relations that are used in defining new concepts. The idea of a *set* is one such term in mathematics, and no attempt will be made to define this word in terms of other words. However, from time to time, such words as *collection* and *class* will be used interchangeably with the word *set*. The following examples are given to illustrate the idea of a set.

Examples 1 The set of prime numbers that are less than 100
2 The set of nonnegative integers
3 The set of persons who have bowled a 300 game
4 The set of factors of 24
5 The set of axioms for the real numbers
6 The set of police captains in Pittsburgh

Observe that each of the sets consists of *elements* that may also be called *members* of the set. To discuss sets and their members with ease and convenience, some notation will be adopted. Usually, capital letters, such as A, B, and so on, will denote sets. Lowercase italic letters, such as a, b, and so on, will denote the elements of a set. The symbol $\in$ will be used to show set membership. For example, we will write the sentence "$a \in B$" to mean "The element a is a member of set B." To denote "is not a member of," we will use the symbol $\notin$. The notation "$b \notin B$" means "The element b is *not* a member of set B."

In each of the examples above, we denoted a set by describing it. A second way to denote a set is by a tabulation of its members. In such a tabulation, the members of the set are listed within braces. Several sets are tabulated below.

Examples 1 {summer, fall, winter, spring}
2 $\{4, 1, 2\}$
3 $\{\frac{1}{2}, \frac{2}{3}, \frac{3}{4}, \frac{4}{5}, \ldots\}$
4 $\{\ldots, \sqrt{-3}, \sqrt{-2}, i, 0, 1, \sqrt{2}, \sqrt{3}, \ldots\}$
5 $\{-52, -51, -50, \ldots, -3\}$

In examples 1 and 2 all of the elements of the sets are listed. When all the elements of a set are listed, the tabulation is a *complete* tabulation. It often is either impossible or impractical to list all the members of a set. In such cases, we make a *partial* tabulation (examples 3, 4, and 5). When a partial tabulation is given, it must be made clear what the omitted elements are. Notice that in examples 3 and 4 the sets continue indefinitely and, therefore, are impossible to tabulate completely. We could have made a complete tabulation of the set in example 5; however, since the set contains 50 elements, it is obviously more convenient to make a partial tabulation.

In example 1, we tabulated the set of seasons of the year. Does {fall, winter, spring, summer} contain the same members as the set {summer, fall, winter, spring}? As you can see, both of these sets are the set of seasons of the year. Therefore, a change in the order in which the elements are tabulated does not change the set membership. We are led to the following definition.

Definition 1/1 If A and B are sets, then A and B are *equal* (denoted by A = B) if and only if each element of A is an element of B and each element of B is an element of A.

It follows from Definition 1/1 that the set of seasons of the year can be tabulated in 4!, or 24, ways, since the set contains 4 elements. The set in example 2 can be tabulated in 3!, or 6, ways. If we were to list all the elements of the set in example 5, this set could be tabulated in 50! ways. The pattern in which the elements are listed for examples 3 and 4 is important because it shows what the unlisted elements are. We would not normally tabulate these sets in any other way; however, it should be clear that others are possible. For example 3, $\{\frac{1}{2}, \frac{2}{3}, \frac{3}{4}, \frac{4}{5}, \ldots\} = \{\ldots, \frac{4}{5}, \frac{3}{4}, \frac{2}{3}, \frac{1}{2}\}$. In what other way can the set in example 4 be tabulated as a partial tabulation?

Two useful sets of numbers are the set of *counting numbers* and the set of *integers*. They are tabulated below.

$$C = \{1, 2, 3, 4, \ldots\}.$$
$$I = \{\ldots, -3, -2, -1, 0, 1, 2, \ldots\}.$$

Throughout this book, we will use the letter C to represent the set of counting numbers and the letter I to represent the set of integers.

A third way of expressing a set is by a *standard description*. A standard description of the set of integers greater than 4 is $\{x \mid x \in I \text{ and } x > 4\}$, which is read as follows: "the set whose members are all x such that x is an integer and x is greater than 4," or, more simply, "the set of all integers greater than 4." The vertical mark is read "such that"; to the right of this symbol is given a condition that x must satisfy. Several other examples of standard descriptions are given below.

Examples 1 $\{x \mid x \in C \text{ and } x \text{ is odd}\}$
2 $\{x \mid x \in C \text{ and } x \text{ is even}\}$
3 $\{x \mid x \in I \text{ and } x \text{ is odd}\}$
4 $\{x \mid x \in I \text{ and } x \text{ is even}\}$

Examples 5 $\{x \mid x \text{ is a day of the week}\}$
6 $\{x \mid x \in C, x \text{ is odd, and } 0 < x < 6\}$

The sets in examples 1, 2, 3, and 4 have the names *odd counting numbers*, *even counting numbers*, *odd integers*, and *even integers*, respectively. The symbols O_C, E_C, O_I, and E_I will be used in this book to represent these sets. We have tabulated these sets below.

$$O_C = \{1, 3, 5, 7, \ldots\}.$$
$$E_C = \{2, 4, 6, 8, \ldots\}.$$
$$O_I = \{\ldots, -3, -1, 1, 3, \ldots\}.$$
$$E_I = \{\ldots, -4, -2, 0, 2, 4, \ldots\}.$$

The sets tabulated above are *infinite* sets because we cannot specify how many members are in each set by means of a nonnegative integer. Several other infinite sets are given below.

Examples 1 $\{x \mid x \in I \text{ and } x > -2\} = \{-1, 0, 1, 2, \ldots\}$.
2 $\{2, 3, 5, 7, 11, 13, 17, \ldots\} = \{x \mid x \in C \text{ and } x \text{ is prime}\}$.
3 $\{\ldots, -14, -7, 0, 7, 14, \ldots\} = \{7x \mid x \in I\}$.

The following sets are *finite* because a nonnegative integer may be used to specify the number of elements in each set.

Examples 1 $\{1, 7, 11\}$
2 $\{x \mid x \text{ is a letter in the Greek alphabet}\}$
3 $\{x \mid x \in C \text{ and } x < 1{,}568{,}432\}$

A particular finite set that merits special notice is the set with no elements in it. This set is referred to as the *empty set* or the *null set*. Two symbols frequently used for the empty set are $\{\ \}$ and $\emptyset$. The empty set is a finite set because the number of elements it contains is indicated by the nonnegative integer 0. Some descriptions of the empty set are given below.

Examples 1 The set of states in the United States bordering Alaska
2 $\{x \mid x \in C \text{ and } x < 1\}$
3 The set of months containing exactly 25 days

Exercises

1 Tabulate each of the following sets.

a The set of months of the year

b The set of planets in the earth's solar system

c The set of states in the United States that are adjacent to the Mississippi River

d The set of counting numbers less than 100

e The set of odd counting numbers greater than 100

f The set of integers greater than -22 and less than 39

g The set of integers greater than 52 and less than -7

h The set of integers that are neither positive nor negative

2 Write a standard description of each of the following sets.

a $\{\ldots, -20, -18, -16, -14\}$

You will find the answers for the exercises that are followed by the word *Answer* in the back of the book.

b {April, June, September, November} *Answer*

c {a, e, i, o, u}

d $\{11, 13, 15, 17, \ldots\}$

e $\{-7, -6, -5, \ldots, 4\}$

3 Tabulate each of the following sets.

a $\{x \mid x$ is a major league baseball team that is located west of the Mississippi River$\}$

b $\{y \mid y \in \mathrm{I}$ and $-3y > 0\}$

c $\{z \mid z$ is a state of the United States bordering on the Gulf of Mexico$\}$

d $\{x \mid x \in \mathrm{C}$ and $x \leqq 999\}$

e $\{z^2 \mid z \in \mathrm{I}$ and $-7 < z < 4\}$ *Answer*

f $\{2y \mid y \in \mathrm{E_C}\}$

g $\left\{y \mid y \in \mathrm{I} \text{ and } \frac{y}{3} < 12\right\}$

h $\{x \mid x \in \mathrm{I},\ 2x > 10, \text{ and } 3x < 25\}$

i $\{w \mid w \in \mathrm{I},\ x \in \mathrm{C}, \text{ and } 2w = x^2\}$ *Answer*

j $\{n \mid n \in \mathrm{C},\ x \in \mathrm{I}, \text{ and } n - 2 = 19x\}$

We have labeled the more difficult exercises, like the following one, with a "diamond."

◆ **k** $\{n \mid n, x \in \mathrm{I},\ n^2 = 2x + 1, \text{ and } n + 1 = 4x\}$

4 Which of the sets given in exercises 1, 2, and 3 are finite?

Subsets of a set **2/1**

Some examples of sets of numbers were given in the previous section. Among them was the set of integers, tabulated below.

$$\mathrm{I} = \{\ldots, -3, -2, -1, 0, 1, 2, 3, \ldots\}.$$

Three other examples of sets of numbers are given below.

Examples 1 $\mathrm{W} = \{0, 1, 2, 3, 4, \ldots\}.$

2 $\mathrm{C} = \{1, 2, 3, 4, \ldots\}.$

3 $\mathrm{I}^- = \{\ldots, -3, -2, -1\}.$

The elements in W are the *whole numbers*; the elements in C, as we noted earlier, are the *counting numbers*; and the elements in I^-

are the *negative integers*. The whole numbers are sometimes referred to as the *nonnegative integers*, and the counting numbers are sometimes referred to as the *positive integers*. The set of positive integers may also be denoted as I^+. Whenever one of these sets is given, it is important that you know precisely what elements are contained in the set since frequent use of these sets will be made throughout this book.

The set of whole numbers is a *subset* of the set of integers, as are the set of counting numbers and the set of negative integers. This means, for example, that every element of W is an element of the set of integers. Since the concept of a subset will be of use as we proceed, a precise statement of the meaning of subset is incorporated in the following definition.

Definition 2/1 If A and B are sets, then A is a *subset* of B if and only if each element of A is an element of B. In other words, A is a subset of B if and only if $x \in A$ implies $x \in B$. That A is a subset of B is denoted by the expression $A \subseteq B$.

The symbol $\subseteq$ is read "included in or equal to." Often, the subset relation is useful in establishing that two sets are equal. An equivalent statement of Definition 1/1 is that $A = B$ if and only if $A \subseteq B$ and $B \subseteq A$. Hence, sets A and B can be shown to be equal by showing that A is a subset of B and that B is a subset of A.

From Definition 2/1 we know that $C \subseteq I$, $C \subseteq W$, $W \subseteq I$, and $I^- \subseteq I$. Actually, these examples illustrate the concept of a *proper subset*. Since every element of C is contained in I but I contains elements (for example, -3 and 0) that are not in C, the set of counting numbers is a proper subset of the set of integers. Similarly, since $0 \in W$ and $0 \notin C$, set C is a proper subset of W. Why is I^- a proper subset of I? Is I a proper subset of I? A precise definition of a proper subset and notation to express the idea are contained in the next definition.

Definition 3/1 If A and B are sets, then A is a *proper subset* of B if and only if A is a subset of B and B contains at least one element not in A. The fact that A is a proper subset of B can be denoted by $A \subset B$. The symbol $\not\subset$ is used to represent "is not a proper subset of."

Two sets of numbers that we will use frequently are the set of *real numbers* and the set of *rational numbers*. We will use the symbols $\mathfrak{R}$ and R, respectively, to represent these sets. The set of rational numbers, which can also be represented by $\{\frac{a}{b} \mid a, b \in I$ and $b \neq 0\}$, is a proper subset of the set of real numbers. Several sets that are proper subsets of both $\mathfrak{R}$ and R are given next.

Examples 1 $\{\frac{a}{b} \mid a, b \in C \text{ and } a + b = 7\} = \{\frac{1}{6}, \frac{2}{5}, \frac{3}{4}, \frac{4}{3}, \frac{5}{2}, \frac{6}{1}\}$.

2 $\{\frac{a}{2} \mid a \in I\} = \{\ldots, -\frac{4}{2}, -\frac{3}{2}, -\frac{2}{2}, -\frac{1}{2}, \frac{0}{2}, \frac{1}{2}, \frac{2}{2}, \frac{3}{2}, \ldots\}$.

3 $\{\frac{7}{a} \mid a \in I \text{ and } a > 3\} = \{\frac{7}{4}, \frac{7}{5}, \frac{7}{6}, \frac{7}{7}, \frac{7}{8}, \ldots\}$.

Suppose that S is any nonempty set. There are two particular subsets of S that are of special interest. As the first of these, notice that, by Definition 2/1, S includes itself as a subset; that is, for any set S, $S \subseteq S$. We say that S is an *improper subset* of itself since S does not contain any elements that are not elements of S. The second of these particular subsets of S is the empty set. The empty set is a proper subset of any nonempty set S because S contains elements that are not contained in $\emptyset$. Thus, $\emptyset \subset S$ for all nonempty sets S.

Now that the meaning of subset has been established, there is an elementary problem in counting that can be solved. Suppose that a set S is finite and has n elements, where n is a nonnegative integer. How many subsets does set S have? To lead to an intelligent guess, later to be proved, first consider some examples.

Examples 1 Consider a set that consists of a single element, the set $A = \{a\}$, for example. The two subsets of $\{a\}$ are tabulated below.

$$A = \{a\}.$$
$$\text{Subsets of A: } \{a\}, \emptyset$$

2 Next consider the set $S = \{a, b\}$, which contains two elements. It has four subsets, tabulated below.

$$S = \{a, b\}.$$
$$\text{Subsets of S: } \{a, b\}, \{a\}, \{b\}, \emptyset$$

3 Now consider the set $T = \{a, b, c\}$, which has three elements. Before you read further, try to determine how many subsets can be formed from set T. The eight subsets of T are tabulated below.

$$T = \{a, b, c\}$$
$$\text{Subsets of T: } \{a, b, c\}, \{a, b\}, \{a, c\},$$
$$\{b, c\}, \{a\}, \{b\}, \{c\}, \emptyset$$

4 As a fourth example, consider the empty set. The only subset of $\emptyset$ is $\emptyset$. Thus, the empty set has exactly one subset.

Perhaps the examples just given are sufficient to suggest the answer to the question raised earlier: How many subsets can be formed from a set S of n elements? If S has n elements and $\mathbb{S}$ is the set of subsets of S, then it is apparent that we are attempting to count the number of elements in $\mathbb{S}$. The notation N(S) will be used to denote the number of members of S; the notation $N(\mathbb{S})$

will be used to denote the number of members of $\mathbb{S}$ or, in other words, the number of subsets of S. By using this notation and the preceding results, we have,

$$\begin{aligned} &\text{if } N(S) = 1, \text{ then } N(\mathbb{S}) = 2 = 2^1; \\ &\text{if } N(S) = 2, \text{ then } N(\mathbb{S}) = 4 = 2^2; \\ &\text{if } N(S) = 3, \text{ then } N(\mathbb{S}) = 8 = 2^3; \\ &\text{if } N(S) = 0, \text{ then } N(\mathbb{S}) = 1 = 2^0. \end{aligned}$$

We might expect from these statements that the number of subsets of a set of n elements is 2^n. This is precisely the case, and we will prove this as the first theorem of the book.

Theorem 1/1 If S is a set containing n elements, where n is a nonnegative integer, and $\mathbb{S}$ is the set of subsets of S, then the number of subsets of S, denoted by $N(\mathbb{S})$, is 2^n.

Proof To establish the theorem, the subsets of S are counted in an orderly fashion. In other words, we want to determine the number of subsets of a set S containing exactly n elements, where $n \geqq 0$.

Suppose that $n = 4$. Then the total number of subsets of S is obtained by the sum.

$$C(4, 0) + C(4, 1) + C(4, 2) + C(4, 3) + C(4, 4),$$

where C(4, 0) represents the number of subsets that can be formed containing zero elements; C(4, 1) represents the number of subsets that can be formed, each containing exactly one element; C(4, 2) represents the number of subsets that can be formed, each containing exactly two elements; C(4, 3) represents the number of subsets that can be formed, each containing exactly three elements; and C(4, 4) represents the number of subsets that can be formed, each containing exactly 4 elements.

Now recall that $C(n, r)$ represents the number of possible combinations of n elements taken r at a time and that

$$C(n, r) = \frac{n!}{r!(n-r)!}, \text{ with } 0! = 1.$$

Thus,

$$\begin{aligned} C(4, 0) + C(4, 1) + C(4, 2) + C(4, 3) + C(4, 4) &= \\ \frac{4!}{0!4!} + \frac{4!}{1!3!} + \frac{4!}{2!2!} + \frac{4!}{3!1!} + \frac{4!}{4!0!} &= \\ 1 + 4 + 6 + 4 + 1 &= 16. \end{aligned}$$

Similarly, the total number of subsets that can be formed from a set of n elements, where $n \geqq 0$, is determined by

$$C(n, 0) + C(n, 1) + C(n, 2) + \ldots + C(n, n).$$

But this sum is just the expansion of $(1 + 1)^n$ by the binomial theorem. Hence,

$$C(n, 0) + C(n, 1) + C(n, 2) + \ldots + C(n, n) = (1 + 1)^n = 2^n,$$

and, consequently,

$$N(\mathbb{S}) = 2^n.$$

This argument establishes a proof of the theorem. A second proof is given below. Read the alternative proof with a view to deciding which proof you find to be more comprehensible.

Alternative proof We form subsets of S by considering each of the elements of S in turn and deciding whether or not to include the element in the subset. If we decide to include no element in the subset, we obtain the empty set. If we decide to include each element of S in the subset, we obtain S itself. Since there are n elements in S, we must make n decisions, and for each decision we have two choices—we either accept or reject the element. Thus, we can make these n decisions in

$$2 \cdot 2 \cdot \ldots \cdot 2 = 2^n \text{ ways.}$$

Hence, $N(\mathbb{S}) = 2^n$.

Exercises

1 Which of the following statements are true?

- **a** $C \subset R$.
- **b** $C \subset C$.
- **c** $R \not\subset \mathfrak{R}$.
- **d** $\mathfrak{R} \subset C$.
- **e** $\mathfrak{R} \not\subset R$.
- **f** $I \subset I^-$.
- **g** $I^- \not\subset \mathfrak{R}$.
- **h** $C \subset I^-$.
- **i** $W \not\subset I$.
- **j** $\mathfrak{R} \not\subset I$. *Answer*
- **k** $\emptyset \subset R$.
- **l** $I \subset R$.
- **m** $I^- \not\subset R$.
- **n** $R \subset W$.
- **o** $I^- \subset F$.

2 In a given plane, let S be the set of all squares; let R be the set of all rectangles; let P be the set of all polygons; let Q be the set of all quadrilaterals; and let T be the set of all triangles. Which of the following statements are true?

- **a** $Q \subseteq P$.
- **b** $R \subseteq S$.
- **c** $T \subseteq P$.
- **d** $R \not\subseteq Q$.
- **e** $T \subseteq T$.
- **f** $P \subseteq R$.
- **g** $T \subseteq Q$.
- **h** $Q \subseteq T$.
- **i** $Q \not\subseteq S$.
- **j** $S \subseteq R$. *Answer*
- **k** $\emptyset \not\subseteq T$.
- **l** $Q \not\subseteq S$.

3 Determine the number of subsets of each of the following sets.

- **a** $\{1, 2, 3, \ldots, 10\}$
- **b** $\{y \mid y \in I^- \text{ and } -8 < -y \leqq 5\}$
- **c** $\emptyset$
- **d** $\{0, 2, 4, 6, 8, \ldots, 20\}$
- **e** $\{x \mid x \in I \text{ and } -3 < x < 6\}$ *Answer*
- **f** $\{3x \mid x \in C \text{ and } x \leqq 100\}$
- **g** $\{-11, -7, -3, \ldots, 41\}$
- **h** C

4 Is there a set with exactly 36 subsets? With exactly 100 subsets? With exactly 512 subsets?

◆ 5 Show that every nonempty finite set has as many subsets with an even number of elements as subsets with an odd number of elements. *Answer*

◆ 6 Suppose that, for sets A, B, and C, $A \subseteq B$, $B \subseteq C$, and $C \subseteq A$. Show that $A = B = C$.

Cartesian product 3/1

In the previous section we discussed some familiar sets—the set of whole numbers, the set of counting numbers, the set of integers, and the set of rational numbers. Each of these, as you know, is a subset of the set of real numbers. This section deals with the set of ordered pairs of real numbers and certain subsets of this set.

Definition 4/1 For any two sets A and B, the *Cartesian product* of A and B, denoted by $A \times B$, is the set of all ordered pairs (a, b), where a is an element of A and b is an element of B. Symbolically,

$$A \times B = \{(a, b) \mid a \in A \text{ and } b \in B\}.$$

For convenience, we will often refer to the Cartesian product of two sets as the *Cartesian set*.

Examples 1 If $A = \{0, 1\}$ and $B = \{5, 8\}$, then
$A \times B = \{(0, 5), (0, 8), (1, 5), (1, 8)\}$.

2 If $A = \{\frac{1}{2}\}$ and $B = \{2, 4\}$, then $A \times B = \{(\frac{1}{2}, 2), (\frac{1}{2}, 4)\}$.

3 If $A = \{\frac{1}{2}\}$ and $B = \{2, 4\}$, then $B \times A = \{(2, \frac{1}{2}), (4, \frac{1}{2})\}$.

4 If $A = \{3, 5\}$, then $A \times A = \{(3, 3), (3, 5), (5, 3), (5, 5)\}$.

For any ordered pair (a, b), we refer to a as the *first component* and to b as the *second component*. Thus, in example 2, the first component of $(\frac{1}{2}, 2)$ is $\frac{1}{2}$ and the second component is 2. In example 3, the first component of $(2, \frac{1}{2})$ is 2 and the second component is $\frac{1}{2}$.

Each point in a plane can be associated with an ordered pair of real numbers, and each ordered pair of real numbers can be associated with a point in the plane. This is done by using a pair of coordinate axes to set up a one-to-one correspondence between $\mathfrak{R} \times \mathfrak{R}$, the set of ordered pairs of real numbers, and the set of points in a plane. For this reason, the plane that is determined by the coordinate axes is called the *real plane*. If the ordered pair (a, b) represents a point in the plane, then we refer to a as the *first coordinate* of the point and to b as the *second coordinate* of the point. Some ordered pairs of real numbers and the points of the plane with which they are associated are represented in Display 1.

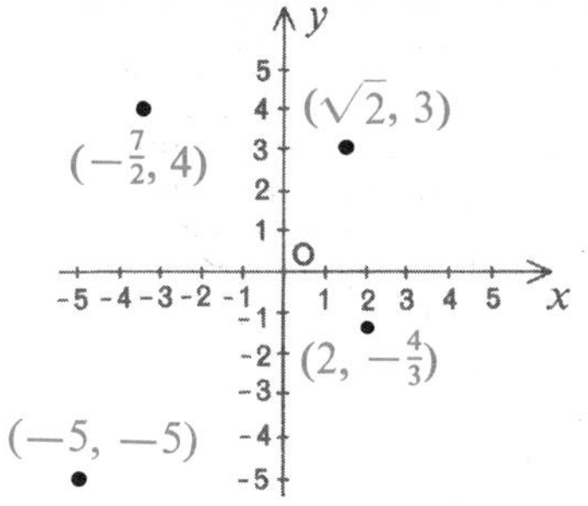

Display 1

To locate the point in the plane associated with a given ordered pair of real numbers, we refer to the first component and locate the point in the x-axis that is associated with this number. We next locate the point in the y-axis that is associated with the second component of the ordered pair. The point associated with the ordered pair is the intersection of the vertical line through the point in the x-axis and the horizontal line through the point in the y-axis. The word ***graph*** is frequently used to denote the set of points associated with a set of ordered pairs of real numbers. Several examples of the graphs of Cartesian sets follow.

Example 1 Display 2 shows a partial graph of I × I, the set of all ordered pairs of integers.

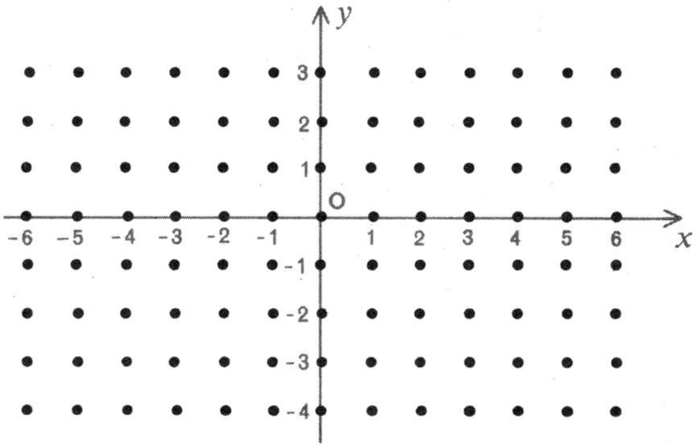

Display 2

As illustrated by this graph, the set of all ordered pairs of integers is a subset of the set of all ordered pairs of real numbers. In other words, $I \times I \subset \mathfrak{R} \times \mathfrak{R}$. Notice that the graph is incomplete since I × I is an infinite set. Show that the set of all ordered pairs of integers is a proper subset of $\mathfrak{R} \times \mathfrak{R}$ by exhibiting an ordered pair of real numbers that is not an ordered pair of integers.

Examples 2 $\{(x, y) \mid x, y \in I, x \leqq 3, \text{ and } y > 4\}$

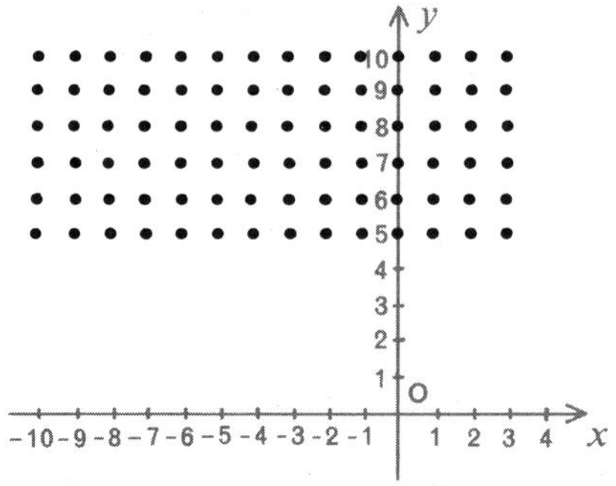

$\{(x, y) \mid x, y \in I, x \leqq 3, \text{ and } y > 4\}$

Display 3

3 $\{(1, 3), \ (-2, 5), \ (6, 0)\}$

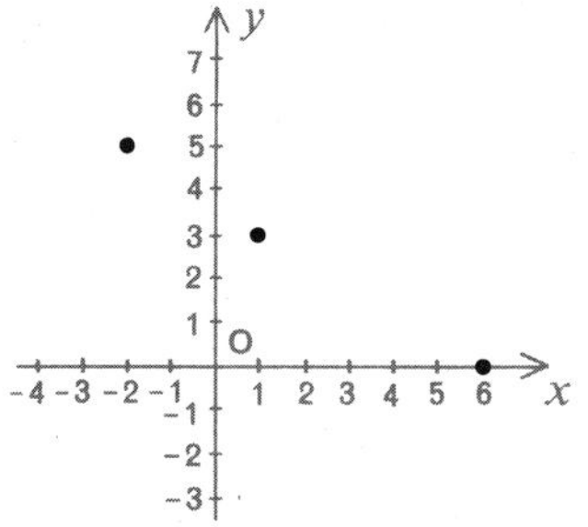

$\{(1, 3), (-2, 5), (6, 0)\}$

Display 4

4 $\{(\pi, -3), \ (4, \sqrt{3})\}$

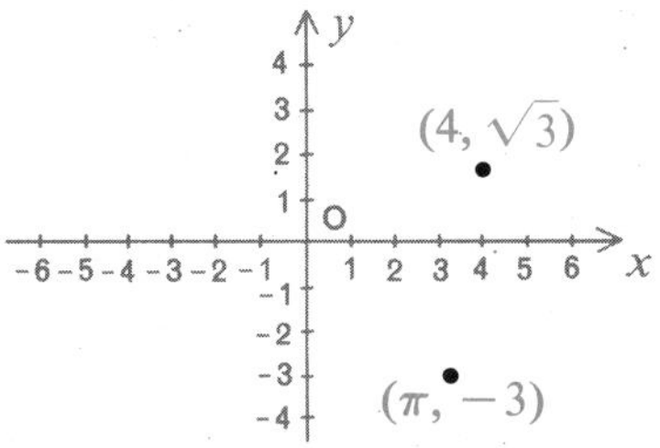

$\{(\pi, -3), (4, \sqrt{3})\}$

Display 5

Explain why the graph of example 2 is an incomplete graph. Why is it possible to display the entire graphs of examples 3 and 4?

It is interesting to note what happens when one of the sets used in forming a Cartesian product is the empty set. If we attempt to form the set of all ordered pairs by choosing first components from the empty set, we find that the set is empty because the empty set has no elements. Thus, the Cartesian product $\emptyset \times S$ is empty for all sets S. Give a similar argument to show that $S \times \emptyset = \emptyset$ for any set S.

In section 2/1, the counting problem associated with the number of subsets of a finite set led to the formula $N(\mathbb{S}) = 2^n$, with $N(S) = n$. A counting problem that is associated with a finite Cartesian set can now be solved.

If set A consists of n elements and set B consists of m elements, then the number of elements (ordered pairs) in the set $A \times B$ is $n \cdot m$. To establish this, observe that there are n choices for the first element of the ordered pair and that each of these n choices may be combined with each of the m elements from set B. Thus, there are $n \cdot m$ elements in the Cartesian set.

Exercises

1 For each of the following, form the Cartesian product $A \times B$.

a $A = \{0, 1\}$ and $B = \{0, 1, 2\}$.

b $A = \{0\}$ and $B = \{1, 2, 3, 4, 5, 6\}$.

c $A = \{x \mid x \in I \text{ and } -2 < x < 2\}$ and $B = \{x \mid x \in C \text{ and } x < 5\}$. *Answer*

d $A = \{x \mid x \in W \text{ and } -5 < x < -1\}$ and $B = \{x \mid x \in W \text{ and } x > 2\}$.

2 Determine the number of elements in each of the following Cartesian products $A \times B$; if $A \times B$ is infinite, list three elements of the set.

a $A = \{x \mid x \in I \text{ and } x < 30\}$ and $B = \{x \mid x \in C \text{ and } x < 30\}$.

b $A = \{x \mid x \in W \text{ and } 2 < x < 10\}$ and $B = \{x \mid x \in I^- \text{ and } x > -12\}$.

c $A = \{x \mid x \in R \text{ and } 3 < x < 4\}$ and $B = \{x \mid x \in I \text{ and } -3 < x < -2\}$.

d $A = \{x \mid x \in C \text{ and } x < 11\}$ and $B = \{x \mid x \in I\}$.

3 Graph the Cartesian product $A \times B$ for each of the following pairs of sets A and B.

a $A = \{x \mid x \in I \text{ and } 2 \leqq x \leqq 6\}$ and $B = \{y \mid y \in I \text{ and } 4 \leqq y \leqq 8\}$.

b $A = \{x \mid x \in \mathfrak{R} \text{ and } 2 \leqq x \leqq 6\}$ and $B = \{y \mid y \in \mathfrak{R} \text{ and } 4 \leqq y \leqq 8\}$.

c $A = \{x \mid x \in I \text{ and } 2 < x < 6\}$ and $B = \{y \mid y \in I \text{ and } 4 < y < 8\}$.

d $A = \{x \mid x \in \mathfrak{R} \text{ and } 2 < x < 6\}$ and $B = \{y \mid y \in \mathfrak{R} \text{ and } 4 < y < 8\}$.

- **4** Show that N(A × B) = N(B × A). *Answer*
- **5** Show that, for nonempty sets A and B, A × B ≠ B × A if A ≠ B.
- **6** Show that, for nonempty sets A, B, and C, if A × B = B × C, then A = B = C.

Relations 4/1

To introduce the idea of a mathematical relation, we will begin with a familiar one—the relation of "less than" on the set of integers. Often this relation is described geometrically in terms of the assumption that there exists a one-to-one correspondence between the set of integers and a subset of the points in the real-number line. A portion of this correspondence is illustrated in Display 6.

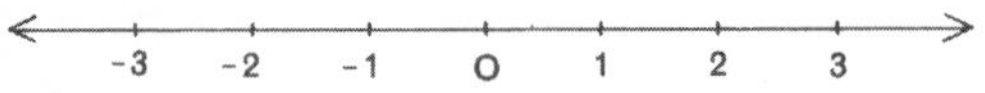

Display 6

Using this correspondence between points and integers, we say that the integer a is less than the integer b if and only if the point in the line associated with a is to the left of the point associated with the integer b. Of course, the order relation "less than" can be defined by using concepts other than that of "to the left of." (In fact, the way in which points and numbers are corresponded depends upon our knowing the order of the integers before we begin.) However, the idea of position in the number line does make the meaning of "less than" clearer. Among the pairs of integers that are related by the order relation "less than" are the ones given in the following statements.

$$-3 < 5. \qquad 11 < 62. \qquad 61 < 2^{10}.$$
$$0 < 6. \qquad -2 < 0. \qquad -15 < -14.$$

Notice that each statement is about a *pair* of integers that are related to each other by the idea of "less than."

In general, we shall use the notation $a \mathrm{R} b$ to express the idea "a is related to b." In this case, we denote the "less than" relation for the pair (a, b) by "$a \mathrm{R} b$ if and only if $a < b$."

First, we will discuss and show graphs of examples of relations on sets of numbers. Then we will define precisely the idea of a relation.

Examples 1 As a first example, a partial graph of the pairs of integers that are related by "less than" is shown below. Notice that the points that correspond to the ordered pairs of integers (x, y) that are related by "x less than y" are represented by dots in the graph.

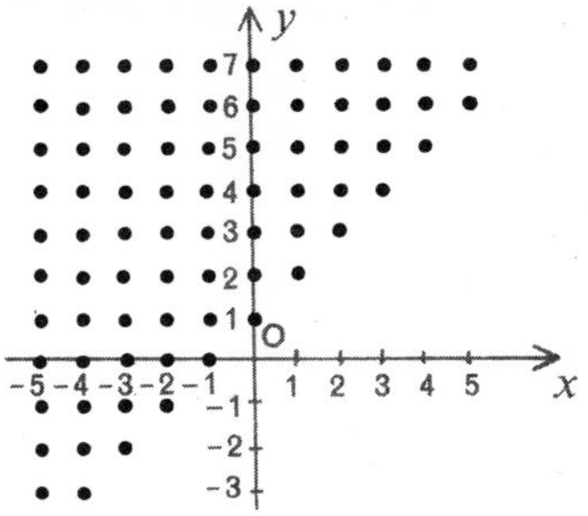

$\{(x, y) \mid x, y \in \mathrm{I} \text{ and } x < y\}$

Display 7

2 Now let us consider the relation of "less than" on the set of real numbers. Some pairs of real numbers that are related by "less than" are given in the following statements:

$$\sqrt{2} < 3. \qquad \pi < 4. \qquad -\tfrac{2}{3} < 0.$$
$$-1.2 < 0. \qquad 2\sqrt{3} < 5. \qquad 4 < 2^3.$$

The set of ordered pairs of real numbers (x, y) that are related by "x less than y" is an example of a relation. A partial graph and a standard description of this set are given in Display 8.

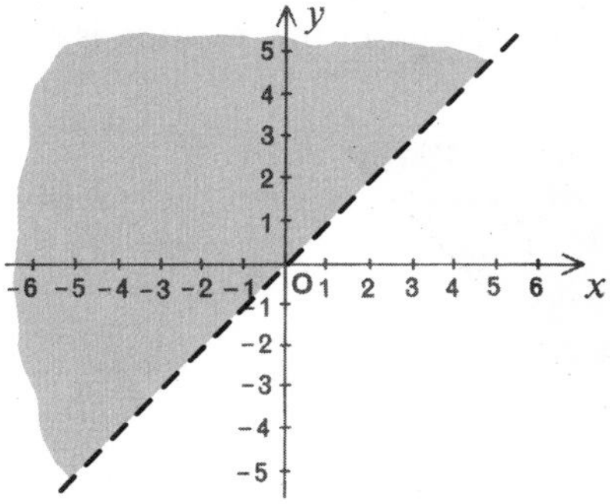

$\{(x, y) \mid x, y \in \mathfrak{R} \text{ and } x < y\}$

Display 8

The relation considered in each of examples 1 and 2 is that of "less than." Another familiar concept is the equality relation, and we can apply this concept to the set of real numbers to yield still another example of a relation.

Examples 3 The relation "equals" on the set of real numbers means that two real numbers are equal if and only if they are the same number. Some pairs of real numbers that are related by equality are (6, 6), (−3, −3), (π, π), and $(\frac{\sqrt{2}}{2}, \frac{\sqrt{2}}{2})$. A partial graph of the ordered pairs that satisfy this relation is shown in Display 9.

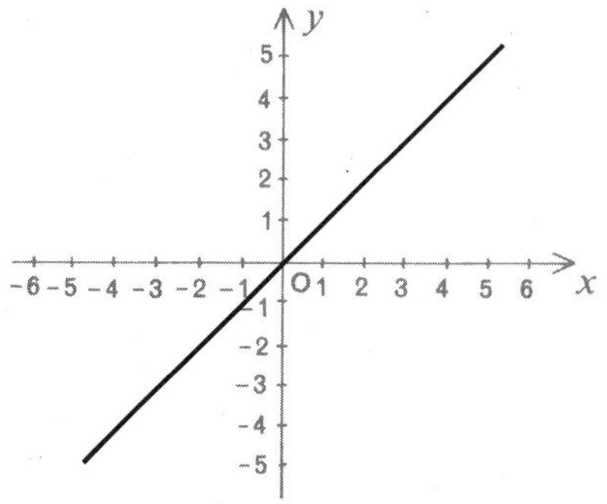

$\{(x, y) \mid x, y \in \Re \text{ and } x = y\}$

Display 9

4 The relations discussed in examples 2 and 3 can be combined to give another example of a relation, that of "less than or equal to," on the set of real numbers. This relation consists of all pairs in the relation of example 2 together with all pairs in the relation of example 3.

We can combine the graphs for examples 2 and 3 to obtain a graph of the relation "less than or equal to" on the set of real numbers. A partial graph of this relation is shown in Display 10.

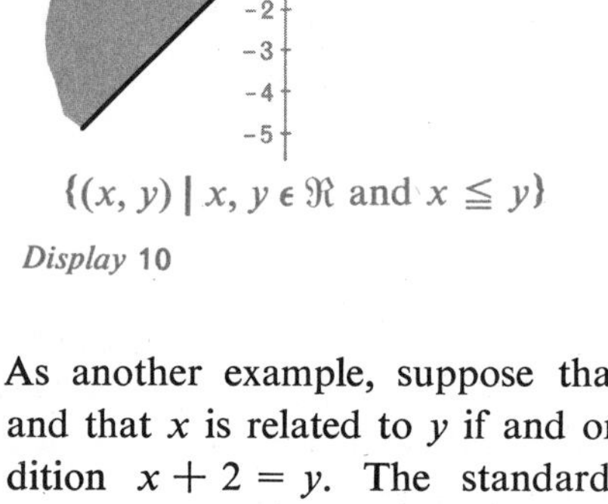

$\{(x, y) \mid x, y \in \Re \text{ and } x \leqq y\}$

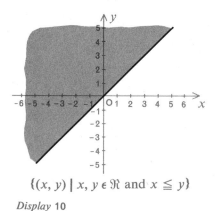

Display 10

5 As another example, suppose that x and y are real numbers and that x is related to y if and only if x and y satisfy the condition $x + 2 = y$. The standard description of this set is

$\{(x, y) \mid x, y \in \Re \text{ and } x + 2 = y\}$. Some ordered pairs (x, y) that satisfy $x + 2 = y$ are listed below.

$$\begin{array}{ll} (0, 2) & (-5, -3) \\ (-2, 0) & (\sqrt{2}, \sqrt{2} + 2) \\ (4, 6) & (3, 5) \end{array}$$

An incomplete graph of this set of ordered pairs is given in Display 11.

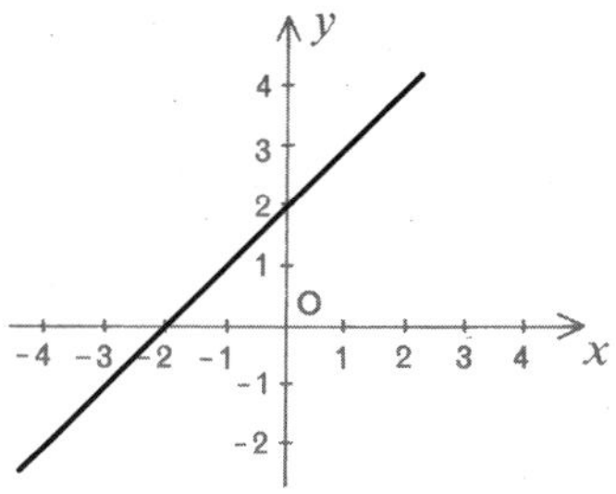

$\{(x, y) \mid x, y \in \Re \text{ and } x + 2 = y\}$

Display 11

The graphs given in this section have been chosen from the set of all possible relations in the real plane. Two reasons for choosing such examples are that relations in the real plane are mathematically important and they commonly occur in earlier mathematical studies. However, we often study relations that do not pertain to numbers. For this reason, the definition of relation is made generally for any two sets.

Definition 5/1 If A and B are sets, then R is a *relation* in A × B if and only if R is a subset of A × B. Symbolically, R is a relation in A × B if and only if $R \subseteq A \times B$. If A = B, then R is a relation *on* A.

Examples 1 through 5 have the common property that each is an infinite relation in an infinite Cartesian set. Lest this lead to an incorrect inference, consider the following examples. Each of these examples is a finite relation on I, although I × I is an infinite Cartesian set.

Examples 6 $\{(x, y) \mid x, y \in I,\ x + 5 = y, \text{ and } 4x + 2 = 2y\} = \{(4, 9)\}$.

7 $\{(x, y) \mid x, y \in I, x < y, \text{ and } -8 < x < -5 \text{ and } y < -3\} =$
$\{(-6, -5), (-6, -4), (-7, -6), (-7, -5), (-7, -4)\}$.

It is possible to have both finite and infinite relations in infinite Cartesian sets because both finite and infinite subsets can be formed from an infinite set. Since it is not possible to form infinite subsets from a finite set, it follows that all relations in $A \times B$, where A and B are finite sets, are finite.

Example 8 An important relation arises from the concept of the absolute value of a real number. Recall that the absolute value of a non-negative real number y (that is, a positive real number or zero) is y and that the absolute value of a negative real number y is $-y$. In the usual absolute value notation, we have:

$$|y| = y \text{ if } y = 0.$$
$$|y| = y \text{ if } y > 0.$$
$$|y| = -y \text{ if } y < 0.$$

By using the concept of absolute value, we can define a relation on $\mathfrak{R}$ by $x \mathrel{R} y$ if and only if $x = |y|$. An incomplete graph of this relation is shown in Display 12.

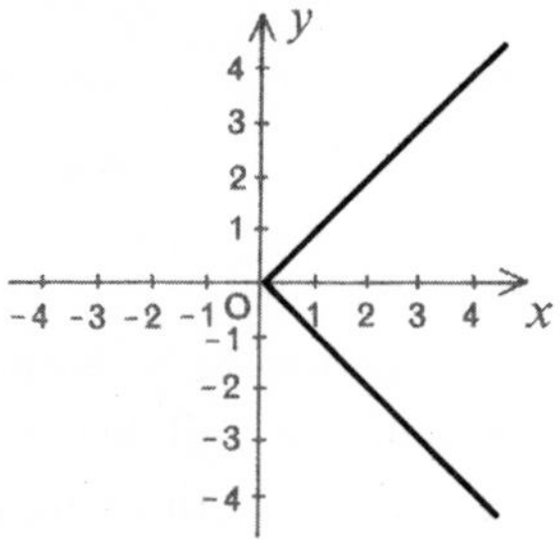

$\{(x, y) \mid x, y \in \mathfrak{R} \text{ and } x = |y|\}$

Display 12

Exercises Draw a graph for each of the following relations.

1 $\{(x, y) \mid x, y \in I \text{ and } y = |x|\}$
2 $\{(x, y) \mid x, y \in \mathfrak{R} \text{ and } y = 3x - 2\}$
3 $\{(x, y) \mid x, y \in \mathfrak{R} \text{ and } x^2 + y^2 = 16\}$
4 $\{(x, y) \mid x, y \in \mathfrak{R} \text{ and } |x| + |y| = 8\}$ *Answer*
5 $\{(x, y) \mid x, y \in I \text{ and } y = x^2\}$
6 $\{(x, y) \mid x, y \in \mathfrak{R} \text{ and } xy = 12\}$
7 $\{(x, y) \mid x, y \in \mathfrak{R},\ y = \frac{1}{2}x \text{ if } x < 0, \text{ and } y = 2x \text{ if } x \geqq 0\}$
8 $\{(x, y) \mid x, y \in I \text{ and } |x + y| = 6\}$
9 $\{(x, y) \mid x, y \in \mathfrak{R} \text{ and } y = \sin x\}$
10 $\{(x, y) \mid x, y \in I \text{ and } (x + y)^2 = x^2 + 2xy + y^2\}$
11 $\{(x, y) \mid x, y \in \mathfrak{R},\ (x + 2)(x - 2) = x^2 - 4, \text{ and } y = 3\}$
12 $\{(x, y) \mid x, y \in \mathfrak{R},\ (x + 1)x = x(x - 1), \text{ and } y = 0\}$
13 $\{(x, y) \mid x, y \in I \text{ and } (|x| - 3)(|y| - 5) = 0\}$ *Answer*

Tabulate each of the following relations in A × B.

14 $A = \{-1, 0, 1, 2, 3, 4\}$. $B = \{1, 2, 3, 4, 5\}$.
$\{(a, b) \mid (a, b) \in A \times B \text{ and } |b^2 - a| = 2\}$

15 $A = \{-4, -2, -\frac{1}{2}, \frac{2}{3}, 5\}$. $B = \{-1\frac{1}{2}, -\frac{2}{3}, 0, \frac{1}{2}, 1\}$.
$\{(a, b) \mid (a, b) \in A \times B \text{ and } 3b < \frac{1}{2}a - 4\}$

16 $A = \{-5, -2, 0, 1, 3, 8, 10\}$.
$B = \{-\frac{5}{3}, -\frac{2}{3}, 0, \frac{1}{6}, \frac{1}{4}, \frac{6}{11}\}$.
$\left\{(a, b) \mid (a, b) \in A \times B \text{ and } b = \frac{a-2}{a+3}\right\}$ *Answer*

Domain and range of a relation

5/1

To illustrate the notions of the domain and the range of a relation, consider the following four examples of relations in A × B. In the graph for examples 1 and 2, dots have been used to represent members of A × B, and those dots that are encircled represent members of the relation.

Example 1 $A = \{1, 2, 3\}$. $B = \{-1, 0, 1\}$.

$A \times B = \{(1, -1), (1, 0), (1, 1), (2, -1), (2, 0), (2, 1), (3, -1), (3, 0), (3, 1)\}$.

$R = \{(1, -1), (1, 0), (3, -1), (3, 0)\}$.

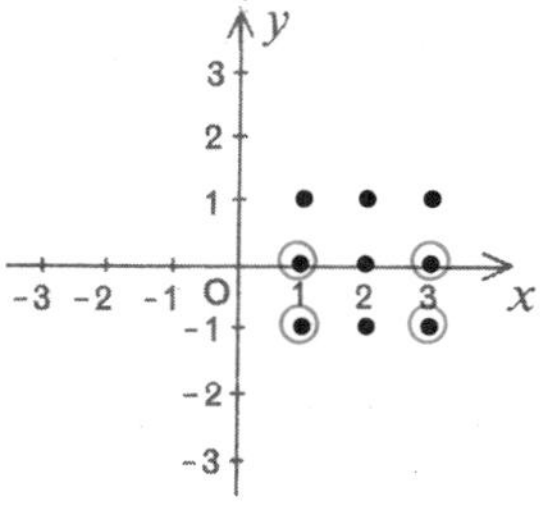

$\{(1, -1), (1, 0), (3, -1), (3, 0)\}$

Display 13

Observe that A and B are different finite sets. The set of first components of the elements of R is a proper subset of A and the set of second components is a proper subset of B. That is, there is an element of R that has 1 for a first component and an element of R that has 3 for a first component (to be precise, there are two of each), but there is no element of R that has 2 for a first component. There is an element of R that has -1 for a second component and, similarly, there is an element of R that has 0 for a second component. Which member of B does not occur as a second component in R?

Examples 2 A = {1, 2, 3}. B = I.
A × B = {(x, y) | x ∈ A and y ∈ I}.
R = {(x, y) | x = 1 and y ∈ I}.

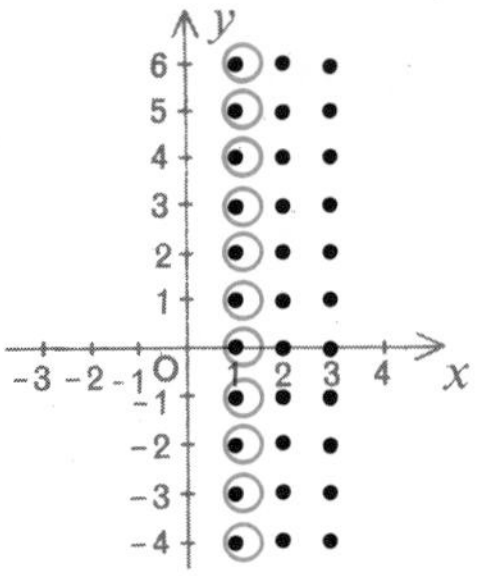

{(x, y) | x = 1 and y ∈ I}

Display 14

A study of the partial graph for example 2 shows that the only first coordinate of any point in the graph of R is 1. However, for each y ∈ B, there is a member of R with y as a second component. Observe that A is finite and that B and R are infinite.

3 A = $\mathfrak{R}$. B = {−1, 0, 1, 2}.
A × B = {(x, y) | x ∈ $\mathfrak{R}$ and y ∈ B}.
R = {(x, y) | x ∈ $\mathfrak{R}$ and y ∈ B}.

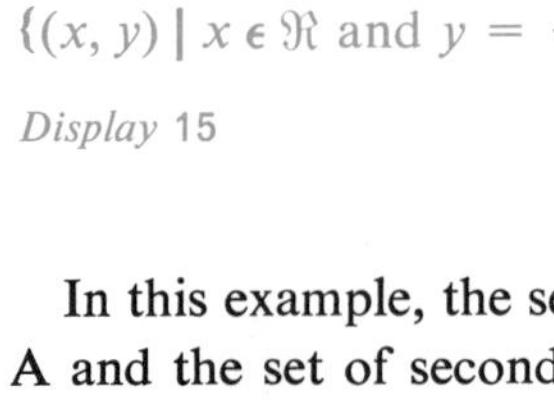

{(x, y) | x ∈ $\mathfrak{R}$ and y = −1, 0, 1, 2}

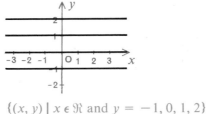

Display 15

In this example, the set of first components of elements of R is A and the set of second components is B. In fact, R is equal to A × B. Observe that A and R are infinite and that B is finite.

4 A = B = $\mathfrak{R}$.
A × A = $\mathfrak{R}$ × $\mathfrak{R}$.
R = {(x, y) | x ∈ I and y ∈ $\mathfrak{R}$}. (See Display 16.)

The sets used in forming the Cartesian product for example 4 are the same infinite set. The set of second components of ele-

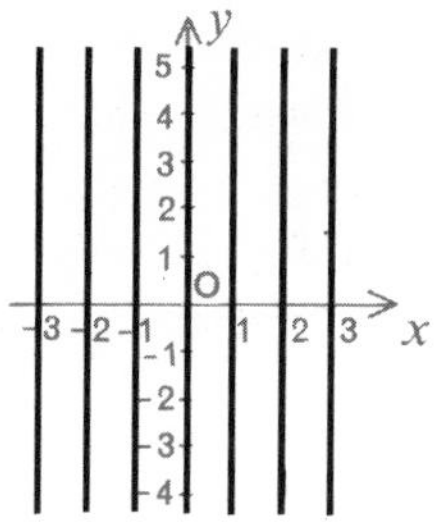

$\{(x, y) \mid x \in \mathrm{I} \text{ and } y \in \mathfrak{R}\}$

Display 16

ments of R is equal to A, but the set of first components is a proper subset of A.

As is apparent from these examples, a variety of situations may exist with respect to relations and the sets from which the elements of a relation obtain their components. Obviously, not all possible cases are covered by these examples. For example, the two sets A and B may both be infinite but distinct. Or, as another case, A and B may both be finite with A = B. However, we now want to consider the subset of A that consists of all first components of elements of R and the subset of B that consists of all second components of elements of R. These sets are formally described in the following definition.

Definition 6/1 If R is a relation in A × B, then the *domain* of R is the subset of all elements $a \in \mathrm{A}$ such that there exists an $(a, b) \in \mathrm{R}$. Similarly, the *range* of R is the subset of all elements $b \in \mathrm{B}$ such that there exists an $(a, b) \in \mathrm{R}$. Symbolically, if $\mathrm{R} \subseteq \mathrm{A} \times \mathrm{B}$, then the domain of R is $\{a \mid a \in \mathrm{A} \text{ and there exists } y \in \mathrm{B} \text{ with } (a, y) \in \mathrm{R}\}$; the range of R is $\{b \mid b \in \mathrm{B} \text{ and there exists } x \in \mathrm{A} \text{ with } (x, b) \in \mathrm{R}\}$.

An alternative way of describing the domain of a relation is as the set of first components of the elements of the relation. Similarly, the range may be described as the set of second components of the relation.

For the relations given in examples 1 through 4, the domains are $\{1, 3\}$, $\{1\}$, $\mathfrak{R}$, and I, respectively. Observe that in examples 1, 2, and 4 the domain is a proper subset of A, but in example 3 the domain is equal to A. The range sets for these relations, listed in order, are: $\{-1, 0\}$, I, $\{-1, 0, 1, 2\}$, and $\mathfrak{R}$. The range in example 1 is a proper subset of B and is equal to B in each of examples 2, 3, and 4.

In summary, the domain of a relation R in A × B can only be either A or a proper subset of A. If the domain and A are the same set, we say that the relation is *from* set A. Similarly, the range of a relation R in A × B must either be B or a proper subset of B. If the range and B are equal, we say that the relation is *onto* set B. If $(a, b) \in$ R, then b is the *image* of a under R. All relations in A × B are said to be *into* set B, but only those relations in which the range is equal to B are described as onto.

Exercises For each of the following relations in A × B, (a) give the domain, (b) give the range, (c) determine if the relation is from A, (d) determine if the relation is onto B, (e) find an image of 0, and (f) find an image of 4. Make graphs for exercises 4, 7, 11, and 18.

1 $\{(x, y) \mid x \in A, y \in B, \text{ and } y = |x|\}$. A = $\mathfrak{R}$. B = I.

2 $\{(x, y) \mid x \in A, y \in B, \text{ and } y = 3x - 2\}$.
A = $\{-5, -\frac{2}{3}, 0, 1, 4\}$. B = $\{-10, -9, -8, \ldots, 17\}$.

3 $\{(x, y) \mid x \in A, y \in B, \text{ and } x^2 + y^2 = 16\}$. A = $\mathfrak{R}$. B = $\mathfrak{R}$.

4 $\{(x, y) \mid x \in A, y \in B, \text{ and } |x| + |y| = 8\}$. A = W. B = I.

5 $\{(x, y) \mid x \in A, y \in B, \text{ and } y = x^2\}$. A = $\mathfrak{R}$. B = $\mathfrak{R}$.

6 $\{(x, y) \mid x \in A, y \in B, \text{ and } xy = 12\}$. A = $\mathfrak{R}$.
B = $\{-5, -\frac{1}{2}, 0, 3, \frac{8}{3}, 10\}$.

7 $\{(x, y) \mid x \in A, y \in B, y = \frac{1}{2}x \text{ if } x < 0, \text{ and } y = 2x \text{ if } x \geqq 0\}$.
A = $\mathfrak{R}$. B = $\mathfrak{R}$.

8 $\{(x, y) \mid x \in A, y \in B, \text{ and } |x + y| = 6\}$.
A = $\{-11, -\frac{17}{6}, 0, \frac{2}{5}, 4, 5\}$. B = $\mathfrak{R}$. *Answer*

9 $\{(x, y) \mid x \in A, y \in B, \text{ and } y = \sin x\}$. A = $\mathfrak{R}$. B = $\mathfrak{R}$.

10 $\{(x, y) \mid x \in A, y \in B, \text{ and } (x + y)^2 = x^2 + 2xy + y^2\}$.
A = E_I. B = I.

11 $\{(x, y) \mid x \in A, y \in B, (x + 2)(x - 2) = x^2 - 4, \text{ and } y = 3\}$.
A = $\mathfrak{R}$. B = O_C.

12 $\{(x, y) \mid x \in A, y \in B, (x + 1)x = x(x - 1), \text{ and } y = 0\}$.
A = W. B = W. *Answer*

13 $\{(x, y) \mid x \in A, y \in B, \text{ and } 9x^2 + 16y^2 - 144 = 0\}$. A = $\mathfrak{R}$.
B = $\mathfrak{R}$.

14 $\{(x, y) \mid x \in A, y \in B, \text{ and } |x + 3| = 5\}$. A = C. B = E_C.

15 $\{(x, y) \mid x \in A, y \in B, \text{ and } x^2 + y^2 - 36 \leqq 0\}$. A = $\mathfrak{R}$. B = $\mathfrak{R}$.

16 $\{(x, y) \mid x \in A, y \in B, \text{ and } 9x^2 - 4y^2 - 36 = 0\}$. A = I. B = I.

17 $\{(x, y) \mid x \in A, y \in B, \text{ and } 25x^2 - 16y^2 + 400 = 0\}$. A = $\mathfrak{R}$.
B = $\mathfrak{R}$.

18 $\{(x, y) \mid x \in A, y \in B, \text{ and } x = y^2\}$.
A = $\{x \mid x \in I \text{ and } x \geqq -10\}$. B = $\mathfrak{R}$.

19 $\{(x, y) \mid x \in A, y \in B, \text{ and } |y - 4| = 2\}$. A = $\mathfrak{R}$. B = $\mathfrak{R}$.

20 $\{(x, y) \mid x \in A, y \in B, \text{ and } (x + y + 2)(x + y - 2) = 0\}$.
A = E_I. B = E_C. *Answer*

Functions 6/1

Certain kinds of relations that have a special property are called *functions*. Examples will be given to illustrate the property that is used to determine which relations are also functions. Study the first two examples with a view toward discovering for yourself a basic difference between the nature of the elements contained in the two relations.

Examples 1 In section 4/1 we considered the relation that consists of all ordered pairs of real numbers (x, y) that satisfy the condition $x = y$. An incomplete graph of this relation is given in Display 17.

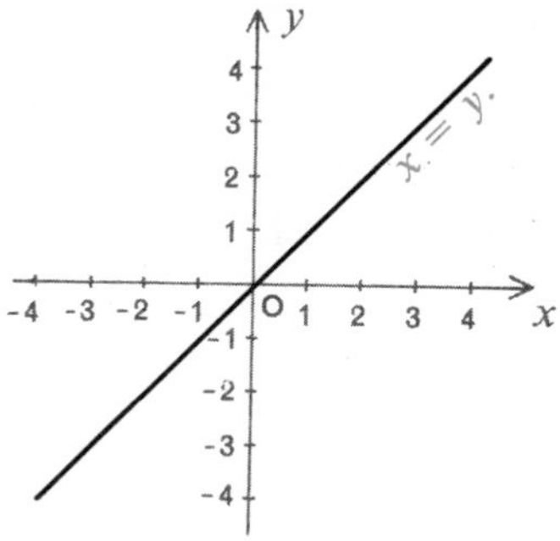

$R_1 = \{(x, y) \mid x, y \in \Re \text{ and } x = y\}$.

Display 17

2 We also considered the relation that consists of all ordered pairs (x, y) satisfying the condition that x is equal to the absolute value of y. An incomplete graph of this relation is shown in Display 18.

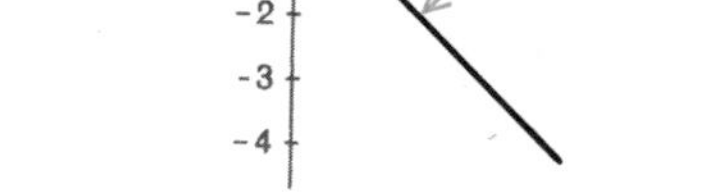

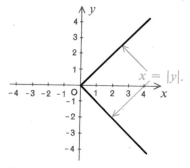

$R_2 = \{(x, y) \mid x, y \in \Re \text{ and } x = |y|\}$.

Display 18

These two relations differ in one very important respect that can be expressed as follows: To each x in the domain of R_1 there corresponds exactly one element in the range of R_1, namely, $y = x$. This statement is not true for the relation R_2. That is, there exist elements x in the domain of R_2 such that $(x, y_1) \in R_2$ and $(x, y_2) \in R_2$ with $y_1 \neq y_2$. To put it another way, there exist first components x in the domain of R_2 that are paired with more than one element of the range. An example of such an element x is 3, because (3, 3) and (3, −3) both belong to R_2. Other examples of such elements are $\frac{5}{4}$, 11.5, $16\frac{1}{2}$, and so on.

As you will see, the distinction between examples 1 and 2 is the distinction between a relation that is a function and one that is not. Before we state this property in a formal definition, let us compare another pair of relations in the same way. First consider the subset of $\mathfrak{R} \times \mathfrak{R}$ that consists of the set of all (x, y) such that $x = y^2$. Then consider the set of all (x, y) such that $y = x^2$. The incomplete graphs of these two relations are given in Displays 19 and 20.

Examples 3 $R_3 = \{(x, y) \mid x, y \in \mathfrak{R} \text{ and } x = y^2\}$.

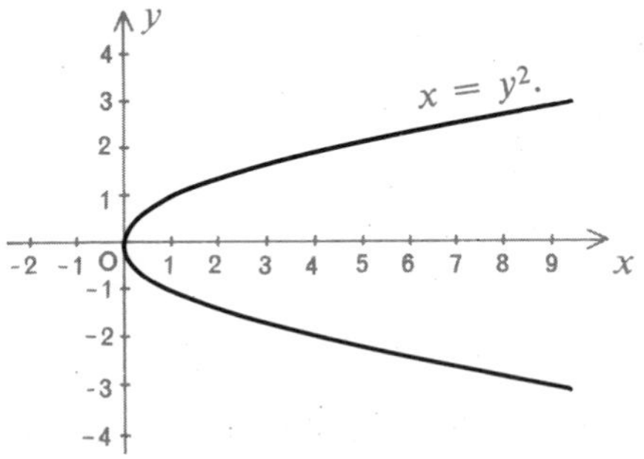

$\{(x, y) \mid x, y \in \mathfrak{R} \text{ and } x = y^2\}$

Display 19

4 $R_4 = \{(x, y) \mid x, y \in \mathfrak{R} \text{ and } y = x^2\}$.

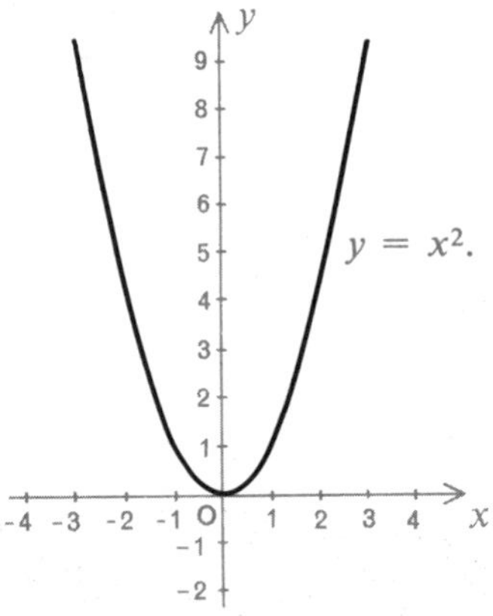

$\{(x, y) \mid x, y \in \mathfrak{R} \text{ and } y = x^2\}$

Display 20

Observe that the difference between R_4 and R_3 is similar to the difference between R_1 and R_2. In R_4, for each element x in the domain, there is a unique element y in the range that corresponds to x. In R_3, for each nonzero element x in the domain, there are two elements y_1 and y_2 that correspond to x. The property of having exactly one element in the range that corresponds to each element in the domain is the property that distinguishes a function from a relation that is not a function. The distinction lies in the property known as *single-valuedness*. A relation is *single-valued* and, hence, is a function if and only if, for each element in the domain of the relation, there is a single element in the range that corresponds to it.

Definition 7/1 If R is a relation in $A \times B$, then R is a *function* if and only if, for each x in the domain of R, there exists exactly one y in the range of R such that $(x, y) \in R$.

Another way of stating Definition 7/1 is: If R is a relation in $A \times B$, then R is a function if and only if $(a, b) \in R$ and $(a, c) \in R$ imply $b = c$.

There are several ways of denoting functions. The letters F and f, the initial letter of the word function, are commonly used; other letters, such as G, H, g, and so forth, are also used. Some different notations that are commonly associated with functions are shown below.

$$\begin{array}{ll} F(x) = y. & f(x) = y. \\ (x)F = y. & (x)f = y. \\ (x, G(x)) & (x, y) \in F. \\ F: x \longrightarrow y & x \xrightarrow{f} y. \end{array}$$

Each of these expresses the same idea; if $(x, y) \in F$, x is an element of the domain of F and y is the element in the range of F that corresponds to x. You should learn to recognize all these different notations; since each of them has special advantages, we intend to use the notation that best suits our purpose at a particular time.

Three specific functions that you have probably studied earlier will now be reviewed.

Example 5 Suppose that S is a set and that $\mathbb{S}$ is the collection of all of the subsets of S. Suppose also that set A is an element of $\mathbb{S}$; that is, A is a subset of S. Associated with this set there is a set of elements that are in S, but are not in A. This subset, called the *complement* of set A with respect to set S, is usually written as follows.

$$\tilde{A} = \{x \mid x \in S \text{ and } x \notin A\}.$$

Notice that if $A = S$, then $\tilde{A} = \emptyset$. Subsets of S may be related to their complement to form a relation in $\mathbb{S} \times \mathbb{S}$. This relation is described by

$$R = \{(A, \tilde{A}) \mid A \in \mathbb{S}\}.$$

The relation R has $\mathbb{S}$ as its domain and also has $\mathbb{S}$ as its range. Therefore, R is from $\mathbb{S}$ and also onto $\mathbb{S}$. Furthermore, R is a function, because, for each A in the domain of R, there is exactly one $\tilde{A}$ in the range of R such that $(A, \tilde{A}) \in R$.

Examples 6 As another example of a function, consider the function that consists of all pairs $(x, -x)$ in $\mathfrak{R} \times \mathfrak{R}$. This function may be expressed as $\{(x, y) \mid x, y \in \mathfrak{R} \text{ and } y = -x\}$. The domain of the function is the set of real numbers; the range is also the set of real numbers. It is single-valued because the additive inverse of a real number is unique. What is the graph of this function?

7 Now consider the set of all ordered pairs of the form $(x, \sqrt{x})$ in $\mathfrak{R} \times \mathfrak{R}$, where x is nonnegative. This relation may be expressed as $\{(x, y) \mid x, y \in \mathfrak{R}, x \geqq 0, \text{ and } y = \sqrt{x}\}$. Because the symbol $\sqrt{\ }$ refers to the nonnegative square root of a number, this relation is a function. The domain of this particular function is the set of nonnegative real numbers; the range is also the set of nonnegative real numbers.

Just as relations are classified by the property of single-valuedness, so functions may be classified according to whether they are one-to-one or many-to-one. To illustrate this property, we will consider the following examples.

Examples 1 $F_1 = \{(x, y) \mid x, y \in \mathfrak{R} \text{ and } y = 3\}$.

2 $F_2 = \{(x, y) \mid x, y \in \mathfrak{R} \text{ and } y = 3 + x\}$.

Each of these sets is a subset of $\mathfrak{R} \times \mathfrak{R}$, and hence, by Definition 5/1, is a relation. Read Definition 7/1 again to be sure that it is clear to you why each of these relations is also a function. Observe that 3 is in the range of F_1; in fact, 3 is the only element in the range. Also note that $(-5, 3)$ and $(1, 3)$, for example, are each elements of F_1. Since there is a second component, 3, with different first components, F_1 is an example of a *many-to-one function.* Thus, we have the following definition of a many-to-one function.

Definition 8/1 If F is a function containing elements (a, c) and (b, c) such that $a \neq b$, then F is *many-to-one*.

Some experimentation, perhaps combined with a study of the graph of F_2, will convince you that for no element c in the range of F_2 is it true that (a, c) and $(b, c) \in F_2$ when $a \neq b$. In other words, no second component of an element of F_2 is paired with more than one first component. So, F_2 is an example of a *one-to-one function*, which is defined below.

Definition 9/1 If F is a function and if (a, c), $(b, c) \in F$ implies that $a = b$, then F is a *one-to-one function*.

Exercises For each of the following relations, determine if the relation is a function. Then, for each relation that is a function, decide whether it is one-to-one or many-to-one. Make graphs for exercises 1, 8, 17, and 22.

1 $\{(x, y) \mid x, y \in \mathfrak{R} \text{ and } y = |x|\}$
2 $\{(x, y) \mid x, y \in \mathfrak{R} \text{ and } y = 3x - 2\}$
3 $\{(x, y) \mid x, y \in \mathfrak{R} \text{ and } x^2 + y^2 = 16\}$
4 $\{(x, y) \mid x, y \in \mathfrak{R} \text{ and } |x| + |y| = 8\}$
5 $\{(x, y) \mid x, y \in \mathfrak{R} \text{ and } y = x^2\}$
6 $\{(x, y) \mid x, y \in \mathfrak{R} \text{ and } xy = 12\}$
7 $\{(x, y) \mid x, y \in \mathfrak{R}, y = \frac{1}{2}x \text{ if } x < 0, \text{ and } y = 2x \text{ if } x \geqq 0\}$
8 $\{(x, y) \mid x, y \in \mathfrak{R} \text{ and } |x + y| = 6\}$
9 $\{(x, y) \mid x, y \in \mathfrak{R} \text{ and } y = \sin x\}$ *Answer*
10 $\{(x, y) \mid x, y \in \mathfrak{R} \text{ and } (x + y)^2 = x^2 + 2xy + y^2\}$
11 $\{(x, y) \mid x, y \in \mathfrak{R}, (x + 1)x = x(x - 1), \text{ and } y = 0\}$
12 $\{(x, y) \mid x, y \in \mathfrak{R} \text{ and } 9x^2 + 16y^2 - 144 = 0\}$
13 $\{(x, y) \mid x, y \in \mathfrak{R} \text{ and } |x + 3| = 5\}$
14 $\{(x, y) \mid x, y \in \mathfrak{R} \text{ and } x^2 + y^2 - 36 \leqq 0\}$
15 $\{(x, y) \mid x, y \in \mathfrak{R} \text{ and } 9x^2 - 4y^2 - 36 = 0\}$
16 $\{(x, y) \mid x, y \in \mathfrak{R} \text{ and } 25x^2 - 16y^2 + 400 = 0\}$
17 $\{(x, y) \mid x, y \in \mathfrak{R} \text{ and } x = y^2\}$
18 $\{(x, y) \mid x, y \in \mathfrak{R} \text{ and } |y - 4| = 2\}$
19 $\{(x, y) \mid x, y \in \mathfrak{R} \text{ and } (x + y + 2)(x + y - 2) = 0\}$
20 $\{(x, y) \mid x, y \in \mathfrak{R} \text{ and } xy = 0\}$
21 $\{(x, y) \mid x, y \in \mathfrak{R} \text{ and } y \text{ is the greatest integer} \leqq x\}$ *Answer*
22 $\{(x, y) \mid x, y \in \mathfrak{R} \text{ and } |y| = |x|\}$
23 $\{(x, y) \mid x, y \in \mathfrak{R} \text{ and } y = \sqrt{16 - x^2}\}$
24 $\{(x, y) \mid x, y \in \mathfrak{R}, y = 1 \text{ if } x \geqq 0, \text{ and } y = -1 \text{ if } x < 0\}$

For each of the following functions in $\mathfrak{R} \times \mathfrak{R}$, determine if the function is one-to-one.

25 $F = \{(x, y) \mid y = \frac{1}{x} \text{ if } x \neq 0 \text{ and } y = 0 \text{ if } x = 0\}$.
26 $F = \{(x, y) \mid y = \frac{1}{x} \text{ and } x \neq 0\}$.
27 $F = \{(x, y) \mid y = x + \frac{1}{x} \text{ and } x \neq 0\}$.

28 $F = \{(x, y) \mid y = 3 \text{ if } -1 \leqq x \leqq 1,\ y = 2x \text{ if } x < -1, \text{ and } y = 2x \text{ if } x > 1\}$.

29 $F = \{(x, y) \mid y = \frac{1}{2}|x + 6| - \frac{1}{2}|x - 6|\}$. *Answer*

30 $F = \{(x, y) \mid y = [\frac{1}{2}|x + 6| - \frac{1}{2}|x - 6|]^2\}$.

31 $F = \{(x, y) \mid y = 0 \text{ if } x \text{ is an integer and } y = x \text{ if } x \text{ is not an integer}\}$.

Binary operations

7/1

The subject of this section—binary operations—is undoubtedly a familiar topic, but the way in which we will think of binary operations may be different from the way you have previously thought of them. Since binary operations are special kinds of functions, keep in mind the definition of a function as various examples of binary operations are presented.

Examples 1 First let us consider the binary operation of addition of counting numbers. With an ordered pair of counting numbers (a, b), there is associated a *sum*, denoted by $a + b$. Specifically, we may think of addition as associating the ordered pair (2, 3) with the sum $2 + 3$, or 5. If the operation of addition (+) is thought of as a function, then, one way to express the sum is

$$(2, 3) \xrightarrow{+} 5.$$

The ordered pair (2, 3) is in the domain of the function + and the operation + is said to *map* the ordered pair (2, 3) onto 5, which is in the range of the function. Since the first and second components of the elements in the domain are each counting numbers and the sum is also a counting number, the operation may be represented more generally by

$$C \times C \xrightarrow{+} C.$$

The domain of the binary operation is the Cartesian product $C \times C$, and the range is included in C. Hence, this operation is a function *from* $C \times C$ into C. Can it be shown that every element of C is contained in the range?

2 Now let us examine the binary operation of multiplication of counting numbers. As an example of the product of two counting numbers, we will consider $5 \cdot 3 = 15$. One way to write this product (in the notation adopted earlier) is

$$(5, 3) \xrightarrow{\cdot} 15.$$

The binary operation multiplication maps the ordered pair (5, 3) onto the product 15. We can represent the operation of multiplication of counting numbers by

$$C \times C \xrightarrow{\cdot} C.$$

The domain of the operation is the Cartesian product C × C. Each element of the range is a counting number. Does the range contain all of C? Is multiplication a function from C × C onto C?

Before you read the next example, observe that the operations of addition and multiplication from C × C are both single-valued. This means that, for a particular pair of counting numbers, there is a unique sum and there is a unique product.

What can you say about the operations of addition and multiplication from I × I into I? Are these operations also functions? What is the domain and range of each of these functions?

3 Now let us examine the set of counting numbers and the operation of subtraction. Associated with every pair of counting numbers (a, b), there is a *difference*, denoted by $a - b$. Although this difference may *not* be contained in C, the difference $a - b$ *is* always contained in I. Thus, with every pair of counting numbers and the operation of subtraction, there is associated an integer. In function notation, we can represent the difference of counting numbers by

$$C \times C \xrightarrow{-} I,$$

which shows the domain to be the Cartesian product C × C and the range to be a subset of I. Is every element of I contained in the range of this function?

4 Consider division of nonzero integers. Associated with every ordered pair of nonzero integers (a, b), there is a *quotient* denoted by $\frac{a}{b}$. This quotient is a rational number, which may or may not be an integer. Thus, division maps pairs of nonzero integers (a, b) onto rational numbers. If we denote the nonzero integers as the union of the positive and the negative integers, that is, as $I^+ \cup I^-$, then we have the function

$$(I^+ \cup I^-) \times (I^+ \cup I^-) \xrightarrow{\div} R.$$

Notice that the domain of this function is not I × I, but is a proper subset of the Cartesian product I × I. This is the case since elements of I × I like (−4, 0), (0, 0), and (0, 3) are not in the domain of the function. Give another example to show that the domain is a proper subset of I × I. Show that the range of this function is a subset of R.

Examples 1 through 4 lead to a general definition of a binary operation. Since operations need not be restricted to a subset of the real numbers, as you will see in the next section, the definition of a binary operation given below is stated for arbitrary sets A and B.

Definition 10/1 If A and B are sets and F is a function whose domain is $A \times A$ and whose range is included in B, then F is a *binary operation.*

Example 1 is a binary operation from $C \times C$ into C; example 2 is from $C \times C$ onto C; example 3 is from $C \times C$ onto I; and example 4 is from $(I^+ \cup I^-) \times (I^+ \cup I^-)$ into R. Observe that the definition requires that a binary operation be single-valued.

Examples 5 In view of the definition of a binary operation, consider the operation of addition of even counting numbers, with $A = E_C$ and $B = E_C$. Recall that the set of even counting numbers is

$$E_C = \{2,\ 4,\ 6,\ 8,\ \ldots\}.$$

It is easy to show that the range of this binary operation is included in E_C because the sum of any two even counting numbers is an even counting number. This is established by the following argument.

$$\begin{aligned} x, y \in E_C \text{ implies } x &= 2m \text{ and } y = 2n;\ m, n \in C. \\ x + y &= 2m + 2n \\ &= 2(m + n) \\ &= 2t,\ t \in C. \\ \text{Therefore, } x + y &\in E_C. \end{aligned}$$

Supply the reason for each step in the computation above. Show that the range of the binary operation is not all of E_C.

6 The operation of multiplication from $E_C \times E_C$ associates with every pair of even counting numbers another even counting number. Can you give an argument similar to the one just given that establishes that the product of two elements of E_C is an element of E_C? Is the range all of E_C? If not, what is the range?

7 Now consider the operation of addition from $O_C \times O_C$. Recall that the set of odd counting numbers is

$$O_C = \{1,\ 3,\ 5,\ 7,\ \ldots\}.$$

The operation of addition associates a sum with every pair of odd counting numbers. This sum is not in O_C; in fact, it is in E_C. Give an argument to verify this. Hence, addition of odd counting numbers is a binary operation that associates an even counting number with every pair of odd counting numbers. Symbolically,

$$O_C \times O_C \xrightarrow{+} E_C.$$

Exercises For each of the functions expressed below, determine (a) the domain, (b) the range, (c) an image of (6, 2), (d) an image of (10, 3). Finally, (e) decide whether or not the function is a binary operation.

1 $\left\{((x, y), z) \mid x, y \in I,\ z \in R, \text{ and } z = \dfrac{x+y}{2}\right\}$ *Answer*

2 $\{((x, y), z) \mid x, y \in R,\ z \in \Re,\ x, y \geqq 0, \text{ and } z = \sqrt{xy}\}$

3 $\{((x, y), z) \mid x, y, z \in \Re,\ x, y \geqq 0, \text{ and } |z| = x + y\}$

4 $\{((x, y), z) \mid x, y, z \in C \text{ and } z = x^y\}$

5 $\left\{((x, y), z) \mid x, y \in R,\ z \in I, \text{ and } z \text{ is the greatest integer that is less than or equal to } \dfrac{x+y}{2}\right\}$

6 $\left\{((x, y), z) \mid x, y \in I^-,\ z \in R, \text{ and } z = \dfrac{x+y}{2xy}\right\}$

7 $\{((x, y), z) \mid x, y, z \in \Re \text{ and } z = (x + y)^2\}$

◆ **8** $\{((x, y), z) \mid x, y, z \in C$ and z is the difference of x and the largest multiple of y that is less than or equal to $x\}$

Union and intersection of sets

8/1

Our study of binary operations in section 7/1 was restricted to the four operations of arithmetic—addition, multiplication, subtraction, and division. In this section and in section 9/1, we will examine some binary operations that are outside the realm of arithmetic.

Just as there are binary operations that associate a third number with an ordered pair of numbers, there are binary operations that associate a third set with an ordered pair of sets. One such operation is defined below.

Definition 11/1 If S is a set, $\mathfrak{S}$ is the collection of subsets of S, and A and B are elements of $\mathfrak{S}$, then the *union* of sets A and B is the set of elements in A *or* in B. Symbolically, the union of A and B is $A \cup B = \{x \mid x \in A \text{ or } x \in B\}$.

The key word in the definition of union is the word *or*. In everyday conversation, we often use "or" in the exclusive sense to mean one or the other, but not both. Here, however, "or" is used in the inclusive sense, which means that the elements in the union may be in *both* of the sets as well as in one or the other. Before we see how the operation of the union of sets fulfills the requirements of Definition 10/1, we will consider examples of the union of sets.

Examples 1 Let S be the set of integers. Two subsets of S are

$$W = \{0, 1, 2, 3, \ldots\},$$
$$I^- = \{\ldots, -3, -2, -1\}.$$

The union of the subsets is

$$W \cup I^- = \{\ldots, -3, -2, -1, 0, 1, 2, 3, \ldots\}.$$

Thus, $W \cup I^- = I = S$.

2 Let S be the set of counting numbers. Consider the subsets

$$A = \{x \mid x \in C \text{ and } x \text{ is prime}\} = \{2, 3, 5, 7, 11, 13, 17, \ldots\},$$
$$B = \{x \mid x \in C \text{ and } x > 7\} = \{8, 9, 10, 11, 12, 13, \ldots\}.$$

Then the union of A and B is the set

$$A \cup B = \{2, 3, 5, 7, 8, 9, 10, 11, 12, 13, 14, 15, 16, 17, \ldots\}.$$

Observe that, in contrast to the first example, the union of the two subsets is not all of set S. What is the complement of $A \cup B$? Remember that the complement of $A \cup B$ is $\{x \mid x \in S \text{ and } x \notin A \cup B\}$.

3 To show how a diagram can be used to illustrate the union of two sets, we now choose the set of real numbers for S and let

$$A = \{x \mid x \in \mathfrak{R} \text{ and } x < -3\},$$
$$B = \{x \mid x \in \mathfrak{R} \text{ and } x > 1\}.$$

The standard description method of writing sets is convenient here because it is impossible to give even a partial tabulation of the infinite sets. The union of the sets is

$$A \cup B = \{x \mid x \in \mathfrak{R} \text{ and } x < -3 \text{ or } x > 1\}.$$

The one-to-one correspondence between the set of real numbers and the set of points in a line enables us to make a graph of $A \cup B$.

$\{x \mid x \in \mathfrak{R} \text{ and } x < -3 \text{ or } x > 1\}$

Display 21

The points in the heavily shaded open rays to the left of -3 and to the right of 1 correspond to the elements in $A \cup B$.

4 Similarly, we can use two-dimensional graphs to illustrate the union of sets of ordered pairs. Let S be the Cartesian product $\mathfrak{R} \times \mathfrak{R}$, and let

$$\begin{aligned} A &= \{(x, y) \mid x, y \in \mathfrak{R} \text{ and } x > y\}, \\ B &= \{(x, y) \mid x, y \in \mathfrak{R} \text{ and } y > 0\}. \end{aligned}$$

Partial graphs of A, of B, and of A ∪ B are given in Display 22.

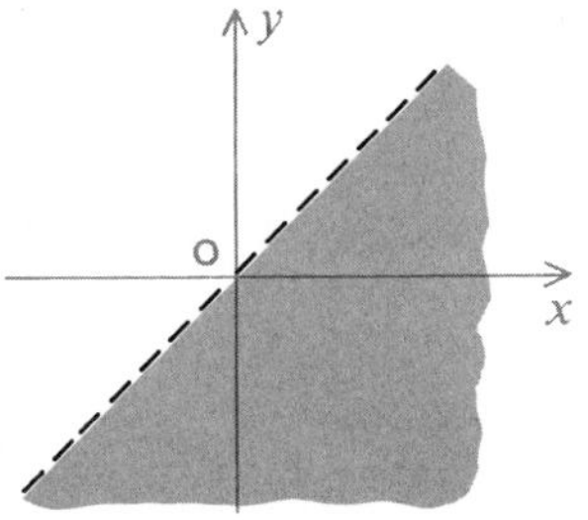

$A = \{(x, y) \mid x, y \in \mathfrak{R} \text{ and } x > y\}.$

Display 22a

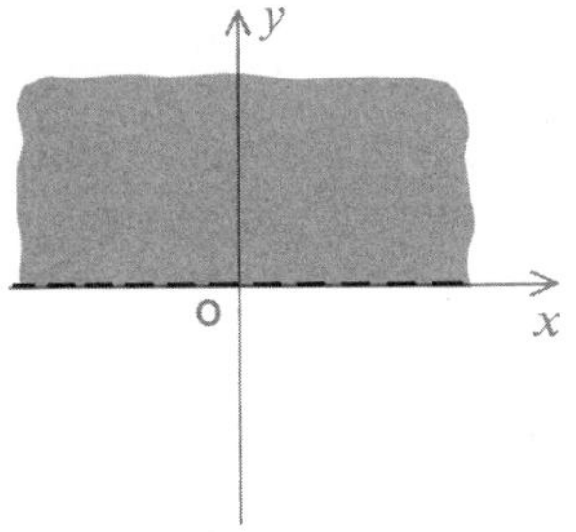

$B = \{(x, y) \mid x, y \in \mathfrak{R} \text{ and } y > 0\}.$

22b

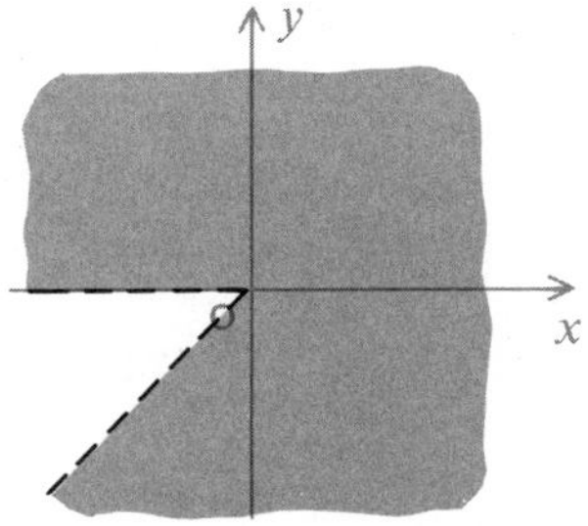

A ∪ B

22c

With these examples in mind, we will now verify that the operation of union of sets is a binary operation. We choose a set S and denote the collection of its subsets by $\mathbb{S}$. For particular sets A and B in $\mathbb{S}$ we represent the operation union by

$$(A, B) \xrightarrow{\cup} (A \cup B).$$

More generally, in terms of Definition 10/1, we have

$$\mathbb{S} \times \mathbb{S} \xrightarrow{\cup} \mathbb{S}.$$

The operation union has as its domain the Cartesian product $\mathbb{S} \times \mathbb{S}$ and has its range in set $\mathbb{S}$. In fact, this function is from $\mathbb{S} \times \mathbb{S}$ onto $\mathbb{S}$. To see that every set P in $\mathbb{S}$ is in the range of the function, observe that $P \cup \emptyset = P$, or $(P, \emptyset) \xrightarrow{\cup} P$.

Next we will define the intersection of sets and show that it, too, is a binary operation.

Definition 12/1 If S is a set, $\mathfrak{S}$ is the collection of subsets of S, and A and B are elements of $\mathfrak{S}$, then the *intersection* of A and B is the set of elements that are in both A and B. Symbolically, the intersection of A and B is $A \cap B = \{x \mid x \in A \text{ and } x \in B\}$.

Examples 1 As a first example, consider the following subsets of the counting numbers. We determined the union of these two sets in example 2 on page 40.

$$A = \{x \mid x \in C \text{ and } x \text{ is prime}\} = \{2, 3, 5, 7, 11, 13, 17, \ldots\},$$
$$B = \{x \mid x \in C \text{ and } x > 7\} = \{8, 9, 10, 11, 12, \ldots\}.$$

The elements common to both of these sets, that is, the intersection of A and B, are

$$A \cap B = \{x \mid x \in C \text{ and } x \text{ is prime and } x \text{ is greater than } 7\}$$
$$= \{11, 13, 17, 19, 23, \ldots\}.$$

2 Now consider the following subsets of C.

$$E_C = \{2, 4, 6, 8, 10, \ldots\},$$
$$O_C = \{1, 3, 5, 7, 9, \ldots\}.$$

Notice that these sets have no elements in common. Therefore,

$$E_C \cap O_C = \emptyset.$$

3 Let set S be the set of ordered pairs of real numbers, $\mathfrak{R} \times \mathfrak{R}$, with

$$A = \{(x, y) \mid x, y \in \mathfrak{R} \text{ and } x = y\},$$
$$B = \{(x, y) \mid x, y \in \mathfrak{R} \text{ and } x = y^2\}.$$

The intersection of A and B can be determined algebraically by solving the system

$$x = y,$$
$$x = y^2.$$

From these conditions, we obtain

$$y^2 - y = 0.$$

This condition is equivalent to

$$y(y - 1) = 0.$$

Thus, $y = 0$ and $y = 1$. Therefore,

$$A \cap B = \{(0, 0), (1, 1)\}.$$

We can also determine $A \cap B$ from the following graphs of relations A and B. We note that the two graphs intersect in points (0, 0) and (1, 1). (See Display 23.)

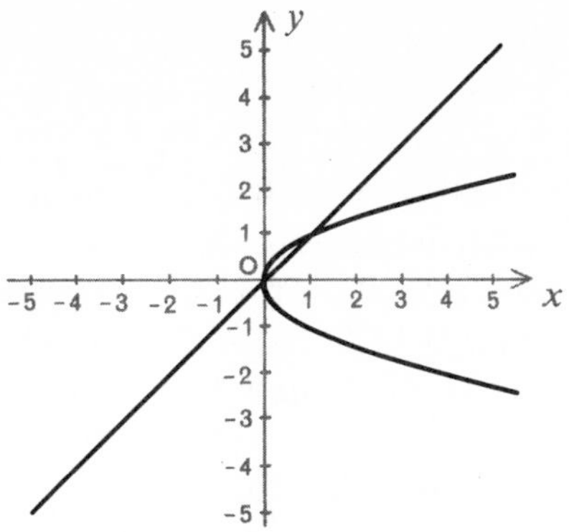

$A \cap B = \{(x, y) \mid x, y \in \Re, x = y, \text{ and } x = y^2\}$.

Display 23

By an argument analogous to the one given for the union of two sets, we can show that intersection of sets is also a binary operation. If S is a set and $\mathbb{S}$ denotes the set of subsets of S, then the function of intersection associates particular pairs of sets with their intersection. Thus,

$$(A, B) \xrightarrow{\cap} (A \cap B).$$

More generally,

$$\mathbb{S} \times \mathbb{S} \xrightarrow{\cap} \mathbb{S}.$$

Since the domain of the binary operation of intersection is $\mathbb{S} \times \mathbb{S}$, this function is from $\mathbb{S} \times \mathbb{S}$. Is the operation also onto $\mathbb{S}$?

Exercises In each of exercises 1 through 11, determine the intersection and the union of sets A and B, which are subsets of $\Re \times \Re$. Make graphs for exercises 1, 4, 7, and 11.

1 $A = \{(x, y) \mid 2x + 3y + 9 = 0\}$. $B = \{(x, y) \mid x - 2y = 13\}$.

2 $A = \{(x, y) \mid x^2 + y^2 = 25\}$. $B = \{(x, y) \mid 2x + y = 5\}$.

3 $A = \{(x, y) \mid 9x^2 + 25y^2 = 225\}$. $B = \{(x, y) \mid 5y = x^2 - 7\}$.

4 $A = \{(x, y) \mid xy = 13\}$. $B = \{(x, y) \mid 2y = 3x^2\}$.

5 $A = \{(x, y) \mid y = 10 - 2x\}$. $B = \{(x, y) \mid x^2 + y^2 = 16\}$.

6 $A = \{(x, y) \mid x^2 + y^2 = 9\}$. $B = \{(x, y) \mid y^2 - x^2 = 9\}$.

7 $A = \{(x, y) \mid |x| = 4\}$. $B = \{(x, y) \mid |y| = 3\}$.

8 $A = \{(x, y) \mid |y| = x^2\}$. $B = \{(x, y) \mid (x - 2)(y - 9) = 0\}$.

9 $A = \{(x, y) \mid y \geqq 0 \text{ and } x = y^2\}$.
$B = \{(x, y) \mid y \leqq 0 \text{ and } x = -y^2\}$.

10 $A = \{(x, y) \mid x \geqq 0 \text{ and } x^2 + y^2 = 16\}$.
$B = \{(x, y) \mid x < 0 \text{ and } 16x^2 + 25y^2 = 400\}$.

11 $A = \{(x, y) \mid -3 \leqq x < 5 \text{ and } y = |x|\}$.
$B = \{(x, y) \mid -3 < x \leqq 5 \text{ and } 4y = x + 15\}$. *Answer*

12 Prove that if A and B are nonempty subsets of S with $A \not\subseteq B$ and $B \not\subseteq A$, then $A \cup B$ is a nonempty subset of S such that $A \cup B \neq A$ and $A \cup B \neq B$.

◆ 13 Prove that if either A or B is an infinite subset of S, then $A \cup B$ is an infinite subset of S.

14 Give an example to show that there exist sets A and B that are infinite subsets of S and $A \cap B$ is infinite. Give another example where A and B are infinite and $A \cap B$ is finite.

15 Prove that if A and B are subsets of S, where $B = \emptyset$, then $A \cup B = A$ and $A \cap B = \emptyset$.

16 Prove that if A and B are subsets of S, then $A \cup B = A$ if and only if $B \subseteq A$.

◆ 17 Prove that if A and B are subsets of S, then $A \cup B = A \cap B$ if and only if $A = B$. *Answer*

18 Let S be a set and let $\mathbb{S}$ be the set of all subsets of S. Show that intersection from $\mathbb{S} \times \mathbb{S}$ is a binary operation.

Composition of functions

9/1

We have already considered binary operations on the elements of certain subsets of the real numbers as well as some examples of binary operations on the subsets of a set. Now we will consider a binary operation on a collection of functions. As you read the first example, try to decide how to define the operation so that ordered pairs of functions are associated with a third function in accordance with Definition 10/1.

Example 1 Let S be the set {1, 2, 3}. A *permutation* of S is a one-to-one function whose domain is S and whose range is S. There are six such permutations of this particular set. They are listed below.

$P_1 = \{(1, 1), (2, 2), (3, 3)\}$. $P_4 = \{(1, 1), (2, 3), (3, 2)\}$.
$P_2 = \{(1, 2), (2, 1), (3, 3)\}$. $P_5 = \{(1, 2), (2, 3), (3, 1)\}$.
$P_3 = \{(1, 3), (2, 2), (3, 1)\}$. $P_6 = \{(1, 3), (2, 1), (3, 2)\}$.

These six permutations include all possible ways of mapping three elements onto themselves. Therefore, it should be clear that no other one-to-one functions can be defined with set S as both the domain and the range.

We will now illustrate how to compose two of the functions given above. To do this, we can use diagrams to show what happens to elements in set S if we first apply one of the functions and then apply a second function. Diagrams for one such composition are given in Display 24.

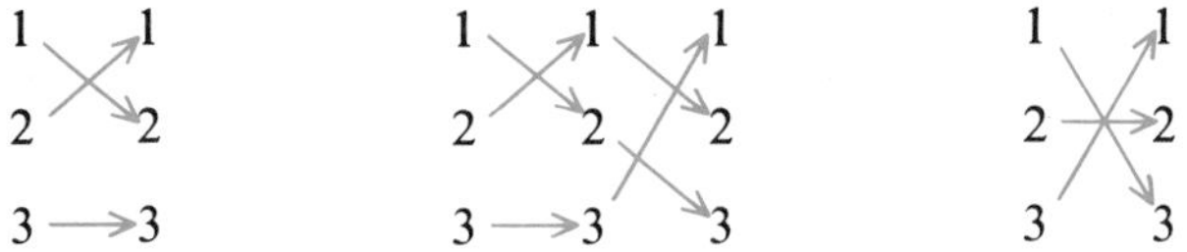

P_2 | $P_2 \circ P_5$ | $P_2 \circ P_5 = P_3$.

Display 24a | 24b | 24c

By following the paths of the arrows through the first two diagrams, we can see the image of an element as it is first acted upon by the permutation P_2 and then acted upon by the permutation P_5. Display 24c shows the result of the composition of P_2 and P_5. The symbol $\circ$ denotes the composition operation. From the diagrams we can see that $P_2 \circ P_5$ is $\{(1, 3), (2, 2), (3, 1)\}$, which is P_3. Thus, when we compose the two functions P_2 and P_5, we obtain the function P_3.

A second diagram that illustrates the composition of permutations P_3 and P_2 is shown in Display 25.

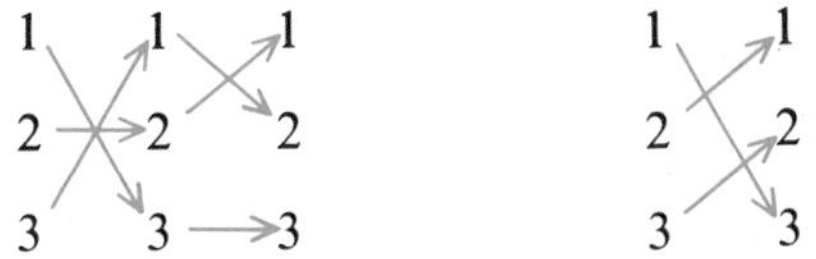

$P_3 \circ P_2$ | $P_3 \circ P_2 = P_6$.

Display 25a | 25b

This particular example deals only with the six functions on the set $S = \{1, 2, 3\}$. Nevertheless, it illustrates how to form a third function from two particular functions. The following definition of *composition* of functions is generalized, but is based on the principle that is illustrated by the specific example.

Definition 13/1 Let A, B, and D be sets and let f be a function whose domain is a subset of A and whose range is a subset of B. Further, let g be a function whose domain includes the range of f and whose range is a subset of D. Then the *composition* of f and g, $f \circ g$, is the function defined by

$$(x)f \circ g = \big((x)f\big)g,$$

where x is any element of A that is in the domain of f.

This process of the "passing on" of image elements of f by the function g is illustrated in Display 26. Observe that, if the image element (x)f is not in the domain of the function g, then it cannot be "passed on" to set D by the function g. From this arises the requirement that the domain of g must include the range of f.

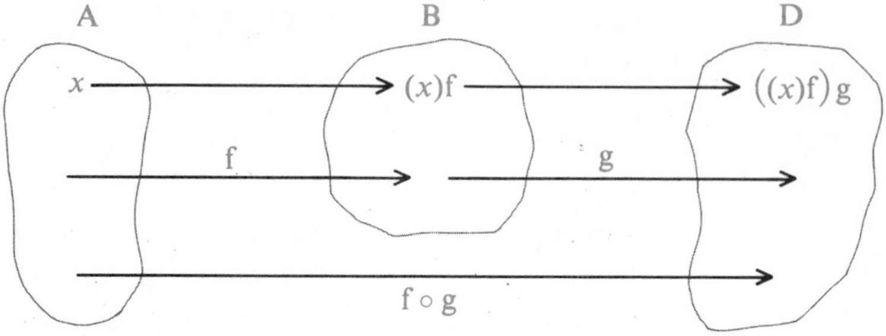

Display 26

Any function whose range is a set of real numbers satisfies the conditions given for function f in Definition 13/1. Such a function is called a *real-valued* function. The next example shows how to form the composition of two real-valued functions.

Examples 2a As a special case, it may happen that by composing two functions, we might map a given element back onto itself. For example, consider the function

$$f = \left\{(x, y) \mid x, y \in \mathfrak{R} \text{ and } y = \frac{3x - 5}{4}\right\}$$

and the function

$$g = \left\{(x, y) \mid x, y \in \mathfrak{R} \text{ and } y = \frac{4x + 5}{3}\right\}.$$

From the definition of composition of functions, for each x in the domain of f,

$$(x)\text{f} \circ \text{g} = \big((x)\text{f}\big)\text{g}.$$

Since the range of f and the domain of g are the same set, $\mathfrak{R}$, we may apply Definition 13/1. We have computed (6)f ∘ g below.

$$6 \searrow$$

$$(6)\text{f} = \frac{3(6) - 5}{4} = \tfrac{13}{4} \searrow$$

$$(\tfrac{13}{4})\text{g} = \frac{4(\frac{13}{4}) + 5}{3} = 6.$$

Hence, (6)f ∘ g = 6.

2b Now notice what happens to another element of $\Re$, -3, under the function $f \circ g$.

$$-3 \searrow (-3)f = \frac{3(-3) - 5}{4} = -\tfrac{7}{2} \searrow (-\tfrac{7}{2})g = \frac{4(-\frac{7}{2}) + 5}{3} = -3.$$

Thus, $(-3)f \circ g = -3$.

From these two examples, we might expect the function $f \circ g$ to be equal to

$$\{(x, y) \mid x, y \in \Re \text{ and } x = y\}.$$

Should this be true, then the composition of the two functions is a function that maps each element onto itself. Such a function is an *identity function.* To verify the assumption that $f \circ g$ is an identity function, we compute algebraically. The function f is given by

$$(x)f = \frac{3x - 5}{4},$$

and the function g is given by

$$(x)g = \frac{4x + 5}{3}.$$

By Definition 13/1, the composite function is given by

$$\begin{aligned}((x)f)g &= \left(\frac{3x - 5}{4}\right)g \\ &= \frac{4(\frac{3x-5}{4}) + 5}{3} \\ &= \frac{3x - 5 + 5}{3} \\ &= \frac{3x}{3} \\ &= x.\end{aligned}$$

This verifies that each element x of the domain of f is mapped onto itself by $f \circ g$. In other words $f \circ g$, for this pair of functions, is an identity function.

In Definition 13/1, we state that $f \circ g$ is a function. At this point, the statement is simply an assertion. However, the assertion can be proved, and we do so in the following theorem.

Theorem 2/1 Let A, B, and D be sets and let f be a function whose domain is included in A and whose range is included in B. Let g be a function whose domain includes the range of f and whose range is included in D. Then the domain of $f \circ g$ is the domain of f, and $f \circ g$ is a function in $A \times D$.

Proof If x is in the domain of f, then $(x)f \circ g = ((x)f)g$. Hence, $(x)f$ is in the domain of g, and this implies that x is in the domain of $f \circ g$. Since f is a function, it is single-valued. This means that, for each x in the domain of f, there is exactly one $(x)f$ in B. But g is also a function and, hence, single-valued. Therefore, for each $(x)f$, there is exactly one $((x)f)g$ in D. This shows that $f \circ g$ is single-valued.

The theorem shows that Definition 13/1 successfully establishes a means of creating a third function from an ordered pair (f, g) of functions, providing, of course, that the range of f is contained in the domain of g. For a particular collection of functions, then, we can exhibit another binary operation.

Examples 3 As an example, think again about the six permutations (functions) on the set $\{1, 2, 3\}$. If we denote this set of six functions by S_6, then the Cartesian product $S_6 \times S_6$ is the set of all ordered pairs of functions. With this set as the domain and the set S_6 as the range, we have an example of a binary operation that is the composition of the given functions. This binary operation can be denoted by

$$(f, g) \xrightarrow{\circ} f \circ g$$

or, more specifically, by

$$S_6 \times S_6 \xrightarrow{\circ} S_6.$$

4 As another example, let $\mathcal{F}$ be the set of all functions whose domain is the real numbers $\mathfrak{R}$ and whose range is a subset of $\mathfrak{R}$. Then the operation of composition from $\mathcal{F} \times \mathcal{F}$ is another example of a binary operation. Using the usual notation, we have

$$\mathcal{F} \times \mathcal{F} \xrightarrow{\circ} \mathcal{F}.$$

These examples are quite useful, and, as we proceed, we will have occasion to refer to them again.

Exercises For exercises 1 through 4, determine (a) the domain and the range of f, (b) the domain and the range of g and indicate whether or not the domain of g contains the range of f, (c) the function h, if it exists, such that $h = f \circ g$, and (d) the domain and the range of h.

1 Let $f = \{(x, y) \mid x, y \in \mathfrak{R} \text{ and } y = 9x^2\}$ and let $g = \{(x, y) \mid x, y \in \mathfrak{R} \text{ and } y = \sqrt{x} + 9\}$.

2 Let $f = \{(x, y) \mid x, y \in \mathfrak{R} \text{ and } y = \sqrt{3x + 1}\}$ and let $g = \{(x, y) \mid x, y \in \mathfrak{R} \text{ and } y = 2x^2\}$.

3 Let f $= \{(x, y) \mid x, y \in \mathfrak{R}$ and $y = x - 4\}$ and let
$g = \left\{(x, y) \mid x, y \in \mathfrak{R} \text{ and } y = \dfrac{3}{2x - 5}\right\}$. *Answer*

4 Let f $= \{(x, y) \mid x, y \in \mathfrak{R}$ and $y = |x - 2|\}$ and let
$g = \{(x, y) \mid x, y \in \mathfrak{R}$ and $y = \sqrt{4 - x}\}$.

5 What change could you make in the domain of f in exercise 3 so that $f \circ g$ would be defined?

6 What change could you make in the domain of f in exercise 4 so that $f \circ g$ would be defined?

For exercises 7 through 10, find examples of functions f and g into $\mathfrak{R}$ that satisfy the given conditions.

7 g is onto and $f \circ g$ is onto.

8 g is onto and $f \circ g$ is not onto.

9 f is not onto and $f \circ g$ is onto. *Answer*

10 f is not onto and $f \circ g$ is not onto.

◆ 11 Prove that, if $f \circ g$ is onto, then g is onto.

Equivalence relations

10/1

In sections 6 through 9 of this chapter, we investigated some of the properties of a special kind of relation called a function. Remember that the distinguishing characteristic of a function is that it is a single-valued relation. Functions are a very important subset of the set of relations, and the type of relation to be discussed in this section is also of importance as one of the unifying concepts of mathematics.

Whereas only one property is used to determine the subset of relations called functions, three properties are needed to select the subset of relations referred to as *equivalence relations*. These three properties will first be discussed in terms of familiar examples.

Example 1 The most frequently encountered equivalence relation in mathematics is the relation of equality. Although the concept of equality may be interpreted differently in different mathematical settings, in ordinary usage, the word *equal* means "identical" or "same." Consider what is meant by the relation of equality on the set of integers. We write $2 + 3 = 5$ and say "two plus three equals five." In this context, we mean that the numerals "five" and "two plus three" represent the same number. Now, the relation of equality on the set of integers satisfies the three properties that are necessary for an equivalence relation. First, each integer is equal to itself; that is, $x = x$ for each $x \in I$. Second, if $x = y$, then $y = x$ for each $x, y \in I$. Third, if $x = y$ and $y = z$, then

$x = z$ for each $x, y, z \in I$. These three properties, which are shared by all equivalence relations, are called the *reflexive*, *symmetric*, and *transitive properties*, respectively.

Examples 2 Another relation that we have already considered is the relation "subset of" for sets. This particular relation does *not* satisfy the three properties mentioned above, as the following discussion will establish. Note that the relation "subset of" is reflexive in subsets; that is, $A \subseteq A$ for all sets A. But observe that the relation "subset of" does not satisfy the symmetric property. To show this, it is sufficient to exhibit subsets A and B of a set S such that A is a subset of B but B is not a subset of A. Is the relation "subset of" transitive for sets? If you believe the relation does not satisfy the property, find a set S with subsets A, B, and C such that $A \subseteq B$ and $B \subseteq C$ are true but $A \subseteq C$ is false. To show that the property does hold, prove that for any sets A, B, and C with $A \subseteq B$ and $B \subseteq C$, it follows that $A \subseteq C$.

3 The relation "less than or equal" on the set of real numbers satisfies two of the properties of an equivalence relation. First, the relation is reflexive. That is, given a real number x, it is true that $x \leqq x$. However, the relation "less than or equal" is not symmetric. To see that the relation does not satisfy the symmetric property, we note that $2 \leqq 3$; but $3 \nleqq 2$. Finally, the relation "less than or equal" does satisfy the transitive property. If x, y, z are real numbers and if $x \leqq y$ and $y \leqq z$, then $x \leqq z$.

So far, we have seen one example of a relation that satisfies the reflexive, symmetric, and transitive properties (example 1) and examples of relations that satisfy only some of these properties (examples 2 and 3). We will now consider another familiar relation and show that it is reflexive, symmetric, and transitive.

4 One of the more important relations not yet discussed in this book is the relation "equivalent to" on the set of rational numbers. The definition of this relation is given below.

Definition 14/1 Let $R = \{\frac{a}{b} \mid a, b \in I, \text{ and } b \neq 0\}$ and let $\frac{a}{b}, \frac{c}{d} \in R$. Then $\frac{a}{b}$ is equivalent to $\frac{c}{d}$, denoted by $\frac{a}{b} \sim \frac{c}{d}$, if and only if $ad = bc$.

We will now establish that the relation "equivalent to" on the set of rational numbers satisfies the reflexive, symmetric, and transitive properties.

Theorem 3/1 If $\frac{a}{b}, \frac{c}{d}$, and $\frac{e}{f} \in R$, then the following properties hold.

1) $\frac{a}{b} \sim \frac{a}{b}$.
2) If $\frac{a}{b} \sim \frac{c}{d}$, then $\frac{c}{d} \sim \frac{a}{b}$.
3) If $\frac{a}{b} \sim \frac{c}{d}$ and $\frac{c}{d} \sim \frac{e}{f}$, then $\frac{a}{b} \sim \frac{e}{f}$.

Proof The proofs of the reflexive and symmetric properties are given below. The proof of transitivity is left as an exercise. These proofs are written in a style not previously used in this book, but one that you probably remember from your geometry course. The steps in the proof are in a column at the left and the reason, or reasons, for each step are in a column at the right. From time to time we will use this form of writing a proof.

Reflexive

$ab = ba.$	Commutative property of multiplication of integers
$\frac{a}{b} \sim \frac{a}{b}.$	Definition of "equivalent to" for elements of R (Definition 14/1)

Symmetric

$\frac{a}{b} \sim \frac{c}{d}.$	Hypothesis
$ad = bc.$	Definition of "equivalent to" for elements of R
$bc = ad.$	Symmetric property of equality for I
$cb = da.$	Commutative property of multiplication of integers
$\frac{c}{d} \sim \frac{a}{b}.$	Definition of "equivalent to" for elements of R

We have seen that some relations discussed in this section satisfy the reflexive, symmetric, and transitive properties and that others do not. We use the condition of satisfying all three of these properties as a means of distinguishing a special set of relations known as *equivalence relations.*

Definition 15/1 A relation R on a set A is an equivalence relation if and only if the relation has the following properties:

1) Reflexive: For each $a \in$ A, $(a, a) \in$ R.
2) Symmetric: If $(a, b) \in$ R, then $(b, a) \in$ R.
3) Transitive: If $(a, b) \in$ R and $(b, c) \in$ R, then $(a, c) \in$ R.

We will conclude this section with two examples not previously discussed.

Example 5 Consider the relation D on I^+, where I^+ is the set of positive integers, of all ordered pairs (a, b) such that a divides b. Recall that a divides b if and only if there exists an integer c such that $ac = b$. Some ordered pairs in the relation D on I^+ are listed below.

$$(2, 6) \in D \text{ because } 2 \cdot 3 = 6.$$
$$(1, 5) \in D \text{ because } 1 \cdot 5 = 5.$$
$$(17, 51) \in D \text{ because } 17 \cdot 3 = 51.$$
$$(8, 24) \in D \text{ because } 8 \cdot 3 = 24.$$
$$(1, n) \in D \text{ because } 1 \cdot n = n.$$
$$(n, n) \in D \text{ because } n \cdot 1 = n.$$

We observe that the relation D on I^+ is reflexive because a divides a for every positive integer a. Why? However, the relation is not symmetric. To establish that the symmetric property does not hold, it is sufficient to find a pair (a, b) such that a divides b, but b does not divide a. Such a pair is (6, 12). Name other pairs for which the symmetric property does not hold. What must be true of a and b if a pair $(a, b) \in D$ satisfies the symmetric property? We establish that the relation D on I^+ is transitive as follows: If a divides b, then there exists $x \in I^+$ such that $ax = b$; and if b divides c, then there exists $y \in I^+$ such that $by = c$. But $ax = b$ and $by = c$ imply that $(ax)y = c$ and, by the associative property of integers, $a(xy) = c$. We know that $x \in I^+$ and $y \in I^+$ imply that $xy \in I^+$. Therefore, a divides c, for there exists an integer $xy \in I^+$ such that $a(xy) = c$. We have just shown that $(a, b) \in D$ and $(b, c) \in D$ together imply that $(a, c) \in D$ and, thus, that the relation D on I^+ is transitive.

Example 6 The final example of this section shows how the domain of a function can be partitioned into subsets such that each element of a particular subset has the same image element in the range of the function.

Let f be a function from A into B. Now, for elements x_1 and x_2 in the domain of f, we define x_1 equivalent to x_2 if and only if $(x_1)f = (x_2)f$. We will show that this is an equivalence relation.

Theorem 4/1 Let A and B be sets in which equality on set B is an equivalence relation and let f be a function from A into B. Let R be the relation defined by $(x_1, x_2) \in R$ if and only if $(x_1)f = (x_2)f$. Then the relation R is an equivalence relation.

Proof In order to establish the reflexive property, we must show that, for each $x \in A$, $(x)f = (x)f$. But equality is reflexive since it is an equivalence relation. Therefore, $(x)f = (x)f$, and $(x, x) \in R$.

Now, to establish the symmetric property, we let $(x_1, x_2) \in R$. In other words, we assume that x_1 and x_2 are elements of A such that $(x_1)f = (x_2)f$. We must now show that (x_2, x_1) is also in the relation R. But it is known that equality on set B satisfies the symmetric property, so $(x_2)f = (x_1)f$. By the definition of R, it follows that $(x_2, x_1) \in R$. Thus, if $(x_1, x_2) \in R$, then $(x_2, x_1) \in R$.

To establish the transitive property for this relation, let (x_1, x_2), $(x_2, x_3) \in R$. That is, suppose that x_1, x_2, and x_3 are elements of A such that $(x_1)f = (x_2)f$ and $(x_2)f = (x_3)f$. By the transitive property of equality on set B, it follows that $(x_1)f = (x_3)f$. Thus, by the definition of R, $(x_1, x_3) \in R$, and the transitive property is established.

It is often helpful to interpret theorems in terms of specific examples, so we list one particular illustration of Theorem 4/1. Let f be a function on the real numbers determined by the condition that $y = (x)f$ is the greatest integer less than or equal to x. Some particular examples of elements in the function are given in the following statements:

$$(\tfrac{1}{2})f = 0. \qquad (-4)f = -4.$$
$$(2\tfrac{1}{4})f = 2. \qquad (\sqrt{2})f = 1.$$
$$(5.2)f = 5. \qquad (-\tfrac{3}{4})f = -1.$$

The partial graph of this function is given in Display 27.

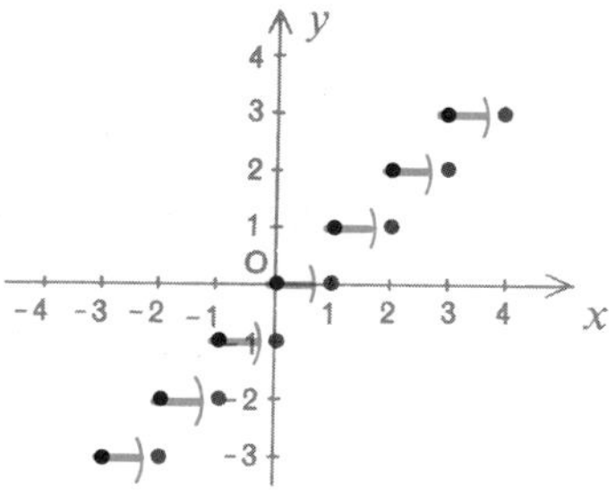

Display 27

Notice that $(\frac{1}{2}, \frac{3}{4}) \in R$ because $\frac{1}{2}$ and $\frac{3}{4}$ both have 0 as their image; similarly, $(-1.5, -2) \in R$ because -1.5 and -2 both have -2 as their image. In general, each integer y in the range of this function is the image of a set of domain elements in the interval $y \leqq x < y + 1$, and every domain element is contained in exactly one such set.

Exercises For exercises 1 through 9, determine which properties of an equivalence relation are satisfied.

1 T is the set of triangles in a plane; $R = \{(x, y) \mid x, y \in T$ and $x \cong y\}$.

2 L is the set of lines in a plane; $R = \{(x, y) \mid x, y \in L$ and $x \parallel y\}$.

3 L is the set of lines in a plane; $R = \{(x, y) \mid x, y \in L$ and $x \perp y\}$.

4 I is the set of integers; $R = \{(x, y) \mid x, y \in I$ and $x < y\}$.

5 M is a set of men; $R = \{(x, y) \mid x, y \in M$ and x is a brother of $y\}$.

6 P is a set of parcels; $R = \{(x, y) \mid x, y \in P$ and x weighs within 1 pound of $y\}$. *Answer*

7 B is a set of boys; $R = \{(x, y) \mid x, y \in B$ and x is not the same age as $y\}$.

8 $\Re$ is the set of real numbers; $R = \{(x, y) \mid x, y \in \Re$ and $|x| = y\}$.

9 J is a set of cities; $R = \{(x, y) \mid x, y \in J$ and x is 50 miles from $y\}$.

◆ **10** Prove that the relation "equivalent to" on the set of rational numbers is transitive.

11 Show that the relation "subset of" for sets does not satisfy the symmetric property.

12 Is the relation "subset of" transitive? Justify your answer.

The integers modulo n

11/1

The sequence of topics—namely, sets, Cartesian sets, relations, and functions—has led to the subject of equivalence relations. Some examples of equivalence relations were discussed in section 10/1. We conclude the chapter with another example of an equivalence relation that utilizes many of the topics discussed previously and that at the same time provides us with a useful example of a mathematical system.

To begin the development of the integers modulo n, we must recall a property of division of integers that you may have first studied in connection with division of counting numbers. We now state this property for integers.

Let a and n be integers with $n > 0$. The *division algorithm* asserts the existence of unique integers q and r such that

$$a = qn + r, 0 \leqq r < n.$$

Example The division algorithm for $n = 3$ is illustrated below.

$$
\begin{array}{r}
a = q \cdot n + r. \\
\hline
\vdots \\
-4 = -2 \cdot 3 + 2. \\
-3 = -1 \cdot 3 + 0. \\
-2 = -1 \cdot 3 + 1. \\
-1 = -1 \cdot 3 + 2. \\
0 = 0 \cdot 3 + 0. \\
1 = 0 \cdot 3 + 1. \\
2 = 0 \cdot 3 + 2. \\
3 = 1 \cdot 3 + 0. \\
4 = 1 \cdot 3 + 1. \\
5 = 1 \cdot 3 + 2. \\
6 = 2 \cdot 3 + 0. \\
7 = 2 \cdot 3 + 1. \\
\vdots
\end{array}
$$

Display 28

Notice that, when the division algorithm is applied to the integers, with n as the fixed integer 3, the same remainder r recurs in a definite pattern. We can form sets of those elements with the same remainder so that there are three disjoint subsets of the integers. The three subsets formed are shown below, and each subset is named by the corresponding remainder for the members of the set: the remainder for each member of the first set is 0, of the second set, 1, and of the third set, 2. We have used a bar above these numerals, $\bar{0}$, $\bar{1}$, and $\bar{2}$, to prevent confusion of the subsets with the integers 0, 1, and 2 that are elements of the subsets.

$$\bar{0} = \{\ldots, -6, -3, 0, 3, 6, 9, \ldots\}.$$
$$\bar{1} = \{\ldots, -5, -2, 1, 4, 7, 10, \ldots\}.$$
$$\bar{2} = \{\ldots, -4, -1, 2, 5, 8, 11, \ldots\}.$$

The example on page 54 shows that there is a relation between the integers in a given subset that arises as a result of expressing them in terms of the division algorithm. We can state this relation as follows. Two integers are related (are members of the same subset) if and only if they have the same remainder in the division algorithm.

Although this example makes clear how to define a relation in what seems to be a natural way, the example is but the special case where $n = 3$. However, it does point the way to defining a more general relation for any positive integer n.

Definition 16/1 Let $a, b \in \mathrm{I}$ and let

$$a = qn + r,$$
$$b = q_1 n + r_1,$$

with $0 \leqq r < n$ and $0 \leqq r_1 < n$, with $n, q, q_1, r, r_1 \in \mathrm{I}$, and with $n > 0$. Then a relation R_n in $\mathrm{I} \times \mathrm{I}$ is defined in the following way: $(a, b) \in \mathrm{R}_n$ if and only if $r = r_1$. If $(a, b) \in \mathrm{R}_n$, then we say that a is *congruent* to b modulo n. Symbolically, $a \equiv b \bmod n$ if and only if $(a, b) \in \mathrm{R}_n$.

To illustrate the definition, we will consider some specific examples.

Example 1 As a first example, we will determine whether or not $(42, 17) \in \mathrm{R}_5$. We can use the division algorithm for integers to express 42 and 17 as follows.

$$42 = 8 \cdot 5 + 2.$$
$$17 = 3 \cdot 5 + 2.$$

Since the remainders are equal, we conclude that $(42, 17) \in \mathrm{R}_5$ is true, or $42 \equiv 17 \bmod 5$.

Example 2 Next, we will determine whether or not $(127, 90) \in R_8$. We can express 127 and 90 in the following way.

$$127 = 15 \cdot 8 + 7.$$
$$90 = 11 \cdot 8 + 2.$$

Since the remainders 7 and 2 are not the same, we conclude that $(127, 90) \notin R_8$. Alternatively, we may write $127 \not\equiv 90 \bmod 8$.

These examples should make clear how to decide the truth or falsity of $(x, y) \in R_n$ for any x, y, and n.

The proof of the following theorem establishes that congruence modulo n is an equivalence relation.

Theorem 5/1 The relation "congruent modulo n" on the set of integers, denoted by R_n, is an equivalence relation.

Proof It is necessary to establish that R_n satisfies the reflexive, symmetric, and transitive properties.

Reflexive

Let $a \in I$ with $a = qn + r$ and $a = q_1n + r_1$. It is required to show that $r = r_1$ and, hence, that $(a, a) \in R_n$. But the division algorithm asserts that, for any given a and n, the numbers q and r are unique. Therefore, $r = r_1$, and $a \equiv a \bmod n$.

Symmetric

If $(a, b) \in R_n$, with $a = qn + r$ and $b = q_1n + r_1$, then $r = r_1$. But by the symmetric property of equality on the set of integers, if $r = r_1$, then $r_1 = r$. Thus, $b = q_1n + r_1$, $a = qn + r$, and $r_1 = r$ imply that $(b, a) \in R_n$. This establishes the symmetric property.

Transitive

If $(a, b) \in R_n$ and $(b, c) \in R_n$ with $a = qn + r$, $b = q_1n + r_1$, and $c = q_2n + r_2$, then $r = r_1$, and $r_1 = r_2$. Since $r = r_1$, $r_1 = r_2$, and the relation equality is transitive on I, it follows that $r = r_2$. Thus, $a = qn + r$, $c = q_2n + r_2$, and $r = r_2$ imply that $(a, c) \in R_n$. This establishes the transitive property.

In the example on page 54, we observed that, when n is chosen to be 3 in $a = qn + r$, precisely three subsets of the integers are formed. These sets are tabulated again below.

$$\bar{0} = \{\ldots, -6, -3, 0, 3, 6, 9, \ldots\}.$$
$$\bar{1} = \{\ldots, -5, -2, 1, 4, 7, 10, \ldots\}.$$
$$\bar{2} = \{\ldots, -4, -1, 2, 5, 8, 11, \ldots\}.$$

The three sets $\bar{0}$, $\bar{1}$, and $\bar{2}$ are called the *equivalence classes* of the integers modulo 3. These subsets of I have two important properties that we will point out. What is $\bar{0} \cap \bar{1}$? What is $\bar{0} \cap \bar{2}$? What is $\bar{1} \cap \bar{2}$? What is the intersection of any two of the three sets? What is $(\bar{0} \cup \bar{1}) \cup \bar{2}$? What is the union of all the subsets? We note the following properties:

1) The intersection of any pair of equivalence classes of the integers modulo 3 is $\emptyset$.
2) The union of the three equivalence classes of the integers modulo 3 is the set of integers.

Here again we are dealing with a special example from which a more general result is apparent.

If we choose an integer $n > 0$ to establish the congruences modulo n, then there are precisely n equivalence classes. The equivalence classes of the integers modulo n are:

$$\begin{aligned}
\bar{0} &= \{\ldots,\ -2n,\ -n,\ 0,\ n,\ 2n,\ \ldots\}.\\
\bar{1} &= \{\ldots,\ -2n+1,\ -n+1,\ 1,\ n+1,\ 2n+1,\ \ldots\}.\\
\bar{2} &= \{\ldots,\ -2n+2,\ -n+2,\ 2,\ n+2,\ 2n+2,\ \ldots\}.\\
&\ \vdots\\
\bar{i} &= \{\ldots,\ -2n+i,\ -n+i,\ i,\ n+i,\ 2n+i,\ \ldots\}.\\
&\ \vdots\\
\overline{n-1} &= \{\ldots,\ -n-1,\ -1,\ n-1,\ 2n-1,\ 3n-1,\ \ldots\}.
\end{aligned}$$

A comparison of these equivalence classes shows that, as for the integers modulo 3, the intersection of any two classes is the empty set and that the union of all n equivalence classes is the set of integers. These results follow from the fact that a unique r does exist for each a and n in the division algorithm, $a = qn + r$, $0 \leqq r < n$. The set of integers modulo n, $\{\bar{0},\ \bar{1},\ \bar{2},\ \ldots,\ \overline{n-1}\}$, is just the set of equivalence classes modulo n.

This discussion suggests that an equivalence relation on a set S subdivides the set into *pairwise disjoint sets* whose union is set S. This is in fact the case, and a statement of the relationship between an equivalence relation on a set and a *partition* (for this is what a collection of subsets with these two properties is called) of the set is contained in Theorem 6/1. No proof of this theorem is given here.

Theorem 6/1 Let S be a set and R an equivalence relation on S. Let S_a denote the set of elements of S that are related to a; that is, let $S_a = \{x \mid x \in S \text{ and } (a, x) \in R\}$. Then the set $\mathcal{P}$ of subsets S_a, where $a \in S$, is called a *partition* of S and has the following properties:

1) Any pair of distinct subsets in $\mathcal{P}$ are disjoint.
2) The union of the subsets in $\mathcal{P}$ is S.

A companion theorem, also not proved here, shows how partitions give rise to equivalence relations.

Theorem 7/1 Let $\mathcal{P}$ be a collection of subsets of S such that any two distinct subsets in $\mathcal{P}$ are disjoint and the union of the subsets in $\mathcal{P}$ is S.

Let a relation R on S be defined by $(a, b) \in R$ if and only if a and b are in the same subset of $\mathcal{P}$. Then R is an equivalence relation on S.

We close this section with a comment about the integers modulo n. There is another method that can be used to develop the system of integers modulo n. We have chosen to use the division algorithm to motivate the definition; an alternative procedure is to use differences to define equivalence classes. This method of development has been included as exercises 2 and 3 in the following set of exercises.

Exercises

1 Determine the set of replacements for x such that the following conditions are satisfied.

a $x \equiv 5 \bmod 8$.
b $x \equiv 6 \bmod 4$.
c $x \equiv 10 \bmod 3$.
d $x \equiv 4 \bmod 9$.
e $x \equiv 2 \bmod 7$.
f $23 \equiv x \bmod 6$.
g $14 \equiv x \bmod 2$.
h $85 \equiv x \bmod 11$.
i $36 \equiv 9 \bmod x$. *Answer*
j $57 \equiv 10 \bmod x$.
k $x \equiv 3 \bmod 5$ and $x \equiv 7 \bmod 12$.
l $x \equiv 10 \bmod 6$ and $x \equiv 7 \bmod 9$. *Answer*
m $x \equiv 1 \bmod 4$ and $x \equiv 6 \bmod 8$.
n $x \equiv 12 \bmod 15$ or $x \equiv 8 \bmod 3$.

◆ 2 Prove that, if $(a, b) \in R_n$, where R_n denotes the relation of congruence modulo n, then there is an integer k such that $a - b = kn$. *Answer*

◆ 3 Prove that, for a positive integer n and integers a and b, if there exists $k \in I$ such that $a - b = kn$, then $(a, b) \in R_n$. *Answer*

4 Consider the equivalence classes of the integers modulo 5. Call these sets $\bar{0}$, $\bar{1}$, $\bar{2}$, $\bar{3}$, and $\bar{4}$. Determine the equivalence class modulo 5 to which each of the following integers belongs.

a $12 + 15$
b $92 + 39$
c $57 + 26$
d $41 + 64$
e $6 + 21$
f $-16 + 25$
g $-31 + 9$
h $37 + 8$
i $36 + 58$
j $53 + 20$
k $78 + 29$
l $13 + 38$
m $-86 + (-12)$
n $-61 + (-18)$

5 Make an addition table for the integers modulo 5. *Answer*

6 Make a multiplication table for the integers modulo 5.

7 Determine the equivalence class of the integers modulo 7 to which each of the following integers belongs.

a 14
b 38
c -27
d 110
e -3
f 86
g -50
h -116

8 Repeat exercise 7, this time for the integers modulo 9.

9 Repeat exercise 7, this time for the integers modulo 12.
10 Make an addition table for the integers modulo 6.
11 Make a multiplication table for the integers modulo 6. *Answer*

Chapter review This test covers many of the main ideas discussed in Chapter 1. There will be two tests for each of the subsequent chapters of this book: a chapter review that covers the material presented in that particular chapter and a cumulative review that covers the major ideas presented thus far in the book.

1 The collection of sets, $\{\{\emptyset\}, \{\emptyset\}\}$, has ~~~ elements.
a 0 b 1 c 2 d 3
2 Give three mathematical descriptions of the empty set.
3 Let S be a set. For subsets A and B of S, A = B if and only if $A \subseteq B$ and $B \subseteq A$. Is equality defined in this way an equivalence relation?
4 Describe the set of all points in Euclidean two-space and denote this set as $\mathfrak{R} \times \mathfrak{R}$. Is $\{(x, y) \mid x, y \in \mathfrak{R},\ x > 0, \text{ and } y < 0\}$ a subset of $\mathfrak{R} \times \mathfrak{R}$? Is this set finite or is it infinite?
5 Let S and T be sets with m and n elements, respectively. How many relations are there in $S \times T$?
6 Let $S = \{1, 2, 3\}$ and $T = \{a, b\}$. List all the functions F in $S \times T$ with domain S_1 and range T_1 as described below.
a $S_1 = S$, $T_1 = \{a\}$.
b $S_1 = \{2\}$, $T_1 = \{b\}$.
c $S_1 = S$, $T_1 = T$.
7 For exercise 6, determine which functions F are one-to-one, which are onto T, and which are both one-to-one and onto.
8 Prove that $(A \cap B) \cup C = (A \cup C) \cap (B \cup C)$ for any sets A, B, and C.
9 Let $R = \{(x, y) \mid x, y \in \mathfrak{R} \text{ and } y = -(x^3)\}$. Is R a function?
10 Let $C \times C \xrightarrow{\star} C$ be the function such that $c \star d = (c + d)d$ for each $c, d \in C$. Is this function a binary operation?
11 Let $S = \{a, b\}$. Write the set of permutations on S in ordered-pair notation. Show that the composition of any two such functions is a permutation on S.
12 Let $S \xrightarrow{f} T$ and $T \xrightarrow{g} W$ be functions. Prove that if the composition $f \circ g$ is one-to-one, then f is one-to-one.
13 Find sets S, T, and W and functions f and g, with $S \xrightarrow{f} T$ and $T \xrightarrow{g} W$, such that f is not onto T but $f \circ g$ is onto W.
14 List the equivalence classes for the integers modulo 6.
15 Let $A = \{2x \mid x \in I\}$. Describe a set B such that $\mathcal{P} = \{A, B\}$ is a partition of I. How are sets A and B commonly described?

Chapter **2**

Groups

12 *Closure of binary operations*

13 *The associative property of binary operations*

14 *Semi-groups and the existence of an identity*

15 *Semi-groups and the existence of inverses*

16 *Properties of groups*

17 *Symmetric groups and permutation groups*

18 *Commutative groups*

19 *Subgroups of a group*

20 *Intersection and union of subgroups*

21 *Cyclic groups*

22 *Classification of cyclic groups*

23* *The Cartesian product of groups*

[* *indicates optional sections.*]

24* *Construction of finite commutative groups*

Introduction

In Chapter 1 we first considered sets, relations, and functions. Then we viewed a binary operation as a special type of function. Now we will again consider sets, together with binary operations, in constructing and analyzing mathematical systems with one binary operation. We will begin the chapter with a discussion of various properties of binary operations. Then, in the remainder of the chapter, we will classify sets with a binary operation according to certain properties that they satisfy.

Closure of binary operations

12/2

Before we turn to the major topic of this section, let us review some notation from Chapter 1. Suppose that A and B are sets and that f is a function whose domain is A × A and whose range is included in B. In short, suppose that f is a binary operation. Such functions may be represented by

$$A \times A \xrightarrow{f} B.$$

Keep in mind that sets A and B are independent in the sense that no restriction, such as $A \subset B$, $B \subset A$, $B \cap A = \emptyset$, or the like, has been necessarily imposed on them. In particular, it is *not* required that $A = B$. We have already discussed examples from arithmetic in which sets A and B are different. Some of these examples are reviewed below.

Examples 1 For set C (the counting numbers), the operation of subtraction is such that the domain is $C \times C$, but the range is not a subset of C. The range is included in set I (the integers). This follows from the fact that the difference of two counting numbers may or may not be a counting number; however, the difference of any two counting numbers is always an integer. Thus, in the expression

$$A \times A \xrightarrow{f} B,$$

$A = C$ and $B = I$.

2 Another example that illustrates the same principle is the binary operation of division from $C \times C$ into R. The domain of this binary operation is $C \times C$, and the range is included in the set of rational numbers. The similarity of this example to example 1 lies in the fact that the quotient of two counting numbers, like the difference of two counting numbers, may or may not be a counting number. Consider, for example, the quotients $\frac{6}{2}$ and $\frac{7}{2}$. The first of these, $\frac{6}{2} = 3$, shows that the quotient of two counting numbers may be a counting number. The second, $\frac{7}{2} = 3\frac{1}{2}$, shows that the quotient is not necessarily a counting number. Therefore, sets A and B in the general notation,

$$A \times A \xrightarrow{f} B,$$

are C and R, respectively.

3 As a third example in which A and B are different sets, consider the binary operation of addition from $O_C \times O_C$. The sum of two odd counting numbers is even, not odd. Consequently, the binary operation of addition of odd counting numbers is such that $A = O_C$ and $B = E_C$.

You can perhaps think of other binary operations in which the set used to form the domain is different from the set that includes the range of the operation. We will now consider several examples of a binary operation in which the sets A and B are equal and in which the range equals set B.

Example 4 The sum of two whole numbers is a whole number and, consequently, A and B are both equal to the set of whole numbers in

$$A \times A \xrightarrow{f} B.$$

In other words,

$$W \times W \xrightarrow{+} W.$$

The list of such examples can be made quite long; so we will collect several examples in this paragraph. Addition of integers is another example in which A and B are equal sets. The binary operation of subtraction from I × I is also one for which A and B are equal sets. Addition of rational numbers is still another example in which the set used in forming the domain and the range are the same set, as is subtraction of rational numbers. Multiplication of integers, multiplication of rational numbers, and division of nonzero rational numbers are three more examples of binary operations, $A \times A \xrightarrow{f} B$, in which A and B are equal sets. The table in Display 29 illustrates these examples and other binary operations in which the set used to form the Cartesian product that is the domain and the set that is the range are the same. Instead of the letter "f," we have used the symbol that commonly denotes the operation in arithmetic.

$W \times W \xrightarrow{+} W.$	$C \times C \xrightarrow{\cdot} C.$	$I \times I \xrightarrow{-} I.$
$I \times I \xrightarrow{+} I.$	$I \times I \xrightarrow{\cdot} I.$	$R \times R \xrightarrow{-} R.$
$R \times R \xrightarrow{+} R.$	$R \times R \xrightarrow{\cdot} R.$	$R \times R \xrightarrow{\div} R.$*
$\mathfrak{R} \times \mathfrak{R} \xrightarrow{+} \mathfrak{R}.$	$\mathfrak{R} \times \mathfrak{R} \xrightarrow{\cdot} \mathfrak{R}.$	$\mathfrak{R} \times \mathfrak{R} \xrightarrow{\div} \mathfrak{R}.$*

Display 29

From the foregoing discussion, it should be clear that we can classify binary operations on the basis of whether or not the range is a subset (proper or improper) of the set used to form the Cartesian product that is the domain. This property is described formally in the definition below.

Definition 17/2 Let f be a function whose domain is A × A and whose range is set B. Then f is said to be *closed* if and only if set B is included in set A. Symbolically, the operation $A \times A \xrightarrow{f} B$ is closed if and only if $B \subseteq A$.

The property that a binary operation must satisfy to be closed is given in Definition 17/2. All of the operations described in Display 29 satisfy Definition 17/2 and, hence, are closed. In the

*For the first of these two examples, R represents the *nonzero* rational numbers. For the second, $\mathfrak{R}$ represents the *nonzero* real numbers.

following discussion, we will use the definition to prove that certain other binary operations satisfy the closure property. First we will consider sets and operations already known to you. Then we will introduce some sets not previously considered in this book, define appropriate operations on them, and show that these operations also satisfy the closure property.

Theorem 8/2 The set of even counting numbers E_C is closed under addition.

You should keep in mind that, when we say, as in Theorem 8/2, that a *set* is closed under a specific operation, we mean that the *operation* from $A \times A$ onto B, where B is a subset of A, is closed. Thus, the theorem could be stated as follows: The binary operation of addition from $E_C \times E_C$ is closed.

In example 5 on page 38 of Chapter 1, we showed that $x, y \in E_C$ implies that $x + y \in E_C$. Hence, the range of the operation is a subset of E_C, and Theorem 8/2 has already been proved. Explain why the range is a proper subset of E_C.

Theorem 9/2 The set of odd counting numbers O_C is closed under multiplication.

Proof Let x and y be odd counting numbers. Then there exist whole numbers m and n such that $x = 2m + 1$ and $y = 2n + 1$. Why? By the properties of whole numbers, we have

$$x \cdot y = (2m + 1)(2n + 1) = 4mn + 2m + 2n + 1.$$

So, $x \cdot y = 2(2mn + m + n) + 1$. Since $2mn + m + n$ is a whole number, $2(2mn + m + n) + 1$ is of the form $2a + 1$, where a is a whole number. Consequently, the product of two odd counting numbers is an odd counting number. Is the range all of O_C?

The examples given so far in this section have dealt with familiar subsets of the real numbers, such as the counting numbers, the integers, and the rational numbers. In the next example, we will also use a subset of the real numbers, but one which may not be as familiar to you as the earlier examples. Therefore, we will first define this set of elements, describe the operations on this set, and then prove the closure property for addition.

Definition 18/2 The set of even integers E_I extended by $\sqrt{2}$, designated by $E_I(\sqrt{2})$, is the subset of all real numbers of the form $a + b\sqrt{2}$ where $a, b \in E_I$. Symbolically,

$$E_I(\sqrt{2}) = \{a + b\sqrt{2} \mid a, b \in E_I\}.$$

Since the set $E_I(\sqrt{2})$ is a subset of the set of real numbers, and since you already know how to find sums and products of real numbers, the following definitions for addition and multiplication should make sense to you and should not require explanation.

If $a + b\sqrt{2}$ and $c + d\sqrt{2}$ are elements of $E_I(\sqrt{2})$, then

$$(a + b\sqrt{2}) + (c + d\sqrt{2}) = (a + c) + (b + d)\sqrt{2},$$

and

$$(a + b\sqrt{2}) \cdot (c + d\sqrt{2}) = (ac + 2bd) + (ad + bc)\sqrt{2}.$$

Some specific examples of sums and products of pairs of elements contained in $E_I(\sqrt{2})$ are given below.

Examples 1 $(2 + 4\sqrt{2}) + (-6 + 8\sqrt{2}) =$
$$\big(2 + (-6)\big) + (4 + 8)\sqrt{2} = -4 + 12\sqrt{2}.$$

2 $\big(6 + (-2\sqrt{2})\big) + \big(-14 + (-4\sqrt{2})\big) =$
$$\big(6 + (-14)\big) + \big(-2 + (-4)\big)\sqrt{2} = -8 + (-6\sqrt{2}).$$

3 $(-4 + 2\sqrt{2}) \cdot \big(-8 + (-2\sqrt{2})\big) =$
$$\big((-4)(-8) + (2)(2)(-2)\big) + \big((-4)(-2) + (2)(-8)\big)\sqrt{2} = 24 + (-8\sqrt{2}).$$

4 $(6 + 0\sqrt{2}) \cdot (-4 + 4\sqrt{2}) =$
$$\big((6)(-4) + (2)(0)(4)\big) + \big((6)(4) + (0)(-4)\big)\sqrt{2} = -24 + 24\sqrt{2}.$$

5 $(2 + 4\sqrt{2}) \cdot \big(2 + (-4\sqrt{2})\big) =$
$$\big((2)(2) + (2)(4)(-4)\big) + \big((2)(-4) + (4)(2)\big)\sqrt{2} = -28 + 0\sqrt{2} = -28.$$

Theorem 10/2 The set $E_I(\sqrt{2})$ is closed under the operation of addition.

Proof The binary operation of addition for elements of $E_I(\sqrt{2})$ has as its domain $E_I(\sqrt{2}) \times E_I(\sqrt{2})$. We will now establish that the sum of two elements of $E_I(\sqrt{2})$ is also an element of $E_I(\sqrt{2})$. The steps in the argument, along with the reason for each step, are given below.

1) $a + b\sqrt{2},\ c + d\sqrt{2} \in E_I(\sqrt{2})$.	Given
2) $(a + b\sqrt{2}) + (c + d\sqrt{2}) = (a + c) + (b + d)\sqrt{2}$.	Definition of addition
3) $a + c \in E_I$.	Closure property of E_I under addition
4) $b + d \in E_I$.	Closure property of E_I under addition
5) $(a + c) + (b + d)\sqrt{2} \in E_I(\sqrt{2})$.	Definition of $E_I(\sqrt{2})$

The binary operation of multiplication from $E_I(\sqrt{2}) \times E_I(\sqrt{2})$ also satisfies the closure property and, by using the preceding argument as a pattern, you should be able to establish this property.

The extension of the even integers by $\sqrt{2}$ is achieved by combining (in the fashion described in Definition 18/2) $\sqrt{2}$ with the set E_I. We will now build a set by extending the integers by the complex number i, which is defined so that $i^2 = -1$. The resulting set is a subset of the complex numbers. This set and corresponding operations are analogous in many ways to $E_I(\sqrt{2})$.

Definition 19/2 The set of integers extended by i, denoted by $G(i)$, is the set of all complex numbers of the form $a + bi$, where $a, b \in I$ and $i^2 = -1$. Symbolically, $G(i) = \{a + bi \mid a, b \in I \text{ and } i^2 = -1\}$.

The set $G(i)$ is called the set of *Gaussian integers* after the famous German mathematician C. F. Gauss (1777-1855). Since $G(i)$ is a subset of the complex numbers, the operations of addition and multiplication of complex numbers may be applied to the elements of $G(i)$. The formulas that yield the sum and product of an arbitrary pair of elements in $G(i)$ are

$$(a + bi) + (c + di) = (a + c) + (b + d)i,$$
$$(a + bi) \cdot (c + di) = (ac - bd) + (ad + bc)i.$$

Some specific examples of sums and products are given below.

Examples 1 $(-3 + 5i) + (6 - 8i) = (-3 + 6) + (5 - 8)i = 3 - 3i.$

2 $(11 - 6i) + (-8 + 4i) = (11 - 8) + (-6 + 4)i = 3 - 2i.$

3 $(3 + 5i) \cdot (2 - 6i) =$
$$\big((3)(2) - (5)(-6)\big) + \big((3)(-6) + (2)(5)\big)i = 36 - 8i.$$

4 $(4 + 0i) \cdot (3 + 4i) =$
$$\big((4)(3) - (0)(4)\big) + \big((4)(4) + (0)(3)\big)i = 12 + 16i.$$

5 $(7 + 2i) \cdot (-7 + 2i) =$
$$\big((7)(-7) - (2)(2)\big) + \big((7)(2) + (2)(-7)\big)i = -53.$$

Theorem 11/2 The set $G(i)$ is closed under the operation of addition.

Proof No reasons are given for the steps in the proof below, and you should supply the appropriate reasons. It will be helpful to reread the proof of Theorem 10/2.

1) $a + bi, c + di \in G(i)$.
2) $(a + bi) + (c + di) = (a + c) + (b + d)i$.
3) $a + c \in I$.
4) $b + d \in I$.
5) $(a + c) + (b + d)i \in G(i)$.

We have already given a definition of the product of two elements in $G(i)$. The following theorem establishes that multiplication from $G(i) \times G(i)$ is a closed binary operation.

Theorem 12/2 The set G(i) is closed under the operation of multiplication.

Proof The steps and the appropriate reasons are stated below.

1) $a + bi, c + di \in G(i)$.	Given
2) $(a + bi) \cdot (c + di) = (ac - bd) + (ad + bc)i$.	Definition of multiplication
3) $ac - bd \in I$.	Closure properties of I under multiplication and subtraction
4) $ad + bc \in I$.	Closure properties of I under multiplication and addition
5) $(ac - bd) + (ad + bc)i \in G(i)$.	Definition of G(i)

The last two examples of closed binary operations to be given in this section involve the set of equivalence classes of the integers modulo n. Recall that, if n is a counting number, then the set of integers modulo n is a set of equivalence classes,

$$I/n = \{\bar{0}, \bar{1}, \bar{2}, \ldots, \overline{n-1}\}.$$

We will now define addition for the set of integers modulo n (denoted by $\oplus_n$ and called *modular addition*), give some examples, and show that this binary operation satisfies the closure property.

Definition 20/2 Let I/n denote the set of equivalence classes of the integers modulo n, with $n \in I$ and $n > 0$; that is, let

$$I/n = \{\bar{0}, \bar{1}, \ldots, \overline{n-1}\}.$$

If $\bar{a}, \bar{b} \in I/n$, with $0 \leqq a < n$ and $0 \leqq b < n$, then the *sum* of $\bar{a}$ and $\bar{b}$, denoted by $\bar{a} \oplus_n \bar{b}$, is $\bar{r}$, where $a + b = qn + r, 0 \leqq r < n$, and $q, r \in I$.

Notice that modular addition is defined in terms of the equivalence classes of I/n. Addition tables for the integers modulo n where $n = 3$ and $n = 5$ are given in Display 30. You should

$n = 3$.

$\oplus_3$	$\bar{0}$	$\bar{1}$	$\bar{2}$
$\bar{0}$	$\bar{0}$	$\bar{1}$	$\bar{2}$
$\bar{1}$	$\bar{1}$	$\bar{2}$	$\bar{0}$
$\bar{2}$	$\bar{2}$	$\bar{0}$	$\bar{1}$

Display 30a

$n = 5$.

$\oplus_5$	$\bar{0}$	$\bar{1}$	$\bar{2}$	$\bar{3}$	$\bar{4}$
$\bar{0}$	$\bar{0}$	$\bar{1}$	$\bar{2}$	$\bar{3}$	$\bar{4}$
$\bar{1}$	$\bar{1}$	$\bar{2}$	$\bar{3}$	$\bar{4}$	$\bar{0}$
$\bar{2}$	$\bar{2}$	$\bar{3}$	$\bar{4}$	$\bar{0}$	$\bar{1}$
$\bar{3}$	$\bar{3}$	$\bar{4}$	$\bar{0}$	$\bar{1}$	$\bar{2}$
$\bar{4}$	$\bar{4}$	$\bar{0}$	$\bar{1}$	$\bar{2}$	$\bar{3}$

30b

study the tables carefully to see how Definition 20/2 has been used to determine the entries in the table. From these examples, it appears that I/n is closed under modular addition. Theorem 13/2 establishes this fact for any positive integer n.

Theorem 13/2 The set of integers modulo n, I/n, is closed under the operation of modular addition.

Proof Definition 20/2 outlines a procedure for obtaining the sum of two equivalence classes. If $\bar{a}$, $\bar{b}$ represent the classes, first the sum of the integers a and b is obtained in the usual way. This sum is then expressed as the sum of a multiple of n and a remainder r by means of the division algorithm. Finally, the equivalence class to which r belongs, that is, $\bar{r}$, is defined to be the sum of $\bar{a}$ and $\bar{b}$. Since r satisfies the condition $0 \leqq r < n$, the equivalence class $\bar{r}$ is in the set of integers modulo n. Hence, $\bar{a} \oplus_n \bar{b}$, which is equal to $\bar{r}$, is in I/n, and the closure property follows.

We will now define *modular multiplication* of the elements of I/n (denoted by $\odot_n$), give some examples, and show that the set I/n is closed under modular multiplication.

Definition 21/2 Let I/n denote the set of equivalence classes of the integers modulo n with $n \in$ I and $n > 0$; that is, let

$$I/n = \{\bar{0}, \bar{1}, \bar{2}, \ldots, \overline{n-1}\}.$$

If $\bar{a}, \bar{b} \in$ I/n, with $0 \leqq a < n$ and $0 \leqq b < n$, then the product of $\bar{a}$ and $\bar{b}$, denoted by $\bar{a} \odot_n \bar{b}$, is $\bar{r}$, where $a \cdot b = qn + r, 0 \leqq r < n$, and $q, r \in$ I.

Multiplication tables for the integers modulo n for the special cases of $n = 3$, 4, and 5 are given in Display 31.

$n = 3$.

$\odot_3$	$\bar{0}$	$\bar{1}$	$\bar{2}$
$\bar{0}$	$\bar{0}$	$\bar{0}$	$\bar{0}$
$\bar{1}$	$\bar{0}$	$\bar{1}$	$\bar{2}$
$\bar{2}$	$\bar{0}$	$\bar{2}$	$\bar{1}$

Display 31a

$n = 4$.

$\odot_4$	$\bar{0}$	$\bar{1}$	$\bar{2}$	$\bar{3}$
$\bar{0}$	$\bar{0}$	$\bar{0}$	$\bar{0}$	$\bar{0}$
$\bar{1}$	$\bar{0}$	$\bar{1}$	$\bar{2}$	$\bar{3}$
$\bar{2}$	$\bar{0}$	$\bar{2}$	$\bar{0}$	$\bar{2}$
$\bar{3}$	$\bar{0}$	$\bar{3}$	$\bar{2}$	$\bar{1}$

31b

$n = 5$.

$\odot_5$	$\bar{0}$	$\bar{1}$	$\bar{2}$	$\bar{3}$	$\bar{4}$
$\bar{0}$	$\bar{0}$	$\bar{0}$	$\bar{0}$	$\bar{0}$	$\bar{0}$
$\bar{1}$	$\bar{0}$	$\bar{1}$	$\bar{2}$	$\bar{3}$	$\bar{4}$
$\bar{2}$	$\bar{0}$	$\bar{2}$	$\bar{4}$	$\bar{1}$	$\bar{3}$
$\bar{3}$	$\bar{0}$	$\bar{3}$	$\bar{1}$	$\bar{4}$	$\bar{2}$
$\bar{4}$	$\bar{0}$	$\bar{4}$	$\bar{3}$	$\bar{2}$	$\bar{1}$

31c

The following theorem concerning closure of modular multiplication can be proved in much the same way that we proved Theorem 13/2. The details of the proof are left as an exercise.

Theorem 14/2 The set I/n is closed under modular multiplication.

In this section we have observed that some binary operations do not satisfy the closure property (examples 1, 2, and 3 on page 61), while others do satisfy this property (all of the remaining examples). It follows that a natural subdivision of binary operations with respect to this property is possible, and the remainder of the chapter is devoted to a study of those binary operations with the closure property. It should be pointed out that in some books the closure property is given as a part of the definition of a binary operation. You should keep this in mind to avoid confusion as you read other books.

It is convenient to have special notation for an arbitrary set with a *closed* binary operation, and we will adopt the symbol (S, ☆) for this purpose. The symbol S denotes the set that is involved, no matter whether the set is the complex numbers, the real numbers, the integers, some subset of one of these sets, or some different set. The symbol ☆ may represent such closed binary operations as addition of real numbers, multiplication of complex numbers, or whatever operation is being considered.

Exercises

1 Decide whether or not the following sets are closed under the given binary operations.

a $(E_C, -)$

b $(E_C, \cdot)$ *Answer*

c $(O_C, \cdot)$

d $(O_C, -)$

e $(I^+, +)$, where I^+ is the set of positive integers

f $(I^+, \cdot)$

g $(I^-, \div)$, where I^- is the set of negative integers

h $(I^-, -)$

i $\left(O_C(\sqrt{3}), +\right) = (\{a + b\sqrt{3} \mid a, b \in O_C\}, +)$.

j $\left(R(\sqrt{2}), \cdot\right) = (\{a + b\sqrt{2} \mid a, b \in R\}, \cdot)$.

k $\left(I(\sqrt[3]{2}), +\right) = (\{a + b\sqrt[3]{2} \mid a, b \in I\}, +)$. *Answer*

l $\left(O_I(\sqrt{2}), \cdot\right) = (\{a + b\sqrt{2} \mid a, b \in O_I\}, \cdot)$.

m $\left(I(\sqrt{2}), -\right) = (\{a + b\sqrt{2} \mid a, b \in I\}, -)$.

n $\left(G(i), -\right) = (\{a + bi \mid a, b \in I \text{ and } i^2 = -1\}, -)$.

o $\left(R(\sqrt{5}), -\right) = (\{a + b\sqrt{5} \mid a, b \in R\}, -)$.

p $\left(I^+(\sqrt{2}), -\right) = (\{a + b\sqrt{5} \mid a, b \in I^+\}, -)$.

q $\left(I(\sqrt[3]{2}), \cdot\right)$. *Answer*

◆ 2 Prove that the set of integers modulo n under the binary operation of modular multiplication given in Definition 21/2 satisfies the closure property.

◆ 3 Let $\mathcal{S}$ be the set of all subsets of a given set. (Remember the null set, $\emptyset$, is a subset of every set.) Prove that $(\mathcal{S}, \cup)$ and $(\mathcal{S}, \cap)$ each satisfy the closure property.

◆ 4 Let A be a nonempty set. Consider the set of all functions f with domain A and range a subset of A. That is, let $A \xrightarrow{f} A$. Let $\mathcal{F}$ represent the set of all such functions and let $\circ$ denote the composition of two functions in $\mathcal{F}$. For all f, g $\in \mathcal{F}$ show that f $\circ$ g $\in \mathcal{F}$; that is, show that the domain of f $\circ$ g is set A and the range is in A. This proves that the binary operation of composition of this special class of functions is closed. *Answer*

5 Prove that

a $(\{7x \mid x \in I\}, +)$ satisfies the closure property.

b $(\{7x \mid x \in I\}, \cdot)$ satisfies the closure property.

c $(\{7x \mid x \in I\}, -)$ satisfies the closure property.

6 Which of the following sets under the given binary operations satisfy the closure property?

a $(I, \star)$, where $x \star y = x^2 + |y|$

b $(I, \star)$, where $x \star y = (xy) - (x + y)$

c $(\mathfrak{R}, \star)$, where $x \star y = x + y + xy$

d $(I^+, \star)$, where $x \star y = (x + y) - xy$

e $(R, \star)$, where $x \star y = x + \frac{1}{2}y$

f $(I, \star)$, where $x \star y = (x - x)y$

g $(E_I, \star)$, where $x \star y = \frac{1}{2}xy$ *Answer*

h $(C, \star)$, where $x \star y = (x + 1)(y + 1)$

i $(\mathfrak{R}, \star)$, where $x \star y = x$

j $(R, \star)$, where $x \star y = |xy|$

k $(I, \star)$, where $x \star y = \max\{x, y\}$; that is, $x \star y = x$ if $x \geqq y$ and $x \star y = y$ if $x < y$

l $(C, \star)$, where $x \star y = [x + y]$; that is, $x \star y$ is the greatest integer less than or equal to $x + y$

Exercises 2 and 3 of section 11/1 established an alternative (equivalent) definition for the equivalence classes of the integers modulo n. The following exercise is directed toward the formulation of an alternative definition for addition from $I/n \times I/n$. An example from $I/5 = \{\bar{0}, \bar{1}, \bar{2}, \bar{3}, \bar{4}\}$ will help in motivating this definition. Observe that

$$\bar{1} \oplus_5 \bar{2} = \bar{3} \text{ since } 3 = 0 \cdot 5 + 3$$

and that

$$\bar{3} \oplus_5 \bar{4} = \bar{2} \text{ since } 7 = 1 \cdot 5 + 2.$$

In the second example, we might write

$$\bar{3} \oplus_5 \bar{4} = \bar{7}.$$

This is permissible since, for I/5, it is true that

$$\bar{7} = \bar{2}.$$

It is the generalization of this idea that leads to the following definition.

Definition 20a/2 (*alternative*) Let I/n denote the set of equivalence classes of the integers modulo n, with $n \in I$, $n > 0$; that is, let $I/n = \{\bar{0}, \bar{1}, \ldots, \overline{n-1}\}$. If $\bar{a}, \bar{b} \in I/n$, then the sum of $\bar{a}$ and $\bar{b}$, denoted by $\bar{a} \oplus_n \bar{b}$, is $\overline{a+b}$.

7 a Show that Definition 20a/2 implies that if $\bar{b} = \bar{c}$, then $\bar{a} \oplus_n \bar{b} = \bar{a} \oplus_n \bar{c}$. [Hint: $\bar{b} = \bar{c}$ implies that $b \equiv c \mod n$.]
b Prove that $\bar{a} \oplus_n \bar{b} = \bar{r}$, where $a \cdot b = qn + r$, $0 \leqq r < n$, and $\bar{a} \oplus_n \bar{b} = \overline{a+b}$ are equivalent definitions. That is, show that $\bar{r} = \overline{a+b}$.

In Definition 21/2 we defined multiplication from $I/n \times I/n$. Consider the following definition for modular multiplication.

Definition 21a/2 (*alternative*) Let I/n denote the set of equivalence classes of the integers modulo n, with $n \in I$, $n > 0$; that is, let $I/n = \{\bar{0}, \bar{1}, \ldots, \overline{n-1}\}$. If $\bar{a}, \bar{b} \in I/n$, then the product of $\bar{a}$ and $\bar{b}$, denoted by $\bar{a} \odot_n \bar{b}$, is $\overline{a \cdot b}$.

8 a Show that, for Definition 21a/2, if $\bar{b} = \bar{c}$, then $\bar{a} \odot_n \bar{b} = \bar{a} \odot_n \bar{c}$.
b Prove that $\bar{a} \odot_n \bar{b} = \bar{r}$, where $a \cdot b = qn + r$, $0 \leqq r < n$, and $\bar{a} \odot_n \bar{b} = \overline{a \cdot b}$ are equivalent definitions; that is, show that $\bar{r} = \overline{a \cdot b}$.

The associative property of binary operations

13/2

Those binary operations that satisfy the closure property have been chosen for special study in this and the following sections. It will be helpful to remember that we have selected from among the set of all relations the set of functions and from among the set of all functions the set of binary operations. We have now made the further restriction to the set of binary operations that are closed. In the next few sections, we will make restrictions on the set of closed binary operations. The goal of this entire process is the development of a mathematical structure known as a *group*.

In this section we will single out those systems with closed binary operations that have the *associative property*, which will be precisely defined a bit later. Some systems with closed binary operations are associative, while others are not; and we will begin with several examples of each kind.

Examples 1 First consider addition of counting numbers. This example is a natural one to consider, since addition of counting numbers is one of the most common operations in mathematics and since it is certainly the earliest example studied in elementary arithmetic. Again, it is important to keep in mind that the operations we are discussing are *binary*; that is, the domain of each operation is a Cartesian product, which may be represented by A × A. This means that the operation is defined on pairs of elements. Yet, at a very early age, you no doubt learned how to compute sums represented by expressions such as $2 + 3 + 5$. In fact, you certainly know how to form sums with three or more addends in different ways. Two different ways to compute the sum $2 + 3 + 5$ are

$$2 + 3 + 5 = (2 + 3) + 5 = 5 + 5 = 10,$$

$$2 + 3 + 5 = 2 + (3 + 5) = 2 + 8 = 10.$$

In essence, what we do is associate the addends so that we have only two. Thus, in the expression $(2 + 3) + 5$, $(2 + 3)$ is one addend and 5 is the other; in $2 + (3 + 5)$, 2 is one addend and $(3 + 5)$ is the other. The associative property assures us that both methods of associating will give the same result.

But addition of counting numbers is not the only binary operation that is associative. In example 2 below, the system is the set of counting numbers and the binary operation is multiplication. In examples 3 and 4 we have computed sums in the set of integers and the set of rational numbers, respectively. These three examples illustrate the associativity of the given operations.

2 $(4 \cdot 3) \cdot 7 = 12 \cdot 7 = 84.$
$4 \cdot (3 \cdot 7) = 4 \cdot 21 = 84.$

3 $(-3 + 2) + 4 = -1 + 4 = 3.$
$-3 + (2 + 4) = -3 + 6 = 3.$

4 $(\frac{1}{2} + 3) + (-\frac{2}{3}) = 3\frac{1}{2} + (-\frac{2}{3}) = 2\frac{5}{6}.$
$\frac{1}{2} + \left(3 + (-\frac{2}{3})\right) = \frac{1}{2} + 2\frac{1}{3} = 2\frac{5}{6}.$

On the other hand, some binary operations do not have this property. Given next are examples chosen from systems that have closed binary operations which are not associative. The operations are not associative because the results are different when the numbers are grouped in different ways. In example 5 the system is (I, −), in example 6 the system is (R, −), and in example 7 the system is (R^+, ÷).

Examples 5 $(6 - 4) - 3 = 2 - 3 = -1.$
$6 - (4 - 3) = 6 - 1 = 5.$

6 $(\frac{1}{3} - 3) - \frac{2}{3} = -2\frac{2}{3} - \frac{2}{3} = -3\frac{1}{3}.$
$\frac{1}{3} - (3 - \frac{2}{3}) = \frac{1}{3} - (2\frac{1}{3}) = -2.$

7 $(\frac{2}{3} \div \frac{1}{2}) \div 5 = \frac{4}{3} \div 5 = \frac{4}{15}.$
$\frac{2}{3} \div (\frac{1}{2} \div 5) = \frac{2}{3} \div \frac{1}{10} = \frac{20}{3}.$

It is now clear that we can extend the concept of a binary operation to include cases in which the sum or product involves more than two numbers. It is also clear that we can associate elements and, in some cases, achieve the same result regardless of how the elements are grouped. Those closed binary operations that give the same result for different groupings of three or more terms are said to be *associative*. A formal statement of this property for a set S and an operation ☆ is given in Definition 22/2.

Definition 22/2 If ☆ is a closed binary operation from S × S, then ☆ is associative if and only if, for each $x, y, z \in S$,

$$(x \star y) \star z = x \star (y \star z).$$

Notice that the word "associative" is well chosen, since the grouping of terms is a process that associates pairs of elements from among the three elements. The examples preceding the definition make clear that some binary operations are associative and that other such familiar binary operations as subtraction and division are not. We will now give several more examples of binary operations with the associative property.

Example 8 As the first of these examples, consider the composition of two functions. In the exercises at the end of the previous section, it was established that, if the range is a subset of the domain, then the binary operation of composition of functions is closed (exercise 4, page 69). We will now show that the closed binary operation of composition of functions on this set of functions satisfies the associative property.

Proving the associative property of composition of functions requires the idea of equality of two functions. The meaning of equality of functions has not yet been stated, but recall that equal usually means identical. This is precisely the meaning of equality that is adopted in the following definition.

Definition 23/2 Let f and g be functions with the same domain A and with ranges included in a set B. Then f = g if and only if, for each $x \in A$, $(x)f = (x)g$.

We can now use Definition 23/2 to show that, when composition of functions is closed, then this binary operation is associative.

Theorem 15/2 Let A be a set of elements and let $\mathcal{F}$ be the set of functions with domain A and range a subset of A. Then set $\mathcal{F}$ under the operation of composition, denoted by $\circ$, is associative. In function notation,

$$(f \circ g) \circ h = f \circ (g \circ h)$$

for all functions f, g, h $\in \mathcal{F}$.

Proof For each $x \in A$, we have

$(x)\big((f \circ g) \circ h\big) = \big((x)(f \circ g)\big)h$	Definition of the composition of $(f \circ g)$ and h
$= \big([(x)f]g\big)h$	Definition of the composition of f and g
$= \big((x)f\big)(g \circ h)$	Definition of the composition of g and h
$= (x)\big(f \circ (g \circ h)\big).$	Definition of the composition of f and $g \circ h$
$(f \circ g) \circ h = f \circ (g \circ h).$	Definition 23/2

Because the proof looks more difficult than it really is, the diagrams in Display 32 are given as an aid in interpreting the proof.

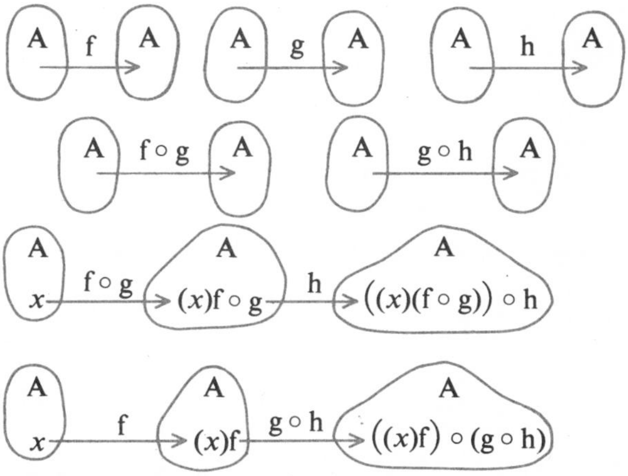

Display 32

We began this chapter with the basic concept of a binary operation and first differentiated closed operations from those that are not closed. Now we have differentiated closed binary operations that are associative from those that are not associative. By this process, we have developed a mathematical system that is called a *semi-group*.

Definition 24/2 If S is a set and ☆ is a closed binary operation on S that satisfies the associative property, then the system (S, ☆) is a *semi-group*.

Observe that, in a semi-group, because of the associative property, the operation can be extended to three (as opposed to two) elements. The associative property makes it possible to define $a \star b \star c$ as either $(a \star b) \star c$ or $a \star (b \star c)$ for each $a, b, c \in S$. It should be clear that the associative property can be extended to include four or five or any finite number of terms. In fact, this is one of the properties we use when we add long columns of figures.

Example 9 In connection with this example, we will define a new binary operation on the set of counting numbers and then determine whether or not it is an associative operation.

Definition 25/2 If C is the set of counting numbers, then for each $a, b \in C$, operation ☆ is defined as

$$a \star b = a + b + ab.$$

Some calculations using this operation are given below.

$$2 \star 3 = 2 + 3 + (2 \cdot 3) = 11.$$
$$1 \star 6 = 1 + 6 + (1 \cdot 6) = 13.$$
$$3 \star 4 = 3 + 4 + (3 \cdot 4) = 19.$$

From Definition 25/2 we know that ☆ is a binary operation from C × C and that it is closed. Why? The domain of the operation is C × C. Prove that the range of the operation is a proper subset of C by finding at least one element of C that is not in the range. The set of counting numbers under the binary operation ☆ just defined is associative, as is proved in the following theorem.

Theorem 16/2 If $a, b \in C$ and the operation ☆ is defined as

$$a \star b = a + b + ab,$$

then (C, ☆) is a semi-group.

Proof To prove Theorem 16/2, we must show that ☆ is a closed binary operation from C × C that satisfies the associative property.

By Definition 25/2 and closure of addition and multiplication of counting numbers, we know that ☆ is a closed binary operation from C × C. The steps below show that ☆ satisfies the associative property. Supply the proper reason (or reasons) for each step.

$$\begin{aligned}(a \star b) \star c &= (a + b + ab) \star c \\ &= (a + b + ab) + c + (a + b + ab)c \\ &= a + b + ab + c + ac + bc + abc.\end{aligned}$$

$$\begin{aligned}a \star (b \star c) &= a \star (b + c + bc) \\ &= a + (b + c + bc) + a(b + c + bc) \\ &= a + b + c + bc + ab + ac + abc \\ &= a + b + ab + c + ac + bc + abc.\end{aligned}$$

Therefore,

$$(a \star b) \star c = a \star (b \star c).$$

Example 10 To conclude this section, we will discuss the integers modulo n under the operation of modular addition and decide if this system is a semi-group. Remember that modular addition from $I/n \times I/n$ is defined as follows for integers a and b:

$$\bar{a} \oplus_n \bar{b} = \bar{r},$$

where $0 \leqq a < n, 0 \leqq b < n$, $a + b = qn + r$, and $0 \leqq r < n$.

Theorem 17/2 The system $(I/n, \oplus_n)$ is a semi-group.

Proof We have established in the proof of Theorem 13/2 that the set I/n under the operation of modular addition is closed. The proof of Theorem 17/2 depends, therefore, upon proving that, for each $\bar{a}, \bar{b}, \bar{c} \in I/n$,

$$(\bar{a} \oplus_n \bar{b}) \oplus_n \bar{c} = \bar{a} \oplus_n (\bar{b} \oplus_n \bar{c}).$$

First, we simplify each side of the equality as follows:

$$\begin{aligned}(\bar{a} \oplus_n \bar{b}) \oplus_n \bar{c} &= \bar{r}_1 \oplus_n \bar{c}, \text{ where } a + b = q_1 n + r_1 \text{ and } 0 \leqq r_1 < n \\ &= \bar{r}_2, \text{ where } r_1 + c = q_2 n + r_2 \text{ and } 0 \leqq r_2 < n. \\ \bar{a} \oplus_n (\bar{b} \oplus_n \bar{c}) &= \bar{a} \oplus_n \bar{r}_3, \text{ where } b + c = q_3 n + r_3 \text{ and } 0 \leqq r_3 < n \\ &= \bar{r}_4, \text{ where } a + r_3 = q_4 n + r_4 \text{ and } 0 \leqq r_4 < n.\end{aligned}$$

In these steps we have used the definition of addition for elements of I/n (Definition 20/2). It remains to show that $\bar{r}_2 = \bar{r}_4$. From the equalities given above, we have

$$\begin{aligned}r_2 &= r_1 + c - q_2 n \\ &= (a + b - q_1 n) + c - q_2 n. \\ r_4 &= a + r_3 - q_4 n \\ &= a + (b + c - q_3 n) - q_4 n.\end{aligned}$$

Either $r_2 \geqq r_4$ or $r_4 \geqq r_2$. Let us assume that $r_2 \geqq r_4$. Now by subtraction,

$$\begin{aligned} r_2 - r_4 &= -q_1 n - q_2 n + q_3 n + q_4 n \\ &= (-q_1 - q_2 + q_3 + q_4)n. \end{aligned}$$

The expression $(-q_1 - q_2 + q_3 + q_4)n$ tells us that the difference of r_2 and r_4 is an integral multiple of n, say kn. Why? That is, $r_2 - r_4 = kn$. Since $r_2 \geqq r_4$ by assumption, $kn \geqq 0$. But $r_2 = r_4 + kn$ and $0 \leqq r_2 - r_4 < n$. Because $r_2 - r_4 = kn$, it follows that $0 \leqq kn < n$. We now have $n > 0$ and $kn \geqq 0$, and $kn < n$. These three conditions are satisfied only if $k = 0$. Hence, $kn = 0$ and $r_2 - r_4 = 0$. Thus, $r_2 = r_4$. This implies that $\bar{r}_2 = \bar{r}_4$. If we had assumed that $r_4 \geqq r_2$, we could have used a similar argument to show that $\bar{r}_4 = \bar{r}_2$. The proof of the theorem is complete.

Exercises

1 Tell which of the systems given below satisfy the associative property.

a $(E_I, \cdot)$
b $(I^+, -)$
c $(E_C, -)$
d $(O_C, \cdot)$
e $(R(\sqrt{2}), +)$
f $(G(i), \cdot)$ *Answer*
g $(R^+, \div)$
h $(O_I(\sqrt{2}), -)$

2 Prove that the system $(\{7x \mid x \in I\}, +)$ satisfies the associative property. Is this system a semi-group?

◆ 3 Let $\mathbb{S}$ be the set of all subsets of a given set S. Prove that $(\mathbb{S}, \cup)$ and $(\mathbb{S}, \cap)$ are both semi-groups. *Answer*

◆ 4 Prove that the set of integers modulo n under modular multiplication forms a semi-group.

5 Which of the following systems are semi-groups?

a $(I, ☆)$, where $x ☆ y = x^2 + |y|$ *Answer*
b $(I^+, ☆)$, where $x ☆ y = (xy) \div (x + y)$
c $(\mathfrak{R}, ☆)$, where $x ☆ y = y^2 - y + x$
d $(R^+, ☆)$, where $x ☆ y = (x + y) \div xy$
e $(R, ☆)$, where $x ☆ y = (x - x)y$
f $(E_C, ☆)$, where $x ☆ y = \frac{1}{2}xy$ *Answer*
g $(I, ☆)$, where $x ☆ y = x$
h $(C, ☆)$, where $x ☆ y = \max\{x, y\}$. That is, $x ☆ y = x$ if $x \geqq y$, and $x ☆ y = y$ if $x < y$.
i $(R, ☆)$, where $x ☆ y = [xy]$. That is, $x ☆ y$ is the greatest integer less than or equal to xy. *Answer*
j $(\mathfrak{R}, ☆)$, where $x ☆ y = |x| + |y|$

Semi-groups and the existence of an identity

14/2

In section 13/2 we observed that a system with a closed binary operation satisfying the associative property is called a semi-group. In this section we will be concerned with a property that some semi-groups satisfy but that others do not. Listed below are several examples of semi-groups that have been chosen so that each also satisfies the property known as the existence of an identity. In each semi-group, the set of elements contains a special element that is called an identity. This element, an *identity element*, is such that, when it is paired with any element x in the domain of the operation, the resulting element—that is, the element in the range—is x. The identity element may be either the first or second component of the pair of domain elements for the operation.

Examples

	Semi-group	*Identity element*	*Example*	*Property*
1	(I, +)	0	$0 + (-4) = -4 + 0 = -4.$	$0 + a = a + 0 = a$ for each $a \in$ I.
2	(C, •)	1	$1 \cdot 8 = 8 \cdot 1 = 8.$	$1 \cdot a = a \cdot 1 = a$ for each $a \in$ C.
3	(R, •)	1	$1 \cdot \frac{2}{3} = \frac{2}{3} \cdot 1 = \frac{2}{3}.$	$1 \cdot a = a \cdot 1 = a$ for each $a \in$ R.
4	(E_I, +)	0	$0 + 6 = 6 + 0 = 6.$	$0 + 2a = 2a + 0 = 2a$ for each $a \in$ I.
5	(O_I, •)	1	$1 \cdot 13 = 13 \cdot 1 = 13.$	$1 \cdot (2a + 1) = (2a + 1) \cdot 1 = 2a + 1$ for each $a \in$ I.
6	(W, +)	0	$0 + 5 = 5 + 0 = 5.$	$0 + a = a + 0 = a$ for each $a \in$ W.

The six examples just given deal with familiar subsets of the real numbers and the operations of addition and multiplication. Later we will see that there are examples of semi-groups with identity elements whose elements are not subsets of the real numbers. But before we proceed to such examples, it is important to note that certain semi-groups which are subsystems of the real numbers do not have an identity element. Three such examples follow.

Examples 7 (C, +) For no element e of C is it true that $e + a = a + e = a$ for each $a \in C$.

8 $(\{7x \mid x \in I\}, \cdot)$ For no element e of $\{7x \mid x \in I\}$ is it true that $e \cdot 7a = 7a \cdot e = 7a$ for each $a \in I$.

9 $(R^+, +)$ For no element e of R^+ is it true that $e + a = a + e = a$ for each $a \in R^+$.

The nine examples we have given show that one property a semi-group may or may not have is the identity-element property. This concept is formally stated in the following definition.

Definition 26/2 If (S, ☆) is a semi-group, then (S, ☆) is a *semi-group with identity* if and only if there exists an element $e \in S$ such that

$$e \star a = a \star e = a$$

for each $a \in S$.

We have used the symbol e to represent an arbitrary identity element in this definition in much the same way that we use ☆ as a symbol to represent the operation of any semi-group. Although the examples on page 77 might lead you to believe that an identity element for a system must always be either 0 or 1, the following examples show that this is not the case.

Example 10 For this example we recall two binary operations discussed in section 8/1, namely, the operations of union and intersection. We will now establish that the set of all subsets of a set forms a semi-group with identity under the binary operation of union and also under intersection. Remember that, for exercise 3 at the end of the previous section, you proved that $(\mathbb{S}, \cup)$ and $(\mathbb{S}, \cap)$ are semi-groups. The following two theorems establish that each of these semi-groups contains an identity element.

Theorem 18/2 If S is a set and $\mathbb{S}$ is the set of subsets of S, then the system $(\mathbb{S}, \cup)$ is a semi-group with identity.

Proof To establish the theorem, it is necessary to exhibit an element of $\mathbb{S}$ that satisfies the property stated in Definition 26/2. Such an element is the empty set $\emptyset$ since

$$\emptyset \cup A = A \cup \emptyset = A$$

for each $A \in \mathbb{S}$.

Theorem 19/2 If S is a set and $\mathbb{S}$ is the set of subsets of S, then the system $(\mathbb{S}, \cap)$ is a semi-group with identity.

Proof An identity element of $(\mathcal{S}, \cap)$ is S since

$$S \cap A = A \cap S = A$$

for each $A \in \mathcal{S}$. Hence, the semi-group $(\mathcal{S}, \cap)$ satisfies the identity property.

Example 11 We will now show that the integers modulo n under modular multiplication form a semi-group with identity.

Theorem 20/2 Let multiplication modulo n, denoted by $\odot_n$, on the set $I/n = \{\bar{0}, \bar{1}, \bar{2}, \ldots, \overline{n-1}\}$ be defined by

$$\bar{a} \odot_n \bar{b} = \bar{r},$$

with $a \cdot b = qn + r$, $0 \leqq r < n$, $0 \leqq a < n$, and $0 \leqq b < n$. Then the system $(I/n, \odot_n)$ is a semi-group with identity.

Proof In exercise 4 of section 13/2, you showed that $(I/n, \odot_n)$ is a semi-group. To show that this semi-group has $\bar{1}$ as an identity element, consider $\bar{a} \in I/n$. Since $0 \leqq a < n$, we know by the division algorithm that

$$\begin{aligned} 1 \cdot a &= a \\ &= 0 \cdot n + a. \end{aligned}$$

Hence, by the definition of multiplication for I/n,

$$\bar{1} \odot_n \bar{a} = \bar{a}.$$

In a similar manner, we can show that $\bar{a} \odot_n \bar{1} = \bar{a}$. Thus, for each $\bar{a} \in I/n$, $\bar{1} \odot_n \bar{a} = \bar{a} \odot_n \bar{1} = \bar{a}$. Hence, $\bar{1}$ is an identity element for $(I/n, \odot_n)$.

Examples 10 and 11 illustrate that there are semi-groups with identity which are not subsystems of the real-number system. The next example shows that it is possible to define an operation on a set so that the semi-group formed does not have the identity-element property of Definition 26/2, but does have a special kind of identity.

Example 12 We define an operation from $C \times C$ by $a \star b = b$ for each $a, b \in C$. From the definition, it is apparent that the domain of the operation is $C \times C$ and that the range of the operation is in C. How do you know that the range of the binary operation contains every element of set C? Some particular examples of this operation are given below.

$$1 \star 3 = 3. \qquad 3 \star 1 = 1. \qquad 2 \star 3 = 3.$$
$$5 \star 7 = 7. \qquad 10 \star 5 = 5. \qquad 5 \star 5 = 5.$$

The observations made so far assure us that the operation $\star$ is a closed binary operation. The system (C, $\star$) also satisfies the associative property, as the following equalities demonstrate:

$$(a \star b) \star c = b \star c = c,$$

$$a \star (b \star c) = a \star c = c.$$

Thus, (C, $\star$) is another example of a semi-group. Now we will investigate the system (C, $\star$) to determine whether or not it has an identity element. If the semi-group has an identity, then there exists an element $e \in$ C such that $e \star a = a \star e = a$ for each $a \in$ C. In particular, if $a = 1$ and e is an identity element, then $1 \star e = 1$. But $1 \star e = e$ by the definition of the operation. Therefore,

$$1 \star e = 1 = e.$$

The assumption that there is an identity element e leads to the conclusion that $e = 1$. But if $a = 2$, then

$$\begin{aligned} a \star e &= 2 \star e \\ &= 2 \star 1 \\ &= 1. \end{aligned}$$

This shows that $2 \star 1 \neq 2$. But $2 \star 1$ should be equal to 2 to satisfy $a \star e = a$ for each $a \in$ C. We have reached a contradiction and, hence, the semi-group (C, $\star$) has no identity element.

We can, however, extend the concept of an identity element as in the following definition, and then we can reconsider example 12 in terms of this definition.

Definition 27/2 The element e_l of a semi-group (S, $\star$) is a *left identity* if and only if, for each $a \in$ S, $e_l \star a = a$. The element e_r of a semi-group (S, $\star$) is a *right identity* if and only if, for each $a \in$ S, $a \star e_r = a$.

For the semi-group (C, $\star$), discussed in the last example, every element of C is a left identity since $x \star a = a$ for each x, $a \in$ C. This means that an infinite number of left identities exist. What about right identities? Let us assume that e_r is a right identity. Then $1 \star e_r = 1$, but $1 \star e_r = e_r$ by the definition of $\star$; therefore, $e_r = 1$. The assumption that e_r is a right identity leads to the conclusion that $e_r = 1$. If $e_r = 1$, then it follows from the definition of $\star$ that $2 \star e_r = 2 \star 1 = 1$. But, if e_r were a right identity, then it should be the case that $2 \star e_r = 2$. Since $1 \neq 2$, the assumption that a right identity exists leads to a contradiction. Therefore, the system (C, $\star$) does not have a right identity.

The operation defined by $a \star b = b$ for each $a, b \in C$ led to an example of a semi-group in which every element of the set serves as a left identity, but no right identity exists.

Exercises

1 Show that each of the following systems has an identity element.

a $(R^+, \cdot)$
b $(I, \cdot)$
c $(G(i), +)$
d $(W(\sqrt{2}), +)$
e $(I(\sqrt{3}), \cdot)$
f $(G(i), \cdot)$ *Answer*
g $(\{2x \mid x \in I\}, +)$

◆ 2 Prove that the semi-group of integers modulo n under addition, represented by $(I/n, \oplus_n)$, satisfies the identity property.

3 Let $\mathbb{S}$ be the set of all subsets of a given set S. Prove that $\emptyset$ is the unique identity for the system $(\mathbb{S}, \cup)$ by assuming that there is another identity $A \neq \emptyset$ for this system and developing a contradiction.

◆ 4 In exercise 3 you proved indirectly that $\emptyset$ is the unique identity for $(\mathbb{S}, \cup)$. Establish this directly by assuming that both $\emptyset$ and A are identities for this system and showing that $A = \emptyset$.

5 Does each of the following systems have an identity element?

a $(\{7x \mid x \in I\}, +)$
b $(E_I, \cdot)$
c $(I, -)$
d $(O_I\sqrt{3}, \cdot)$
e $(O_C, +)$

6 Prove that $\bar{0}$ is the unique identity element of $(I/n, \oplus_n)$. *Answer*

7 Find left or right identities for each of the following systems.

a $(I, -)$
b $(R^+, \div)$
c $(E_I, \div)$
d $(\mathfrak{R}, -)$
e $(R(\sqrt{2}), -)$

◆ 8 Let A be a given set. Let $\mathcal{F}$ be the set of all functions with domain A and range included in A. Consider the operation of composition of functions on the elements of $\mathcal{F}$. Find an identity element for this system; that is, find a function $h \in \mathcal{F}$ such that, for each $f \in \mathcal{F}$, $f \circ h = h \circ f = f$. This requires that you find an $h \in \mathcal{F}$ so that, for each $x \in A$ and each $f \in \mathcal{F}$, $(x)f \circ h = (x)h \circ f = (x)f$. *Answer*

9 Determine whether or not each of the following systems satisfies the identity property. For those that do not satisfy the identity property, determine whether or not left identities exist and whether or not right identities exist.

a $(\mathfrak{R}, \star)$, where $x \star y = x + y + xy$
b $(\mathfrak{R}, \star)$, where $x \star y = \frac{1}{2}xy$ *Answer*
c $(I, \star)$; where $x \star y = (x - x)y$
d $(C, \star)$, where $x \star y = x$

e $(E_I, \star)$, where $x \star y = \max \{x, y\}$; that is, $x \star y = x$ if $x \geqq y$ and $x \star y = y$ if $x < y$

f $(I, \star)$, where $x \star y = [x + y]$; that is, $x \star y$ is the greatest integer less than or equal to $x + y$ *Answer*

g $(R, \star)$, where $x \star y = |x|\,|y|$

h $(C, \star)$, where $x \star y = [x]\,[y]$; that is, $x \star y$ is the product of the greatest integer less than or equal to x and the greatest integer less than or equal to y

15/2 Semi-groups and the existence of inverses

In this section we will discuss only those mathematical systems in which the given binary operation is closed and associative and for which there exists an identity element; in short, we will be dealing with semi-groups with identity. Some of the systems of this kind that we have studied so far are listed in Display 33.

Semi-groups with identity

$(W, +)$	$(I, \cdot)$	$(R, +)$	$(\{7x \mid x \in I\}, +)$
$(C, \cdot)$	$(R^+, \cdot)$	$(G(i), +)$	
$(I, +)$	$(O_I, \cdot)$	$(G(i), \cdot)$	

Display **33**

We have almost reached our goal of defining the mathematical system known as a group. The property to be discussed here is the one property still needed. Some of the systems in Display 33 have the required property, and some do not. The property we have in mind may be stated as follows: For each element a in the system, there is another element, denoted by a', such that $a' \star a = a \star a' = e$, where e represents an identity element of the system and $\star$ represents the binary operation. If a and a' are elements of a mathematical system such that $a' \star a = a \star a' = e$, then a' is an *inverse* of a and a is an inverse of a'.

We can classify the examples in Display 33 according to whether or not they have an inverse property. Those that do satisfy the property that each element has an inverse are given next, along with a specific example of an element and its inverse and a general statement of the inverse property. Notice that, if the operation is addition, the inverse of a is denoted by $-a$; if the operation is multiplication, the inverse of a is denoted by $\frac{1}{a}$.

Examples

	System	Identity element	Example of inverse property	Inverse property
1	(I, $+$)	0	$-2+2=2+(-2) = 0.$	$-a+a=a+(-a)=0$ for each $a \in$ I.
2	(R^+, $\cdot$)	1	$\frac{4}{3}\cdot\frac{3}{4}=\frac{3}{4}\cdot\frac{4}{3}=1.$	$\frac{1}{a}\cdot a=a\cdot\frac{1}{a}=1$ for each $a \in R^+$.
3	(R, $+$)	0	$\frac{4}{3}+(-\frac{4}{3}) = -\frac{4}{3}+\frac{4}{3}=0.$	$-a+a=a+(-a)=0$ for each $a \in$ R.
4	$\big($G(i), $+\big)$	0	$\big(-3+(-4i)\big)+(3+4i)=(3+4i)+\big(-3+(-4i)\big)=0.$	$\big(-a+(-bi)\big)+(a+bi)=(a+bi)+\big(-a+(-bi)\big)=0$ for each $a+bi \in$ G(i).
5	($\{7x \mid x \in$ I$\}$, $+$)	0	$-21+21=21+(-21)=0.$	$7(-a)+7a=7a+7(-a)=0$ for each $a \in$ I.

The examples from Display 33 that do *not* satisfy the inverse property are given below. For each system, a particular element that does not have an inverse is also given.

	System	Element with no inverse
6	(W, $+$)	3
7	(C, $\cdot$)	13
8	(I, $\cdot$)	-4
9	(O_I, $\cdot$)	$2^{10}+1$
10	$\big($G(i), $\cdot\big)$	$3+0i$

The general definition of the inverse property for any system (S, ☆) follows.

Definition 28/2 Let (S, ☆) be a semi-group with an identity element denoted by e. Then the system (S, ☆) has an *inverse property* if and only if, for each $a \in$ S, there exists an element of S, denoted by a', such that $a' ☆ a = a ☆ a' = e$. The element a' is an inverse of a and a is an inverse of a'.

It has already been established that the set of all subsets of a set S under the operations of union and intersection are examples of semi-groups with identity. Therefore, it is relevant to ask whether or not these two particular systems have the property that each element has an inverse. Theorems 21/2 and 22/2 establish that these two systems do *not* have inverse properties.

Theorem 21/2 The semi-group $(\mathcal{S}, \cup)$, consisting of the set of all subsets $\mathcal{S}$ of a nonempty set S under the operation of union, does not satisfy the inverse property.

Proof We have previously established that an identity of the system $(\mathcal{S}, \cup)$ is $\emptyset$. The empty set is the only identity for this system. We also know, by the definition of operation union, that

$$A \cup S = S \cup A = S,$$

for each $A \in \mathcal{S}$. But $S \neq \emptyset$. Hence, the element S of $\mathcal{S}$ has no inverse. Therefore, the system does not satisfy the inverse property.

Theorem 22/2 The semi-group $(\mathcal{S}, \cap)$, consisting of the set of all subsets $\mathcal{S}$ of a nonempty set S under the operation of intersection, does not satisfy the inverse property.

Proof We have previously established that an identity of the system $(\mathcal{S}, \cap)$ is set S. The only identity for this system is set S. We also know, by the definition of the operation of intersection, that

$$A \cap \emptyset = \emptyset \cap A = \emptyset,$$

for each $A \in \mathcal{S}$. But $\emptyset \neq S$. Hence, the element $\emptyset$ of $\mathcal{S}$ has no inverse. Therefore, the system does not satisfy the inverse-element property.

See if you can prove Theorems 21/2 and 22/2 by choosing other particular sets that have no inverse. Suppose that $S = \emptyset$. Would the semi-groups $(\mathcal{S}, \cup)$ and $(\mathcal{S}, \cap)$ have inverse properties?

Now let us consider the general system of integers modulo n under modular addition. We have shown earlier that $(I/n, \oplus_n)$ is a semi-group with identity. Therefore, to prove the following theorem, we must show that the system $(I/n, \oplus_n)$ contains an inverse for each element of I/n.

Theorem 23/2 The system of integers modulo n under the operation $\oplus_n$, $(I/n, \oplus_n)$, is a semi-group with identity that satisfies the inverse property.

Proof To prove Theorem 23/2, we must show that, for each $\bar{a} \in I/n$, there exists an $\bar{a}' \in I/n$ such that $\bar{a}' \oplus_n \bar{a} = \bar{a} \oplus_n \bar{a}' = \bar{0}$. Now, if n and a are integers, we know that

$$\begin{aligned}(n - a) + a &= n \\ &= 1 \cdot n + 0\end{aligned}$$

and that

$$\begin{aligned}a + (n - a) &= n \\ &= 1 \cdot n + 0.\end{aligned}$$

Thus, if there exists an additive inverse of $\bar{a}$ in I/n, where $I/n = \{\bar{0}, \bar{1}, \bar{2}, \ldots, \overline{n-1}\}$, then it must be $\overline{n-a}$. By Definition 20/2,

$$\overline{n-a} \oplus_n \bar{a} = \bar{0},$$
$$\bar{a} \oplus_n \overline{n-a} = \bar{0}.$$

Since $\bar{0}$ is an additive identity of I/n, we have shown that, for each $\bar{a} \in I/n$, $\overline{n-a}$ is the additive inverse of $\bar{a}$. Therefore, the proof of the theorem is complete.

Exercises

1 Prove that $(I/n, \odot_n)$ does not satisfy the inverse property. [Hint: Consider $(I/4, \odot_4)$.]
2 Show that $1 + 2i$ does not have an inverse in $(G(i), \cdot)$.
3 Which elements in $(G(i), \cdot)$ have inverses? *Answer*
4 Show that $(R(\sqrt{2}), \cdot)$ does not satisfy the inverse property.
5 Which elements in $(R(\sqrt{2}), \cdot)$ have inverses?
6 Show that $(I(\sqrt{2}), \cdot)$ does not satisfy the inverse property.
7 Which elements in $(I(\sqrt{2}), \cdot)$ have inverses?

Let set A be the set of nonnegative real numbers. Consider the set $\mathcal{F}$ of all functions that have domain A and range included in A. We know that set $\mathcal{F}$ under the operation of composition forms a semi-group with identity. This identity is unique, and it is the function $\{(x, x) \mid x \in A\}$. That is, if we denote the identity function by e, we have $(x)e = x$ for each $x \in A$. We wish to explore the question: Does $\mathcal{F}$ under composition satisfy the inverse property? For each $f \in \mathcal{F}$, we are looking for a function $f' \in \mathcal{F}$ such that $f' \circ f = f \circ f' = e$; that is, if $x \in A$, $(x)f' \circ f = (x)f \circ f' = (x)e = x$. If such a function f′ exists, it is an inverse of f, and f is an inverse of f′.

8 In each of the following exercises, find, if possible, an inverse $f' \in \mathcal{F}$ of the function f.

a $(x)f = 3x$.
b $(x)f = \frac{1}{2}x$.
c $(x)f = 2x + 5$.
d $(x)f = -3x + 2$.
e $(x)f = \dfrac{4x + 2}{3}$. *Answer*
f $(x)f = x^2$.
g $(x)f = \sqrt{x}$.
h $(x)f = \frac{1}{2}x^3$.
i $(x)f = 2\sqrt[3]{x}$.
j $(x)f = \sqrt[3]{2x}$.
k $(x)f = \sqrt{2x^2 + 3}$. *Answer*
l $(x)f = \sqrt{x^2 + 5}$.
m $(x)f = |x|$.
n $(x)f = |x - 2|$.

9 Does $(\mathcal{F}, \circ)$ as described above have the inverse property? If not, name an element of $\mathcal{F}$ that has no inverse.

10 Determine which of the following systems have an inverse property.

If $x \star y = x + y + xy$:

a (R, ☆) *Answer*

b (I, ☆)

If $x \star y = \frac{1}{2}xy$:

c ($\mathfrak{R}$, ☆)

d (E_I, ☆)

If $x \star y = [xy]$:

e (C, ☆)

f ($\mathfrak{R}$, ☆)

If $x \star y = |x| + |y|$:

g (I, ☆)

h (C, ☆)

Properties of groups 16/2

In each of the four preceding sections, we emphasized a single property of binary operations—first closure, then associativity, next identity, and, finally, the inverse property. Now we will study these properties from a slightly different viewpoint by considering systems (S, ☆) that satisfy all four of the properties. To begin with, we will recall the sequence of ideas that has been developed in the systems that we are now considering.

In Chapter 1 we began with Cartesian products in general. We then went on to consider, first, relations; next, relations that are functions; and finally, functions that are binary operations. So far in this chapter, we have studied systems that are called semi-groups, which are systems with binary operations that are closed and associative; next, semi-groups with an identity element; and then, semi-groups with identity and inverses.

The development just described has led us to the mathematical system that is called a *group*. We will be analyzing groups and their properties throughout the rest of this chapter. A formal definition of a group will be given a bit later, but first we will discuss some examples of systems that satisfy the four basic group properties; that is, the closure, associative, identity, and inverse properties.

Examples 1 The first of these examples is the set of integers modulo 4 under modular addition. We can illustrate the binary operation of the system ($I/4$, $\oplus_4$) with the addition table shown in Display 34.

Since each of the entries in the table is an element of $\{\bar{0}, \bar{1}, \bar{2}, \bar{3}\}$, we know that $(I/4, \oplus_4)$ satisfies the *closure property*.

$\oplus_4$	$\bar{0}$	$\bar{1}$	$\bar{2}$	$\bar{3}$
$\bar{0}$	$\bar{0}$	$\bar{1}$	$\bar{2}$	$\bar{3}$
$\bar{1}$	$\bar{1}$	$\bar{2}$	$\bar{3}$	$\bar{0}$
$\bar{2}$	$\bar{2}$	$\bar{3}$	$\bar{0}$	$\bar{1}$
$\bar{3}$	$\bar{3}$	$\bar{0}$	$\bar{1}$	$\bar{2}$

Display 34

One way to verify the *associative property* would be to compute all possible cases. However, such an approach would mean verifying sixty-four $(4 \cdot 4 \cdot 4)$ different cases. It is simpler to verify the associative property by using the definition of addition for this system, and, in fact, this was done for the integers modulo n in Theorem 17/2. We observe from Display 34 that the element $\bar{0}$ is an *additive identity* of the system. Why? Furthermore, each of the elements in the set has an *additive inverse*: an inverse of $\bar{0}$ is $\bar{0}$; an inverse of $\bar{2}$ is $\bar{2}$; and $\bar{1}$ and $\bar{3}$ are inverses of each other. Consequently, the mathematical system $(I/4, \oplus_4)$ forms a group.

2 Next we will consider the subset of the complex numbers $\{1, i, -1, -i\}$ under the operation of multiplication. Remember that the complex number i is defined so that $i^2 = -1$. A multiplication table for this system is given in Display 35.

$\cdot$	1	i	-1	$-i$
1	1	i	-1	$-i$
i	i	-1	$-i$	1
-1	-1	$-i$	1	i
$-i$	$-i$	1	i	-1

Display 35

We see from the table that this system has the *closure property* because each entry is an element of $\{1, i, -1, -i\}$. The *associative property* follows from the fact that $\{1, i, -1, -i\}$ is a subset of the set of complex numbers, and we know that multiplication of complex numbers is associative. Also, the table illustrates that an *identity* of this system is 1. Furthermore, each element of the system has a *multiplicative inverse*: an inverse of 1 is 1; an inverse of -1 is -1; an inverse of i is $-i$; an inverse of $-i$ is i. Consequently, $(\{1, i, -1, -i\}, \cdot)$ forms a group.

Examples 1 and 2 show that the operation of a group may be either modular addition or multiplication. As you will see later, even other operations may be used in forming a group; that is why we have used the symbol ☆ to denote the group operation in the following definition.

Definition 29/2 Let G be a nonempty set and let ☆ be a binary operation with domain $G \times G$. Then the mathematical system (G, ☆) is a group if and only if the following four properties are satisfied:

Closure 1 For each $a, b \in G$, $a ☆ b \in G$.

Associative 2 For each $a, b, c \in G$, $(a ☆ b) ☆ c = a ☆ (b ☆ c)$.

Identity 3 There exists an element $e \in G$ such that, for each $a \in G$, $e ☆ a = a ☆ e = a$.

Inverse 4 For each $a \in G$, there exists an element $a' \in G$ such that $a' ☆ a = a ☆ a' = e$.

Because of the closure property, the operation ☆ is from $G \times G$ into G. The operation is actually onto G because the range is all of G. If no confusion can arise, we will sometimes refer to the group simply as G with no mention of the operation ☆.

Most of our examples so far have been tied to the real-number system because of our familiarity with it. However, we need not restrict our examples of groups to familiar subsystems of the real numbers or complex numbers. Therefore, we will now consider an example involving a new operation on real numbers.

Example 3 Given the ordered pairs of numbers (a, b) and (c, d), with a and c elements of the set of nonzero real numbers, denoted by $\mathfrak{R}^+ \cup \mathfrak{R}^-$, and b and d elements of $\mathfrak{R}$, we define the operation ☆ as follows:

$$(a, b) ☆ (c, d) = (ac, bc + d).$$

For convenience, we will use (H, ☆) to designate this system. Notice that H is a set of ordered pairs (a, b), with $a \in (\mathfrak{R}^+ \cup \mathfrak{R}^-)$ and $b \in \mathfrak{R}$. That is, $H = (\mathfrak{R}^+ \cup \mathfrak{R}^-) \times \mathfrak{R}$. We have used the definition of operation ☆ to compute the following "products" in the system.

$$(2, 1) ☆ (3, \tfrac{1}{2}) = (2 \cdot 3, 1 \cdot 3 + \tfrac{1}{2}) = (6, \tfrac{7}{2}).$$

$$(-1, 0) ☆ (4, \tfrac{3}{2}) = (-1 \cdot 4, 0 \cdot 4 + \tfrac{3}{2}) = (-4, \tfrac{3}{2}).$$

$$(\sqrt{2}, 5) ☆ (-2, -4) = \big(\sqrt{2} \cdot (-2), 5 \cdot (-2) + (-4)\big) = (-2\sqrt{2}, -14).$$

Now we will verify that (H, ☆) satisfies the closure, associative, identity, and inverse properties of a group. Recall that the closure property requires that each "product" be an element of the set used to form the domain of ☆. Since $H = (\mathfrak{R}^+ \cup \mathfrak{R}^-) \times \mathfrak{R}$, the domain of ☆ is

$$[(\mathfrak{R}^+ \cup \mathfrak{R}^-) \times \mathfrak{R}] \times [(\mathfrak{R}^+ \cup \mathfrak{R}^-) \times \mathfrak{R}].$$

To establish the *closure property*, we must show that the "product" of (a, b) and (c, d), $(ac, bc + d)$, is in $(\mathfrak{R}^+ \cup \mathfrak{R}^-) \times \mathfrak{R}$. By the definition of H, a and c are real numbers different from 0. It follows that ac, the first component of $(ac, bc + d)$, is in $\mathfrak{R}^+ \cup \mathfrak{R}^-$. Why? Show that $bc + d \in \mathfrak{R}$. Hence, $(ac, bc + d)$ is an element of $(\mathfrak{R}^+ \cup \mathfrak{R}^-) \times \mathfrak{R}$. This completes the proof of the closure property of the operation ☆.

The computation given below verifies that the operation ☆ satisfies the *associative property*. Let (x, y), (z, w), and (u, v) be elements of $(\mathfrak{R}^+ \cup \mathfrak{R}^-) \times \mathfrak{R}$.

$$\begin{aligned}\big((x, y) \star (z, w)\big) \star (u, v) &= (xz, yz + w) \star (u, v)\\ &= \big((xz)u, (yz + w)u + v\big)\\ &= \big((xz)u, (yz)u + wu + v\big)\\ &= (xzu, yzu + wu + v).\end{aligned}$$

$$\begin{aligned}(x, y) \star \big((z, w) \star (u, v)\big) &= (x, y) \star (zu, wu + v)\\ &= \big(x(zu), y(zu) + wu + v\big)\\ &= (xzu, yzu + wu + v).\end{aligned}$$

You should be able to justify each of these steps.

We next turn to the verification of the *identity property*. In most of the examples that have been studied previously, simple inspection showed that an identity exists and also which element it is. For this system, an identity, if it exists, is not obvious. It is necessary, therefore, to determine what the identity might be.

Suppose that there exists an element (u, v) in H such that, for each $(a, b) \in H$,

$$(a, b) \star (u, v) = (a, b).$$

But, by the definition of ☆,

$$(a, b) \star (u, v) = (au, bu + v).$$

Hence, if (u, v) is an identity, $(au, bu + v) = (a, b)$. It follows that $au = a$, because ordered pairs are equal only if their components are equal. But, since this condition implies that $u = 1$, it follows that if the element (u, v) is to serve as an identity, then u must be equal to 1. Further, the second components of $(au, bu + v)$ and (a, b) must also be equal. The following steps show that $bu + v = b$

if and only if $v = 0$. Since we have decided that $u = 1$, we have

$$\begin{aligned} bu + v &= b \cdot 1 + v \\ &= b + v \\ &= b + 0 \\ &= b. \end{aligned}$$

Thus, we see that if (u, v) is an identity, it must be the ordered pair $(1, 0)$. [You should show that the results are the same if you work with $(u, v) \star (a, b) = (a, b)$.] Although this argument shows that, if there is an identity element, then it is $(1, 0)$, the argument does not verify that $(1, 0)$ is an identity. To verify that $(1, 0)$ is actually an identity, we must show that $(1, 0) \star (a, b) = (a, b) \star (1, 0) = (a, b)$ for each $(a, b) \in$ H. The following steps complete the proof of the identity property.

$$\begin{aligned} (1, 0) \star (a, b) &= (1 \cdot a, 0 \cdot a + b) \\ &= (a, b). \\ (a, b) \star (1, 0) &= (a \cdot 1, b \cdot 1 + 0) \\ &= (a, b). \end{aligned}$$

Give the reasons for each of these steps.

Because we have now established that $(1, 0)$ is an identity element in the system (H, $\star$), we can determine if the system also has the *inverse property*. (Explain why it follows that, if the identity property does not hold for a particular system, then the inverse property cannot hold, either.) We can determine an inverse of an arbitrary element of (H, $\star$) in much the same way as we determined an identity of the system; that is, we will assume that (u, v) is the inverse of (a, b) and establish what must be true of u and v. Suppose that

$$(a, b) \star (u, v) = (1, 0).$$

But, by the definition of $\star$,

$$(a, b) \star (u, v) = (au, bu + v).$$

Hence, it must be the case that

$$(au, bu + v) = (1, 0).$$

Therefore, if (u, v) is an inverse of (a, b), then $au = 1$, which is true only if $u = \frac{1}{a}$. Recall that, in the definition of (H, $\star$), we required the first component of any ordered pair (a, b) to be different from zero. It is now apparent why this requirement was necessary. If this were not the case, it would not be possible to find an inverse for each (a, b). Why? Now we want to determine v so that $(a, b) \star (u, v) = (1, 0)$, in other words, so that

$$bu + v = 0.$$

But, since $u = \frac{1}{a}$,

$$\begin{aligned} bu + v &= b\frac{1}{a} + v \\ &= \frac{b}{a} + v. \end{aligned}$$

Hence, $\frac{b}{a} + v = 0$, or $v = -\frac{b}{a}$. The assumption that (u, v) is the inverse of (a, b) has led to the conclusion that (u, v) is $\left(\frac{1}{a}, -\frac{b}{a}\right)$. Now we need only to establish that $\left(\frac{1}{a}, -\frac{b}{a}\right)$ is in fact an inverse of (a, b). In the following steps we show that $\left(\frac{1}{a}, -\frac{b}{a}\right) \star (a, b)$ and $(a, b) \star \left(\frac{1}{a}, -\frac{b}{a}\right)$ yield $(1, 0)$, an identity of the system.

$$\begin{aligned} \left(\frac{1}{a}, -\frac{b}{a}\right) \star (a, b) &= \left(\frac{1}{a} \cdot a, -\frac{b}{a} \cdot a + b\right) \\ &= \left(\frac{a}{a}, -b + b\right) \\ &= (1, 0). \end{aligned}$$

$$\begin{aligned} (a, b) \star \left(\frac{1}{a}, -\frac{b}{a}\right) &= \left(a \cdot \frac{1}{a}, b \cdot \frac{1}{a} + (-\frac{b}{a})\right) \\ &= \left(\frac{a}{a}, \frac{b}{a} + (-\frac{b}{a})\right) \\ &= (1, 0). \end{aligned}$$

By verifying the closure, associative, identity, and inverse properties, we have shown that the system (H, ☆) meets the requirements of Definition 29/2 and, hence, is a group.

We should point out here that the four properties of a group are independent, which means that no one of the properties implies another. As we have seen, the integers under subtraction satisfy only the closure property; the even integers under multiplication satisfy the closure and associative properties; and the whole numbers under addition satisfy only the closure, associative, and identity properties. So, it is possible for a given system to have one, two, or three of the properties without having all four. On the other hand, any system that satisfies these four properties also satisfies certain other properties that are implied by the group properties. Several examples of such properties are left for you to prove in the exercises at the end of this section, but two properties that are satisfied by all groups are proved as theorems in the following discussion. To illustrate the first one, we use an example from your earlier mathematical training.

Example You know that (I, +) is a group. A property that is satisfied by (I, +) is that it is always possible to find integral solutions for linear equations like those given below.

a) $6 + x = 5$. c) $a + x = b$. e) $y + 3 = 7$.
b) $-3 + x = 2$. d) $y + (-2) = -4$. f) $y + a = b$.

The solutions of the preceding equations are, respectively:

a) $x = (-6) + 5 = -1$. d) $y = -4 + 2 = -2$.
b) $x = 3 + 2 = 5$. e) $y = 7 + (-3) = 4$.
c) $x = -a + b$. f) $y = b + (-a) = b - a$.

As a matter of fact, it is possible to solve linear equations in *any* group. This group property is a consequent of the four basic group properties, and Theorem 24/2 not only shows that such solutions exist, but also shows what form each solution must take.

Theorem 24/2 If (G, ☆) is a group, with $a, b \in G$, then there exist unique elements $x, y \in G$ such that

1) $a ☆ x = b$

and

2) $y ☆ a = b$.

Furthermore, if a' is an inverse of a, then $x = a' ☆ b$ and $y = b ☆ a'$.

Proof If we solve for x in $a ☆ x = b$, we have the following steps:

$$a ☆ x = b.$$
$$a' ☆ (a ☆ x) = a' ☆ b.$$
$$(a' ☆ a) ☆ x = a' ☆ b.$$
$$e ☆ x = a' ☆ b.$$
$$x = a' ☆ b.$$

Justify each step. How do you know that $a' ☆ b \in G$? Verify that $a' ☆ b$ is the solution of $a ☆ x = b$.

Similarly, if we solve for y in $y ☆ a = b$, we have

$$y ☆ a = b.$$
$$(y ☆ a) ☆ a' = b ☆ a'.$$
$$y ☆ (a ☆ a') = b ☆ a'.$$
$$y ☆ e = b ☆ a'.$$
$$y = b ☆ a'.$$

Verify that $b \star a'$ is the solution of $y \star a = b$. The proof of the theorem is complete.

Example Theorem 24/2 shows that linear equations can be solved in any group; so, in particular, it is possible to solve equations in the group (H, $\star$) of example 3 on page 88. Suppose that we want to determine the solution of

$$(2, -3) \star (u, v) = (\tfrac{1}{2}, 4).$$

From Theorem 24/2, we know that (u, v) is the "product" of an inverse of $(2, -3)$ and $(\frac{1}{2}, 4)$. Because an inverse of each $(a, b) \in \mathrm{H}$ is $\left(\frac{1}{a}, -\frac{b}{a}\right)$, we know that an inverse of $(2, -3)$ is $(\frac{1}{2}, \frac{3}{2})$. Therefore,

$$\begin{aligned}(u, v) &= (\tfrac{1}{2}, \tfrac{3}{2}) \star (\tfrac{1}{2}, 4)\\ &= (\tfrac{1}{4}, \tfrac{3}{4} + 4)\\ &= (\tfrac{1}{4}, \tfrac{19}{4}).\end{aligned}$$

By using the definition of $\star$ in (H, $\star$), we can check the solution $(\frac{1}{4}, \frac{19}{4})$ as follows:

$$\begin{aligned}(2, -3) \star (\tfrac{1}{4}, \tfrac{19}{4}) &= (\tfrac{2}{4}, -\tfrac{3}{4} + \tfrac{19}{4})\\ &= (\tfrac{1}{2}, 4).\end{aligned}$$

We will now consider another property that is satisfied by every group. We know that, if (G, $\star$) is a group and $a \in \mathrm{G}$, then an inverse of a is an element of G. In fact, this is one of the four properties of a group. We also know that an inverse of $a \star b$, denoted by $(a \star b)'$, is in G if a and b are in G. The following theorem shows that if a and b are in G, then an inverse of $a \star b$ is equal to $b' \star a'$.

Theorem 25/2 If (G, $\star$) is a group, with $a, b \in \mathrm{G}$, and a' and b' are inverses of the elements a and b, respectively, then an inverse of $a \star b$ is $b' \star a'$. Symbolically, $(a \star b)' = b' \star a'$.

Proof To prove Theorem 25/2, we must show that $(b' \star a') \star (a \star b) = e$ and also that $(a \star b) \star (b' \star a') = e$. This is accomplished in the steps at the bottom of this page and the top of the following page. You should supply reasons for each of the steps.

$$\begin{aligned}(b' \star a') \star (a \star b) &= b' \star \big(a' \star (a \star b)\big)\\ &= b' \star \big((a' \star a) \star b\big)\\ &= b' \star (e \star b)\\ &= b' \star b\\ &= e.\end{aligned}$$

$$\begin{aligned}(a \star b) \star (b' \star a') &= a \star \big(b \star (b' \star a')\big) \\ &= a \star \big((b \star b') \star a'\big) \\ &= a \star (e \star a') \\ &= a \star a' \\ &= e.\end{aligned}$$

Theorem 25/2 enables us to use the formula $(a \star b)' = b' \star a'$ to find an inverse of the product $a \star b$. This formula may be applied to any mathematical system that is a group; so, in particular, it applies to the group (H, ☆) in example 3, page 88. To illustrate, let us compute an inverse of $(7, \sqrt{2}) \star (-\frac{1}{2}, 5)$. By our earlier work, we know that an inverse of $(7, \sqrt{2})$ is $(\frac{1}{7}, -\frac{\sqrt{2}}{7})$ and that an inverse of $(-\frac{1}{2}, 5)$ is $(-2, 10)$. By Theorem 25/2, an inverse of $(7, \sqrt{2}) \star (-\frac{1}{2}, 5)$ is $(-2, 10) \star (\frac{1}{7}, -\frac{\sqrt{2}}{7})$. Then, by the definition of the operation ☆, we have

$$(-2, 10) \star (\tfrac{1}{7}, -\tfrac{\sqrt{2}}{7}) = (-\tfrac{2}{7}, \tfrac{10 - \sqrt{2}}{7}).$$

The following computation verifies that the correct inverse has been obtained.

$$\begin{aligned}(-\tfrac{2}{7}, \tfrac{10 - \sqrt{2}}{7}) \star [(7, \sqrt{2}) \star (-\tfrac{1}{2}, 5)] &= (-\tfrac{2}{7}, \tfrac{10 - \sqrt{2}}{7}) \star (-\tfrac{7}{2}, -\tfrac{\sqrt{2}}{2} + 5) \\ &= (1, \tfrac{-10 + \sqrt{2}}{2} + \tfrac{10 - \sqrt{2}}{2}) \\ &= (1, 0).\end{aligned}$$

$$\begin{aligned}[(7, \sqrt{2}) \star (-\tfrac{1}{2}, 5)] \star (-\tfrac{2}{7}, \tfrac{10 - \sqrt{2}}{7}) &= (-\tfrac{7}{2}, \tfrac{-\sqrt{2}}{2} + 5) \star (-\tfrac{2}{7}, \tfrac{10 - \sqrt{2}}{7}) \\ &= (1, \tfrac{\sqrt{2} - 10}{7} + \tfrac{10 - \sqrt{2}}{7}) \\ &= (1, 0).\end{aligned}$$

Exercises

1 Give reasons for each step in the proof (on page 89) that (H, ☆) satisfies the associative property.

2 Give reasons for each step in the proof (on page 90) that (1, 0) is an identity of (H, ☆).

3 Give reasons for each step in the proof (on page 91) that $\left(\frac{1}{a}, -\frac{b}{a}\right)$ is an inverse of (a, b) in (H, ☆).

4 Give reasons for each step in the proof of Theorem 24/2 on page 92.

5 Give reasons for each step in the proof of Theorem 25/2 on pages 93-94.

6 Show that $(\{1, -1\}, \cdot)$ is a group.

7 Consider the Cartesian product $\mathfrak{R} \times \mathfrak{R}$. For ordered pairs (a, b) and (c, d) of $\mathfrak{R} \times \mathfrak{R}$, we define the operation $\circ$ by

$$(a, b) \circ (c, d) = (a + c, b + d).$$

Call this system $(V, \circ)$. Show that $(V, \circ)$ is a group.

8 Determine which of the following systems are groups.

a $(\mathfrak{R}, +)$
b $(I/n, \odot_n)$
c $(G(i), +)$
d $(\mathfrak{R}, \cdot)$
e $(I/n, \oplus_n)$
f $(I, +)$
g $(I, -)$
h $(G(i), \cdot)$ *Answer*
i $(R(\sqrt{2}), +)$
j $(R(\sqrt{2}), \cdot)$
k $(\{x \mid x \in \mathfrak{R} \text{ and } x \neq 0\}, \cdot)$
l $(\{x \mid x \in R \text{ and } x > 0\}, \cdot)$
m $(\{2x \mid x \in I\}, +)$
n $(\{x \mid x \in \mathfrak{R} \text{ and } x \notin R\}, +)$ *Answer*
o $(\{x\sqrt{2} \mid x \in \mathfrak{R} \text{ and } x \neq 0\}, \cdot)$
p $(\{x \mid x \in \mathfrak{R} \text{ and } x \notin R\}, \cdot)$

9 Determine which of the following systems are groups.

Let $x \star y = x + y + xy$:
a $(R, \star)$
b $(C, \star)$

Let $x \star y = \frac{1}{2}xy$:
c $(\mathfrak{R}, \star)$
d $(E_I, \star)$

Let $x \star y = [x + y]$:
e $(I, \star)$
f $(R, \star)$

Let $x \star y = [x] \cdot [y]$:
g $(C, \star)$
h $(\mathfrak{R}, \star)$

10 Prove that there is a unique identity element of a group. *Answer*

11 Prove that each element of a group has a unique inverse. *Answer*

12 Prove that if a is a group element, then $(a')' = a$; that is, prove that the inverse of the inverse of a is a.

13 Prove that if G is a group, $a, b, x \in G$, and $a \circ x = b \circ x$, then $a = b$. This is the *right cancellation law.* *Answer*

14 Prove that if G is a group, $a, b, y \in G$, and $y \circ a = y \circ b$, then $a = b$. This is the *left cancellation law.*

◆ **15** Prove that if $(G, \star)$ is a semi-group that has a left identity e_l, and each element a of G has a left inverse a'_l, then G is a group. This is an alternative definition of a group. [Hint: Use the fact that $a \star a'_l = a \star (a'_l \star a) \star a'_l$.] *Answer*

◆ **16** Prove that if G is a semi-group such that G has a right identity e_r, and each element a of G has a right inverse a'_r, then G is a group. This also is an alternative definition of a group.

◆ **17** Prove that if $(G, \circ)$ is a nonempty semi-group such that the equations $x \circ a = b$ and $a \circ y = b$ have solutions x and y in G for each $a, b \in G$, then G is a group. This is an alternative definition of a group. *Answer*

18 Let $\circ$ be the operation of a group from $G \times G$ into G. Show that $\circ$ maps $G \times G$ *onto* G; that is, if $x \in G$, then there are elements $a, b \in G$ such that $a \circ b = x$.

19 If (G, ∘) is a group and there exists an $x \in G$ such that $x \circ x = x$, prove that $x = e$, the identity.

20 Find x in $a \star x \star a = b$, where a, b, x are elements of the group (G, ☆).

21 In the integers modulo 11, solve the following equations.

a $\bar{x} \oplus_{11} \bar{3} = \bar{8}$.

b $\bar{4} \oplus_{11} \bar{x} = \bar{0}$.

c $\bar{x} \oplus_{11} \bar{2} = \bar{0}$.

d $(\bar{3} \oplus_{11} \bar{5}) \oplus_{11} \bar{x} = \bar{0}$.

e $\bar{0} = \bar{x} \oplus_{11} (\bar{1} \oplus_{11} \bar{4})$.

f $\bar{9} \oplus_{11} \bar{x} = \bar{6}$.

g $\bar{x} \oplus_{11} \bar{7} = \bar{3} \oplus_{11} \bar{7}$.

h $\bar{5} \oplus_{11} \overline{10} = \bar{5} \oplus_{11} \bar{x}$.

◆ **22** Determine all groups of two elements; that is, write the operation table for each different group of two elements a and b. [Hint: The entries must be either a or b since groups satisfy the closure property.]

◆ **23** Determine all groups of three elements as in exercise 22.

24 Consider the function

$$f = \{(x, y) \mid y = ax + b, \text{ with } a \neq 0, a, b \in R, \text{ and } x \in \mathfrak{R}\}.$$

Prove that the set of all functions $\mathcal{F}$ of the form f constitutes a group under the operation of composition. *Answer*

◆ **25** Let (G, ☆) be a group with an even number of elements. Prove that there exists at least one nonidentity element $a \in G$ such that $a \star a$ is the identity of G.

Symmetric groups and permutation groups

17/2

Much of the elementary theory of groups grew out of problems in geometry. Indeed, there are still areas of study in physics, for example, where the description of physical motions in the plane and in space leads to a study of certain group properties. While such topics are outside the scope of this book, in this section we will discuss examples of groups that may be used to represent such geometric functions as transformations in a plane or in space. We begin by reconsidering permutations, which we first discussed in connection with the noncommutative operation of composition.

You will recall that a permutation is a one-to-one function from a given set S onto the set S. The six permutations from set $S_3 = \{1, 2, 3\}$ onto itself are tabulated below. We will use these permutations to form some examples of groups.

$P_1 = \{(1, 1), (2, 2), (3, 3)\}$. $P_4 = \{(1, 1), (2, 3), (3, 2)\}$.
$P_2 = \{(1, 2), (2, 1), (3, 3)\}$. $P_5 = \{(1, 2), (2, 3), (3, 1)\}$.
$P_3 = \{(1, 3), (2, 2), (3, 1)\}$. $P_6 = \{(1, 3), (2, 1), (3, 2)\}$.

Example 1 These six permutations correspond in a natural way to certain motions of a triangle. We will restrict our attention just now to those motions that are *rotations* of an equilateral triangle in a plane. The elements P_1, P_5, and P_6, for example, can be interpreted as counterclockwise rotations of an equilateral triangle about its centroid* in a plane. Display 36 illustrates how the permutations P_1, P_5, and P_6 can be made to correspond to rotations of an equilateral triangle whose vertices are labeled 1, 2, and 3.

P_1: Rotation of 0° (or 360°)

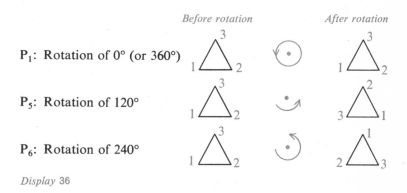

P_5: Rotation of 120°

P_6: Rotation of 240°

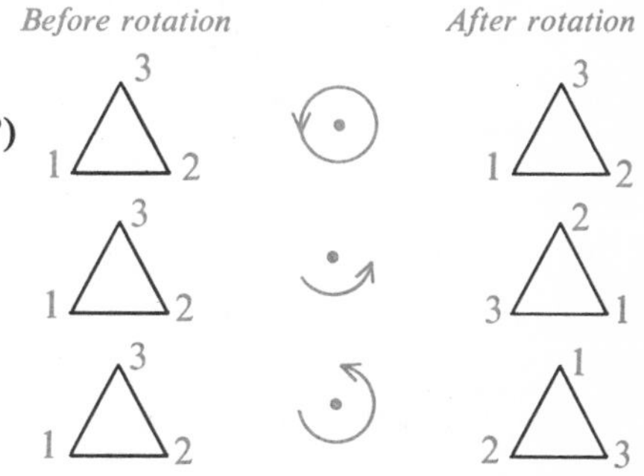

Display 36

Since permutations are special kinds of functions, Definition 13/1 (page 45) for the composition of functions applies to the elements of $\{P_1, P_5, P_6\}$. The composition table for this set of permutations is given in Display 37 on page 98. The entries in this table are obtained either by considering the permutations as rotations of a triangle in a plane or by using the definition of the composition of functions. Thus, in terms of rotations, $P_5 \circ P_6$ is a rotation of 120° followed by a rotation of 240°, which is equal to a rotation of 360°. In terms of permutations, $P_5 \circ P_6$ is the permutation $\{(1, 2), (2, 3), (3, 1)\}$, followed

*The centroid of a triangle is the point in which the medians of the triangle intersect.

by the permutation {(1, 3), (2, 1), (3, 2)}, which is equal to the permutation P_1.

$\circ$	P_1	P_5	P_6
P_1	P_1	P_5	P_6
P_5	P_5	P_6	P_1
P_6	P_6	P_1	P_5

Display 37

Because all the entries in the table are members of $\{P_1, P_5, P_6\}$, the table in Display 37 shows that the operation of composition from $\{P_1, P_5, P_6\}$ is *closed.* That the *associative property* also holds can be determined by checking all possible cases. However, in section 13/2, we proved that the operation of composition of functions, when applied to a set of functions that have a common domain and also have their range in that set, is an associative operation (Theorem 15/2). Hence, the associative property must hold in this case. From Display 37, it is apparent that the permutation P_1 is the *identity element* of the system. The table also illustrates that the inverse property holds because the inverse of P_1 is P_1; the inverse of P_5 is P_6; and the inverse of P_6 is P_5. If we use G to denote the set consisting of the three permutations P_1, P_5, and P_6, and if we use $\circ$ to denote the operation of composition of functions, then the system $(G, \circ)$ forms a *group.*

Before we consider a second example of a group with permutations as elements, it will be helpful to have a new way of writing permutations. The notation to be introduced will make it simpler to see the results of the operation of composition. Permutations P_1, P_5, and P_6 are shown below in *two-line* notation. The numbers in the first row are the first components of the ordered pairs in the given permutation, and the numbers in the second row are the second components of the ordered pairs.

$$P_1: \begin{pmatrix} 1 & 2 & 3 \\ 1 & 2 & 3 \end{pmatrix}$$

$$P_5: \begin{pmatrix} 1 & 2 & 3 \\ 2 & 3 & 1 \end{pmatrix}$$

$$P_6: \begin{pmatrix} 1 & 2 & 3 \\ 3 & 1 & 2 \end{pmatrix}$$

In terms of the rotations of an equilateral triangle, the entries in the first row of each permutation represent the vertices of the triangle before the rotation; the entries in the second row represent the positions, with respect to their original positions, of the vertices after the rotation. If we wish to compute the product of two of these permutations, then we use reasoning similar to that used in section 9/1, where composition of permutations was first presented. The two-line notation just introduced is now used to illustrate the composition of pairs of elements of $\{P_1, P_5, P_6\}$.

$$P_1 \circ P_1 = \begin{pmatrix} 1 & 2 & 3 \\ 1 & 2 & 3 \end{pmatrix} \circ \begin{pmatrix} 1 & 2 & 3 \\ 1 & 2 & 3 \end{pmatrix} = \begin{pmatrix} 1 & 2 & 3 \\ 1 & 2 & 3 \end{pmatrix} = P_1.$$

$$P_1 \circ P_5 = \begin{pmatrix} 1 & 2 & 3 \\ 1 & 2 & 3 \end{pmatrix} \circ \begin{pmatrix} 1 & 2 & 3 \\ 2 & 3 & 1 \end{pmatrix} = \begin{pmatrix} 1 & 2 & 3 \\ 2 & 3 & 1 \end{pmatrix} = P_5.$$

$$P_1 \circ P_6 = \begin{pmatrix} 1 & 2 & 3 \\ 1 & 2 & 3 \end{pmatrix} \circ \begin{pmatrix} 1 & 2 & 3 \\ 3 & 1 & 2 \end{pmatrix} = \begin{pmatrix} 1 & 2 & 3 \\ 3 & 1 & 2 \end{pmatrix} = P_6.$$

$$P_5 \circ P_1 = \begin{pmatrix} 1 & 2 & 3 \\ 2 & 3 & 1 \end{pmatrix} \circ \begin{pmatrix} 1 & 2 & 3 \\ 1 & 2 & 3 \end{pmatrix} = \begin{pmatrix} 1 & 2 & 3 \\ 2 & 3 & 1 \end{pmatrix} = P_5.$$

$$P_5 \circ P_5 = \begin{pmatrix} 1 & 2 & 3 \\ 2 & 3 & 1 \end{pmatrix} \circ \begin{pmatrix} 1 & 2 & 3 \\ 2 & 3 & 1 \end{pmatrix} = \begin{pmatrix} 1 & 2 & 3 \\ 3 & 1 & 2 \end{pmatrix} = P_6.$$

$$P_5 \circ P_6 = \begin{pmatrix} 1 & 2 & 3 \\ 2 & 3 & 1 \end{pmatrix} \circ \begin{pmatrix} 1 & 2 & 3 \\ 3 & 1 & 2 \end{pmatrix} = \begin{pmatrix} 1 & 2 & 3 \\ 1 & 2 & 3 \end{pmatrix} = P_1.$$

$$P_6 \circ P_1 = \begin{pmatrix} 1 & 2 & 3 \\ 3 & 1 & 2 \end{pmatrix} \circ \begin{pmatrix} 1 & 2 & 3 \\ 1 & 2 & 3 \end{pmatrix} = \begin{pmatrix} 1 & 2 & 3 \\ 3 & 1 & 2 \end{pmatrix} = P_6.$$

$$P_6 \circ P_5 = \begin{pmatrix} 1 & 2 & 3 \\ 3 & 1 & 2 \end{pmatrix} \circ \begin{pmatrix} 1 & 2 & 3 \\ 2 & 3 & 1 \end{pmatrix} = \begin{pmatrix} 1 & 2 & 3 \\ 1 & 2 & 3 \end{pmatrix} = P_1.$$

$$P_6 \circ P_6 = \begin{pmatrix} 1 & 2 & 3 \\ 3 & 1 & 2 \end{pmatrix} \circ \begin{pmatrix} 1 & 2 & 3 \\ 3 & 1 & 2 \end{pmatrix} = \begin{pmatrix} 1 & 2 & 3 \\ 2 & 3 & 1 \end{pmatrix} = P_5.$$

To show how the composition of two functions can be determined by simple inspection, consider $P_5 \circ P_1$. From the two-line representation of P_5, we see that 1 is mapped onto 2; in P_1, 2 is mapped onto 2. Thus, in $P_5 \circ P_1$, 1 is mapped onto 2. Similarly, 2 is mapped onto 3 in P_5 and 3 is mapped onto 3 in P_1; hence, in $P_5 \circ P_1$, 2 is mapped onto 3. Finally, 3 is mapped onto 1 in P_5 and 1 is mapped onto 1 in P_1; therefore, 3 is mapped onto 1 in $P_5 \circ P_1$. Thus, $P_5 \circ P_1 = P_5$.

Example 2 We have seen that permutations P_1, P_5, and P_6 correspond to certain rotations of an equilateral triangle in a plane. The remaining three permutations on S_3, which have been denoted by P_2, P_3, and P_4, also can be made to correspond to motions of an equilateral triangle. To illustrate the correspondence, we will again use a triangle whose vertices are denoted by 1, 2, and 3. The motions to which P_2, P_3, and P_4 correspond are *reflections* about certain lines in the plane of the triangle. Illustrations of these three reflections are given in Display 38.

P_2: Reflection about the bisector of $\angle 3$

$$\begin{pmatrix} 1 & 2 & 3 \\ 2 & 1 & 3 \end{pmatrix}$$

P_3: Reflection about the bisector of $\angle 2$

$$\begin{pmatrix} 1 & 2 & 3 \\ 3 & 2 & 1 \end{pmatrix}$$

P_4: Reflection about the bisector of $\angle 1$

$$\begin{pmatrix} 1 & 2 & 3 \\ 1 & 3 & 2 \end{pmatrix}$$

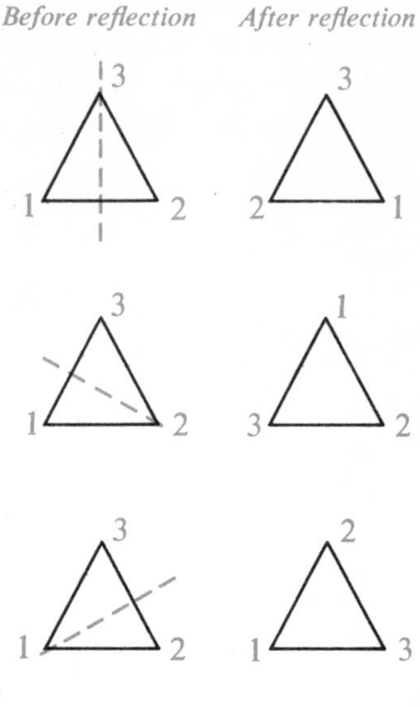

Display 38

Notice that these reflections of the equilateral triangle are mappings of the sides and vertices onto each other so that in each case two vertices and the corresponding opposite sides are interchanged.

The products of the pairs of permutations in $\{P_2, P_3, P_4\}$ are shown below in two-line form.

$$P_2 \circ P_2 = \begin{pmatrix} 1 & 2 & 3 \\ 2 & 1 & 3 \end{pmatrix} \circ \begin{pmatrix} 1 & 2 & 3 \\ 2 & 1 & 3 \end{pmatrix} = \begin{pmatrix} 1 & 2 & 3 \\ 1 & 2 & 3 \end{pmatrix} = P_1.$$

$$P_2 \circ P_3 = \begin{pmatrix} 1 & 2 & 3 \\ 2 & 1 & 3 \end{pmatrix} \circ \begin{pmatrix} 1 & 2 & 3 \\ 3 & 2 & 1 \end{pmatrix} = \begin{pmatrix} 1 & 2 & 3 \\ 2 & 3 & 1 \end{pmatrix} = P_5.$$

$$P_2 \circ P_4 = \begin{pmatrix} 1 & 2 & 3 \\ 2 & 1 & 3 \end{pmatrix} \circ \begin{pmatrix} 1 & 2 & 3 \\ 1 & 3 & 2 \end{pmatrix} = \begin{pmatrix} 1 & 2 & 3 \\ 3 & 1 & 2 \end{pmatrix} = P_6.$$

$$P_3 \circ P_2 = \begin{pmatrix} 1 & 2 & 3 \\ 3 & 2 & 1 \end{pmatrix} \circ \begin{pmatrix} 1 & 2 & 3 \\ 2 & 1 & 3 \end{pmatrix} = \begin{pmatrix} 1 & 2 & 3 \\ 3 & 1 & 2 \end{pmatrix} = P_6.$$

$$P_3 \circ P_3 = \begin{pmatrix} 1 & 2 & 3 \\ 3 & 2 & 1 \end{pmatrix} \circ \begin{pmatrix} 1 & 2 & 3 \\ 3 & 2 & 1 \end{pmatrix} = \begin{pmatrix} 1 & 2 & 3 \\ 1 & 2 & 3 \end{pmatrix} = P_1.$$

$$P_3 \circ P_4 = \begin{pmatrix} 1 & 2 & 3 \\ 3 & 2 & 1 \end{pmatrix} \circ \begin{pmatrix} 1 & 2 & 3 \\ 1 & 3 & 2 \end{pmatrix} = \begin{pmatrix} 1 & 2 & 3 \\ 2 & 3 & 1 \end{pmatrix} = P_5.$$

$$P_4 \circ P_2 = \begin{pmatrix} 1 & 2 & 3 \\ 1 & 3 & 2 \end{pmatrix} \circ \begin{pmatrix} 1 & 2 & 3 \\ 2 & 1 & 3 \end{pmatrix} = \begin{pmatrix} 1 & 2 & 3 \\ 2 & 3 & 1 \end{pmatrix} = P_5.$$

$$P_4 \circ P_3 = \begin{pmatrix} 1 & 2 & 3 \\ 1 & 3 & 2 \end{pmatrix} \circ \begin{pmatrix} 1 & 2 & 3 \\ 3 & 2 & 1 \end{pmatrix} = \begin{pmatrix} 1 & 2 & 3 \\ 3 & 1 & 2 \end{pmatrix} = P_6.$$

$$P_4 \circ P_4 = \begin{pmatrix} 1 & 2 & 3 \\ 1 & 3 & 2 \end{pmatrix} \circ \begin{pmatrix} 1 & 2 & 3 \\ 1 & 3 & 2 \end{pmatrix} = \begin{pmatrix} 1 & 2 & 3 \\ 1 & 2 & 3 \end{pmatrix} = P_1.$$

The method used in these computations is, of course, not the only one available, and it is instructive to verify the results by viewing each composition as corresponding to successive reflections of an equilateral triangle.

The above computations show that the operation of composition on the set of permutations $\{P_2, P_3, P_4\}$ is not closed. Hence, $\{P_2, P_3, P_4\}$ under the operation of composition does not form a group. It is interesting to note that we obtained an element of $\{P_1, P_5, P_6\}$ as a result of each computation above. Therefore, in terms of motions of an equilateral triangle in a plane, the composition of any two of the reflections P_2, P_3, and P_4 is a rotation.

Example 3 We have seen that $(\{P_1, P_5, P_6\}, \circ)$ is a group and that $\{P_2, P_3, P_4\}$ under the operation of composition is not a group. Now let us examine $\{P_1, P_5, P_6\} \cup \{P_2, P_3, P_4\}$, or $\{P_1, P_2, P_3, P_4, P_5, P_6\}$, under the operation of composition to determine whether or not this system is a group. We will begin by exhibiting a composition table for $\{P_1, P_2, P_3, P_4, P_5, P_6\}$ under operation $\circ$ (Display 39).

$\circ$	P_1	P_2	P_3	P_4	P_5	P_6
P_1	P_1	P_2	P_3	P_4	P_5	P_6
P_2	P_2	P_1	P_5	P_6	P_3	P_4
P_3	P_3	P_6	P_1	P_5	P_4	P_2
P_4	P_4	P_5	P_6	P_1	P_2	P_3
P_5	P_5	P_4	P_2	P_3	P_6	P_1
P_6	P_6	P_3	P_4	P_2	P_1	P_5

Display 39

Notice that the compositions of the pairs of permutations in $\{P_1, P_2, P_3, P_4, P_5, P_6\}$ are again permutations in this set. Consequently, the operation of composition is *closed* in

$\{P_1, P_2, P_3, P_4, P_5, P_6\}$. Since the permutations are functions and since we have shown that composition of functions of this type is associative, it follows that the operation of composition in this set has the *associative property*. The permutation P_1 is the *identity* of this mathematical system, and each element in the system has an *inverse*. The inverse of P_1 is P_1; the inverse of P_2 is P_2; the inverse of P_3 is P_3. What is the inverse of P_4? Of P_5? Of P_6?

Because the set of permutations on $S_3 = \{1, 2, 3\}$ under the operation of composition satisfies the four basic group properties, it follows that the system $(\{P_1, P_2, P_3, P_4, P_5, P_6\}, \circ)$ is a group. This group is often called the group of motions of an equilateral triangle.

Example 4 In the preceding examples, we have restricted the discussion to the set of permutations on $\{1, 2, 3\}$, but the groups in examples 1 and 3 are only special cases of a more general group. The set of permutations on $\{1, 2, \ldots, n\}$ is also a group under the operation of composition. This claim is established in Theorem 26/2.

Theorem 26/2 If $S_n = \{1, 2, \ldots, n\}$, G_n is the set of all permutations from S_n onto S_n and $\circ$ is the operation of composition of functions in G_n, then the mathematical system $(G_n, \circ)$ is a group.

Proof This theorem will be proved by verifying each of the group properties. To begin, note that each of the functions in set G_n has set S_n as both its domain and range. Consequently, for any two functions, each of which has S_n as its domain, the function that is the composition of these two functions also has S_n as its domain. Since permutations are always onto functions, each of the functions in set G_n is onto S_n. It follows that the composition of two functions in G_n will also be onto S_n. Finally, because each function is one-to-one, their composition is one-to-one. Therefore, we are guaranteed that the composition of two permutations in set G_n is also in G_n (in other words, operation $\circ$ is from $G_n \times G_n$ onto G_n), and that the operation satisfies the *closure property*.

The *associative property* has been generally proved earlier for composition of certain types of functions. Since permutations are of this type, we know that the associative property is satisfied by the operation of composition on G_n, the set of permutations from S_n onto S_n.

To establish the third group property, we must show that set G_n under the operation of composition has an *identity* element. We will show that the identity element of this system is the permutation that leaves every element of set S_n fixed. If this assertion is true, then the identity element is the permutation

$$e = \begin{pmatrix} 1 & 2 & 3 & \dots & n \\ 1 & 2 & 3 & \dots & n \end{pmatrix}.$$

In the notation usually used for functions, the claim is that the identity permutation is given by

$$(x)e = x \text{ for each } x \in S_n.$$

We will use this notation to verify that the permutation we have denoted by e is the identity of the system. To this end, let f be any permutation in G_n, and let x be any element in S_n. Then

$$\begin{aligned}(x)(e \circ f) &= \big((x)e\big)f = (x)f,\\ (x)(f \circ e) &= \big((x)f\big)e = (x)f.\end{aligned}$$

These formulas show that the image of any element x of S_n under the functions $e \circ f$ and $f \circ e$ is the same as the image of the element x under the function f. By the definition of equality of functions, this implies that $e \circ f = f \circ e = f$, and the identity property is satisfied.

Because the system $(G_n, \circ)$ has an identity element, which is the *identity function*, it is now possible to decide if this system also satisfies the *inverse property*. The verification of this fourth property will show that $(G_n, \circ)$ is a group. Let f be any permutation in G_n and let x be any element in S_n. Then we define f′ by

$$\big((x)f\big)f' = x.$$

By the definition of a permutation in S_n, every element of S_n is of the form $(x)f$ for some $x \in S_n$. Hence, function f′ is from S_n. Why? Also, function f′ is onto S_n. Why? As a result of these two observations, it follows that f′ is a permutation of S_n. Why? It remains to show that $f' \circ f = f \circ f' = e$. By the definition of equality of functions, it is sufficient to show that $(x)(f' \circ f) = (x)(f \circ f') = (x)e = x$ for any element x of S_n.

We will first show that $f' \circ f = e$. Let $x \in S_n$. Since f is one-to-one from S_n onto S_n, there exists a unique $y \in S_n$ such that $(y)f = x$. Then, using the definition of f′, we have

$$\begin{aligned}(x)(f' \circ f) &= \big((x)f'\big)f\\ &= \big([(y)f]f'\big)f\\ &= (y)f\\ &= x\\ &= (x)e.\end{aligned}$$

Since $x(f' \circ f) = (x)e$, $f' \circ f = e$. Be sure that you can supply reasons for each step in the above argument.

The computation below shows that $f \circ f' = e$.

$$(x)(f \circ f') = \big((x)f\big)f' = x = (x)e.$$

Thus, we have shown that every permutation $f \in G_n$ has an inverse.

Each of the four properties of a group has been verified; so we have established that the set of all permutations on $\{1, 2, \ldots, n\}$ forms a group under the operation of composition of functions. A precise definition of this group is given below.

Definition 30/2 If $S_n = \{1, 2, \ldots, n\}$ and if G_n is the set of all permutations from S_n onto S_n with $\circ$ the operation of composition of permutations, then the group $(G_n, \circ)$ is the *symmetric group on* S_n.

It is possible, of course, to consider subsets of the symmetric group on $\{1, 2, \ldots, n\}$. In fact, we did just this in the first example of this section, where we developed a group using only three of the six permutations of the set of all permutations on $S_3 = \{1, 2, 3\}$. This group was the set of permutations $\{P_1, P_5, P_6\}$ under the operation of composition. We now define groups of this type.

Definition 31/2 If $(G_n, \circ)$ is a symmetric group and T is a subset of G_n such that $(T, \circ)$ is a group, then $(T, \circ)$ is a *permutation group*.

From Definitions 30/2 and 31/2, we see that the group of motions of an equilateral triangle, $(\{P_1, P_2, P_3, P_4, P_5, P_6\}, \circ)$, is the symmetric group $(G_3, \circ)$ and that $(\{P_1, P_5, P_6\}, \circ)$ is a permutation group.

We will conclude the discussion in this section with two more particular examples of permutation groups. These two groups will involve subsets of the symmetric group G_4.

Example 5 The elements of this group can be associated with certain rotations of a square in the plane. To describe these rotations, we label the vertices of a square with the numerals 1, 2, 3, and 4. Display 40 illustrates the positions of the vertices of the square before and after four particular counterclockwise rotations through multiples of 90° about the centroid of the square. The usual two-line notation for the corresponding permutation is given for each of the four rotations.

The table for the composition of the four permutations illustrated in Display 40 is given in Display 41. The entries in the table may be checked by using the definition of composition of functions or by determining the results of two successive rotations.

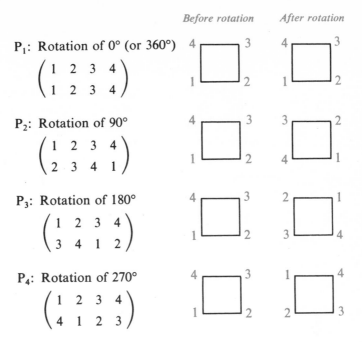

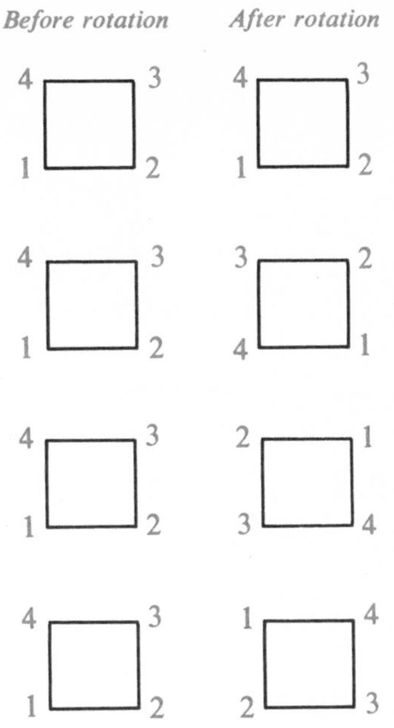

P_1: Rotation of 0° (or 360°)

$$\begin{pmatrix} 1 & 2 & 3 & 4 \\ 1 & 2 & 3 & 4 \end{pmatrix}$$

P_2: Rotation of 90°

$$\begin{pmatrix} 1 & 2 & 3 & 4 \\ 2 & 3 & 4 & 1 \end{pmatrix}$$

P_3: Rotation of 180°

$$\begin{pmatrix} 1 & 2 & 3 & 4 \\ 3 & 4 & 1 & 2 \end{pmatrix}$$

P_4: Rotation of 270°

$$\begin{pmatrix} 1 & 2 & 3 & 4 \\ 4 & 1 & 2 & 3 \end{pmatrix}$$

Display 40

$\circ$	P_1	P_2	P_3	P_4
P_1	P_1	P_2	P_3	P_4
P_2	P_2	P_3	P_4	P_1
P_3	P_3	P_4	P_1	P_2
P_4	P_4	P_1	P_2	P_3

Display 41

The entries in the table can be used to verify that the four permutations P_1, P_2, P_3, and P_4 under the operation of composition form another example of a permutation group. We will comment only briefly on each of the four properties. Observe that the entries in the table are elements of the set $\{P_1, P_2, P_3, P_4\}$; hence, the *closure property* is satisfied. The *associative property* is satisfied because composition of these kinds of functions is associative. Determine which of the four elements is the *identity* of the system. Each element of the system has an *inverse*, as follows: The inverse of P_1 is P_1; the inverse of P_2 is P_4; the inverse of P_3 is P_3; and the inverse of P_4 is P_2. In summary, the set of rotations of a square, $\{P_1, P_2, P_3, P_4\}$, under the operation of composition forms a permutation group.

Before turning to the next example, let us compare the motions of a square with the motions of an equilateral triangle that we considered in examples 1, 2, and 3 of this section. The three rotations of a triangle, P_1, P_5, P_6, form a *permutation group* under the operation of composition. Under the operation composition, the union of the set of three reflections of a triangle about each of the angle bisectors, $\{P_2, P_3, P_4\}$, and the set of three rotations of a triangle about its centroid, $\{P_1, P_5, P_6\}$, yields the system $(\{P_1, P_2, P_3, P_4, P_5, P_6\}, \circ)$, which we know from Definition 30/2 is the symmetric group $(G_3, \circ)$. We established in example 5 that the set of four rotations of a square, $\{P_1, P_2, P_3, P_4\}$, under composition forms a permutation group. We will now combine the set of four rotations of a square with the set of reflections of a square about its diagonals to see if the resulting set of permutations under the operation of composition is a permutation group. Display 42 illustrates the reflections of a square about its diagonals.

Before reflection *After reflection*

P_5: Reflection about the diagonal joining vertices 1 and 3

$$\begin{pmatrix} 1 & 2 & 3 & 4 \\ 1 & 4 & 3 & 2 \end{pmatrix}$$

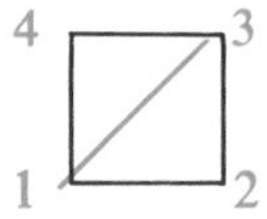

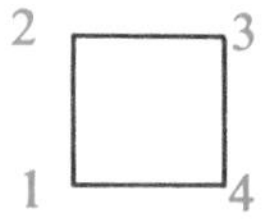

P_6: Reflection about the diagonal joining vertices 2 and 4

$$\begin{pmatrix} 1 & 2 & 3 & 4 \\ 3 & 2 & 1 & 4 \end{pmatrix}$$

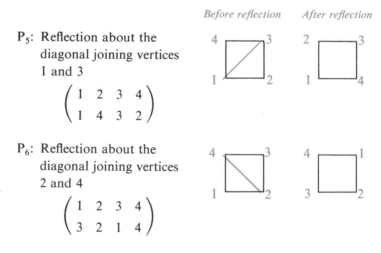

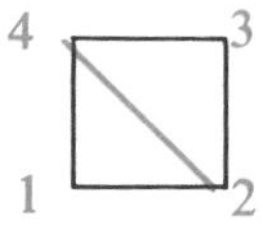

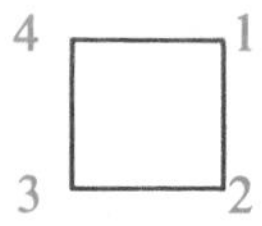

Display 42

Example 6 Suppose that we form the union of the set of permutations $\{P_5, P_6\}$ and the set of four rotations $\{P_1, P_2, P_3, P_4\}$ considered in example 5. A hasty assumption might be that this set under composition is a group. However, this is not the case, as is shown by computing the "product" of the two permutations listed below.

$$P_6 \circ P_2 = \begin{pmatrix} 1 & 2 & 3 & 4 \\ 3 & 2 & 1 & 4 \end{pmatrix} \circ \begin{pmatrix} 1 & 2 & 3 & 4 \\ 2 & 3 & 4 & 1 \end{pmatrix} = \begin{pmatrix} 1 & 2 & 3 & 4 \\ 4 & 3 & 2 & 1 \end{pmatrix}$$

Notice that $P_6 \circ P_2$ can be interpreted as a reflection in a vertical line bisecting opposite sides of the square. Since this "product" is not an element of $\{P_1, P_2, P_3, P_4, P_5, P_6\}$, the closure property does *not* hold. Consequently, this set under the operation of composition is *not* a group.

However, we can combine two more motions of a square with the set of six rotations and reflections already given and thereby obtain a group. The two other permutations that we need are reflections in the lines that are the perpendicular bisectors of pairs of opposite sides of the square. These reflections are shown in Display 43 along with the corresponding permutations.

P_7: Reflection about the line ℓ_1

$$\begin{pmatrix} 1 & 2 & 3 & 4 \\ 2 & 1 & 4 & 3 \end{pmatrix}$$

P_8: Reflection about the line ℓ_2

$$\begin{pmatrix} 1 & 2 & 3 & 4 \\ 4 & 3 & 2 & 1 \end{pmatrix}$$

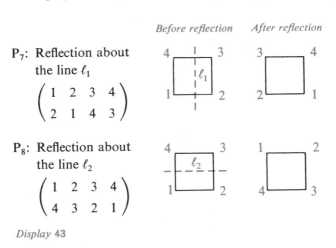

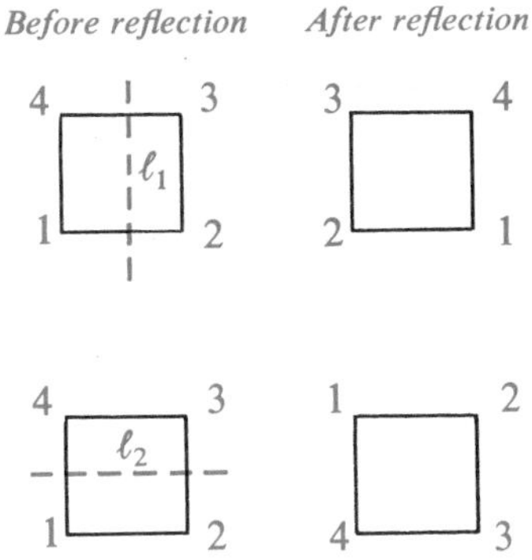

Display 43

We now have a set of eight permutations that correspond to motions of a square. These elements are listed below in two different categories: rotations and reflections. Keep in mind that P_5 and P_6 are reflections about diagonals and that P_7 and P_8 are reflections about lines joining midpoints of opposite sides.

Rotations	*Reflections*
$P_1: \begin{pmatrix} 1 & 2 & 3 & 4 \\ 1 & 2 & 3 & 4 \end{pmatrix}$	$P_5: \begin{pmatrix} 1 & 2 & 3 & 4 \\ 1 & 4 & 3 & 2 \end{pmatrix}$
$P_2: \begin{pmatrix} 1 & 2 & 3 & 4 \\ 2 & 3 & 4 & 1 \end{pmatrix}$	$P_6: \begin{pmatrix} 1 & 2 & 3 & 4 \\ 3 & 2 & 1 & 4 \end{pmatrix}$
$P_3: \begin{pmatrix} 1 & 2 & 3 & 4 \\ 3 & 4 & 1 & 2 \end{pmatrix}$	$P_7: \begin{pmatrix} 1 & 2 & 3 & 4 \\ 2 & 1 & 4 & 3 \end{pmatrix}$
$P_4: \begin{pmatrix} 1 & 2 & 3 & 4 \\ 4 & 1 & 2 & 3 \end{pmatrix}$	$P_8: \begin{pmatrix} 1 & 2 & 3 & 4 \\ 4 & 3 & 2 & 1 \end{pmatrix}$

The composition table for these eight permutations is given in Display 44 on the following page. You should use the definition of the composition of two functions or the idea of successive motions of a square to verify the entries in the table.

$\circ$	P_1	P_2	P_3	P_4	P_5	P_6	P_7	P_8
P_1	P_1	P_2	P_3	P_4	P_5	P_6	P_7	P_8
P_2	P_2	P_3	P_4	P_1	P_8	P_7	P_5	P_6
P_3	P_3	P_4	P_1	P_2	P_6	P_5	P_8	P_7
P_4	P_4	P_1	P_2	P_3	P_7	P_8	P_6	P_5
P_5	P_5	P_7	P_6	P_8	P_1	P_3	P_2	P_4
P_6	P_6	P_8	P_5	P_7	P_3	P_1	P_4	P_2
P_7	P_7	P_6	P_8	P_5	P_4	P_2	P_1	P_3
P_8	P_8	P_5	P_7	P_6	P_2	P_4	P_3	P_1

Display 44

From the table we see that this set of eight permutations on $\{1, 2, 3, 4\}$ satisfies the *closure property*. The *associative property* is valid because the composition of functions of this type is associative. The *identity* element in this system is the permutation P_1. Each of the permutations has an *inverse* in the set, as described below.

The inverse of P_1 is P_1; the inverse of P_2 is P_4; the inverse of P_3 is P_3; the inverse of P_4 is P_2; the inverse of P_5 is P_5; the inverse of P_6 is P_6; the inverse of P_7 is P_7; and the inverse of P_8 is P_8.

This establishes that the set $\{P_1, P_2, P_3, P_4, P_5, P_6, P_7, P_8\}$ under composition forms a permutation group. This group is called the group of motions of a square.

Exercises

1 The symmetric group on S_3 is usually denoted as G_3. This is, of course, the set of permutations on $\{1, 2, 3\}$. The six permutations in G_3 are listed on page 97 as P_1, P_2, P_3, P_4, P_5, and P_6. Which of the following subsets of G_3 are permutation groups under the operation of composition?

a $\{P_1\}$
b $\{P_4\}$
c $\{P_1, P_2\}$
d $\{P_1, P_3\}$
e $\{P_1, P_4\}$
f $\{P_1, P_5\}$
g $\{P_2, P_3\}$
h $\{P_1, P_5, P_6\}$
i $\{P_2, P_3, P_4\}$
j $\{P_1, P_2, P_3\}$
k $\{P_2, P_4, P_6\}$
l $\{P_1, P_2, P_3, P_4, P_5\}$

2 Consider an isosceles triangle that is not equilateral. Find the set of motions associated with this figure in a plane; that is, the set of motions which map the figure onto itself. Does this set under composition form a group?

3 Consider the symmetric group on S_2; that is, G_2. How many elements does G_2 contain? Form the table for G_2. How many permutation groups are included in G_2?

4 Consider the symmetric group on S_4; that is, G_4. How many elements does G_4 contain? Eight of the permutations in G_4 are given on page 107 as $P_1, P_2, \ldots, P_8$. Which of the following subsets of G_4 form permutation groups? *Answer*

a $\{P_1\}$
b $\{P_3\}$
c $\{P_1, P_3\}$
d $\{P_1, P_2, P_3\}$
e $\{P_1, P_2, P_3, P_4\}$
f $\{P_1, P_3, P_7, P_8\}$
g $\{P_1, P_3, P_5, P_6\}$
h $\{P_1, P_2, P_3, P_4, P_7\}$
i $\{P_1, P_2, P_3, P_5, P_6\}$
j $\{P_1, P_2, P_3, P_4, P_7, P_8\}$

Consider the subset of the symmetric group G_4 given below in the two-line notation. Use this set of permutations in connection with exercises 5, 6, and 7.

$$P_a: \begin{pmatrix} 1 & 2 & 3 & 4 \\ 1 & 2 & 3 & 4 \end{pmatrix} \quad P_c: \begin{pmatrix} 1 & 2 & 3 & 4 \\ 1 & 3 & 2 & 4 \end{pmatrix} \quad P_e: \begin{pmatrix} 1 & 2 & 3 & 4 \\ 1 & 4 & 2 & 3 \end{pmatrix}$$

$$P_b: \begin{pmatrix} 1 & 2 & 3 & 4 \\ 1 & 2 & 4 & 3 \end{pmatrix} \quad P_d: \begin{pmatrix} 1 & 2 & 3 & 4 \\ 1 & 4 & 3 & 2 \end{pmatrix} \quad P_f: \begin{pmatrix} 1 & 2 & 3 & 4 \\ 1 & 3 & 4 & 2 \end{pmatrix}$$

5 Which of these permutations belong to the group of motions of a square?

6 Make a composition table for $(\{P_a, P_b, P_c, P_d, P_e, P_f\}, \circ)$ and show that this system is a permutation group.

7 Which of the following subsets of G_4 form permutation groups?

a $\{P_a\}$
b $\{P_a, P_b\}$
c $\{P_a, P_c\}$
d $\{P_a, P_e\}$
e $\{P_a, P_e, P_f\}$
f $\{P_a, P_b, P_d\}$
g $\{P_a, P_b, P_e, P_f\}$
h $\{P_a, P_c, P_d, P_e, P_f\}$

8 Consider a rectangle that is not a square. Find the set of motions of this figure in a plane. Does this set under composition form a group?

9 Find the inverses in G_5 of the following permutations.

a $\begin{pmatrix} 1 & 2 & 3 & 4 & 5 \\ 2 & 3 & 4 & 5 & 1 \end{pmatrix}$ *Answer*

b $\begin{pmatrix} 1 & 2 & 3 & 4 & 5 \\ 3 & 4 & 5 & 2 & 1 \end{pmatrix}$

c $\begin{pmatrix} 1 & 2 & 3 & 4 & 5 \\ 3 & 2 & 4 & 1 & 5 \end{pmatrix}$

d $\begin{pmatrix} 1 & 2 & 3 & 4 & 5 \\ 1 & 2 & 3 & 4 & 5 \end{pmatrix}$

10 How many elements does $(G_n, \circ)$ contain? *Answer*

The permutation on the set $\{1, 2, \ldots, n\}$, given in the two-line form by

$$C: \begin{pmatrix} 1 & 2 & 3 & \ldots & k & \ldots & n \\ 2 & 3 & 4 & \ldots & k+1 & \ldots & 1 \end{pmatrix};$$

is called the *full cycle* of the symmetric group G_n. Since the full cycle is a permutation on the set $\{1, 2, \ldots, n\}$, each symmetric group contains a full cycle.

◆ **11** Determine whether the full cycle is contained in each of the following groups discussed in the text.

a The rotations of an equilateral triangle

b The motions of an equilateral triangle (the symmetric group G_3)

c The rotations of a square

d The motions of a square

◆ **12** Determine whether the full cycle is contained in each of the groups described in exercises 1 and 4.

◆ **13** If P is a permutation on the set $\{1, 2, \ldots, n\}$, we define $P^2 = P \circ P$, $P^3 = P \circ P \circ P$, and $P^k = P \circ P \circ \ldots \circ P$ (with k "factors" of P) for any integer $k > 0$.

a Compute P_5^k for $k = 1, 2, \ldots, 5$, where P_5 is the rotation of a triangle described on page 97.

b Compute P_2^k for $k = 1, 2, \ldots, 8$, where P_2 is the rotation of the square described on page 107.

◆ **14** Determine the full cycle of G_5. Compute the powers of the cycle from 1 through 5; write these permutations in two-line form. Make a composition table for these permutations. *Answer*

15 Determine the full cycle of G_6. Compute the powers of the cycle from 1 through 6; write these permutations in two-line form. Make a composition table for these permutations.

16 From exercises 14 and 15, what conjecture would you make about the nth power of the full cycle of G_n? *Answer*

17 Since the composition of permutations has previously been proved to be associative, the composition of the set of powers from 1 to n of the full cycle of G_n is associative. From exercises 14 and 15, what conjecture would you make about closure in the set consisting of the set of powers from 1 to n of the full cycle of G_n under the operation of composition?

18 Use the composition table you constructed for exercise 14 to determine an inverse for each element of the set of powers from 1 to 5 of the full cycle of G_5.

19 Use the composition table you constructed for exercise 15 to determine an inverse for each element of the set of powers from 1 to 6 of the full cycle of G_6.

20 From exercises 18 and 19, what conjecture would you make about the existence of inverses in the set of powers from 1 to n of the full cycle of G_n?

21 In view of your answers to exercises 16, 17, and 20, what can you conclude about the system composed of the set of powers from 1 to n of the full cycle of G_n under the operation of composition? *Answer*

Commutative groups 18/2

The previous section was devoted to the study of a special kind of group called a symmetric group and certain subsystems of symmetric groups called permutation groups. The distinguishing characteristic of symmetric and permutation groups is that the elements are permutations. Now we will discuss another classification of groups, but this separation of groups into the categories of *commutative* and *noncommutative* depends upon a property of the group operation rather than upon the nature of the elements of the group.

Let us begin by reconsidering several familiar subsystems of the real numbers that satisfy the four group properties. Five such subsystems are listed below.

Examples 1 (I, +)

2 (R, +)

3 $(R^+, \cdot)$

4 $(\{2x \mid x \in I\}, +)$

5 $(\{x \mid x \in \mathfrak{R} \text{ and } x \neq 0\}, \cdot)$

Each of these systems has a property that is called the *commutative property*. For those examples that have addition as the operation, the property is expressed as follows: If a and b are elements in the group, then $a + b = b + a$. In those examples for which the operation is multiplication, the property is expressed as $a \cdot b = b \cdot a$. Informally, the property can be stated as follows: "The order in which the elements occur in the operation does not affect the result of the operation." A formal definition of the class of groups with the commutative property is given below.

Definition 32/2 If (G, ☆) is a group, then (G, ☆) is a *commutative group* if and only if, for each $a, b \in G$, $a \text{ ☆ } b = b \text{ ☆ } a$.

Although it is true that the groups in mathematics with which you are probably most familiar are commutative groups, there are noncommutative operations in mathematics and there are many noncommutative operations that occur in everyday affairs. As an illustration, the operation of putting on your socks and then your shoes does not yield the same result as the operation of putting on your shoes and then your socks. To convince yourself that there are many other such examples, think of several acts that you perform in a certain order that would not result in the same outcome if the order of events were reversed.

Since you may not have thought of noncommutative operations in mathematics (indeed, you may have thought that all operations were commutative), we shall now exhibit a noncommutative group.

In section 17/2, we showed that the set of six motions of a triangle, which we later noted is the set G_3 of all permutations on $S_3 = \{1, 2, 3\}$, under the operation of composition forms a group. However, this group is *not* commutative. To show that $(G_3, \circ)$ is not commutative, it is sufficient to find two elements P_i and P_j in G_3 such that the result of composition of the elements is altered if the elements occur in a different order. Two such elements are P_6 and P_4. The following computations show that $P_6 \circ P_4 \neq P_4 \circ P_6$.

$$P_6 \circ P_4 = \begin{pmatrix} 1 & 2 & 3 \\ 3 & 1 & 2 \end{pmatrix} \circ \begin{pmatrix} 1 & 2 & 3 \\ 1 & 3 & 2 \end{pmatrix} = \begin{pmatrix} 1 & 2 & 3 \\ 2 & 1 & 3 \end{pmatrix} = P_2.$$

$$P_4 \circ P_6 = \begin{pmatrix} 1 & 2 & 3 \\ 1 & 3 & 2 \end{pmatrix} \circ \begin{pmatrix} 1 & 2 & 3 \\ 3 & 1 & 2 \end{pmatrix} = \begin{pmatrix} 1 & 2 & 3 \\ 3 & 2 & 1 \end{pmatrix} = P_3.$$

Since the result of the operation of composition in this case depends upon which permutation occurs first, we have demonstrated that $(G_3, \circ)$ is not a commutative group. You should use the permutations listed on page 97 to find other pairs that do not commute. Now that we have one example of a noncommutative group, a generalization of this result shows that there are infinitely many noncommutative groups. The theorem below establishes this generalization.

Theorem 27/2 If S_n is the set $\{1, 2, \ldots, n\}$ with $n \geqq 3$, and G_n is the set of all permutations on S_n, then the symmetric group $(G_n, \circ)$ is noncommutative.

Proof To establish the theorem, it is sufficient to exhibit two permutations in G_n such that the result of composition of the permutations does depend upon the order in which the elements occur. The example discussed earlier for G_3 points to a way of selecting the following pair of elements in G_n.

$$\begin{pmatrix} 1 & 2 & 3 & 4 & \dots & n \\ 3 & 1 & 2 & 4 & \dots & n \end{pmatrix} \circ \begin{pmatrix} 1 & 2 & 3 & 4 & \dots & n \\ 1 & 3 & 2 & 4 & \dots & n \end{pmatrix} = \begin{pmatrix} 1 & 2 & 3 & 4 & \dots & n \\ 2 & 1 & 3 & 4 & \dots & n \end{pmatrix}.$$

$$\begin{pmatrix} 1 & 2 & 3 & 4 & \dots & n \\ 1 & 3 & 2 & 4 & \dots & n \end{pmatrix} \circ \begin{pmatrix} 1 & 2 & 3 & 4 & \dots & n \\ 3 & 1 & 2 & 4 & \dots & n \end{pmatrix} = \begin{pmatrix} 1 & 2 & 3 & 4 & \dots & n \\ 3 & 2 & 1 & 4 & \dots & n \end{pmatrix}.$$

The two products are not equal because 1, 2, and 3 are mapped differently in the two permutations. Since the resultant permutations in the two computations are not the same, the group is not commutative and the proof of the theorem is completed.

The commutative property serves to separate the set of all groups into two natural classes: those that are *commutative* and those that are *noncommutative*. Each of these kinds of groups has an important role in mathematics. At the present time, much research is being done into the nature of infinite commutative groups. There are also still many unsolved problems in the theory of noncommutative groups.

We have just seen that symmetric groups on three or more elements do not possess the commutative property. We will now examine two other systems to determine if they are commutative groups.

Example 1 For the first of these two examples, let n be a counting number and let a and b be any elements in the set of integers. We define a binary operation $\star_n$ as follows:

$$a \star_n b = a + b - n.$$

Note that the set involved in this example is the set of integers and the operation $\star_n$ has I × I as its domain. Some "products" in the system (I, $\star_n$) are given below.

$$2 \star_n 3 = 2 + 3 - n.$$
$$5 \star_n -4 = 5 + (-4) - n.$$
$$-1 \star_n 1 = -1 + 1 - n.$$

Observe that the "products" will be different for different choices of n. If we choose $n = 3$, then the examples above become:

$$2 \star_3 3 = 2 + 3 - 3 = 2.$$
$$5 \star_3 -4 = 5 + (-4) - 3 = -2.$$
$$-1 \star_3 1 = -1 + 1 - 3 = -3.$$

The overall picture of the effect of this operation is best seen through a partial "multiplication" table. For $n = 3$ the table for the integers from -3 through $+3$ is given in Display 45 on the following page.

$\star_3$	−3	−2	−1	0	1	2	3
3	−3	−2	−1	0	1	2	3
2	−4	−3	−2	−1	0	1	2
1	−5	−4	−3	−2	−1	0	1
0	−6	−5	−4	−3	−2	−1	0
−1	−7	−6	−5	−4	−3	−2	−1
−2	−8	−7	−6	−5	−4	−3	−2
−3	−9	−8	−7	−6	−5	−4	−3

Display **45**

Although the entries in the table are given for $n = 3$, remember that we are interested in establishing that, for *each* replacement of n, the system is a group. We will now verify the four group properties.

Since addition and subtraction are closed in the set of integers, we know that $a + b - n$ is an integer. Therefore, the binary operation $\star_n$ as defined on the set $I \times I$ satisfies the *closure property*.

The *associative property* for this operation can be verified by the following two computations:

$$\begin{aligned}(a \star_n b) \star_n c &= (a + b - n) \star_n c \\ &= (a + b - n) + c - n \\ &= a + b + c - 2n.\end{aligned}$$

$$\begin{aligned}a \star_n (b \star_n c) &= a \star_n (b + c - n) \\ &= a + (b + c - n) - n \\ &= a + b + c - 2n.\end{aligned}$$

Since these computations show that $(a \star_n b) \star_n c = a \star_n (b \star_n c)$, for all $a, b, c \in I$, it follows that operation $\star_n$ is associative.

Now we will verify that there is an *identity* for this mathematical system. In order to discover which element is the identity, we will first assume the existence of such an identity e and use the conditions that it must satisfy to determine which element in $(I, \star_n)$ is equal to e. By the definition of identity, we know that e must satisfy the condition

$$a \star_n e = a.$$

But, by the definition of $\star_n$,

$$a \star_n e = a + e - n.$$

Hence,

$$a = a + e - n,$$

which implies that

$$e = n.$$

We have just shown that *if* an identity exists, then it must be n. However, we have not actually shown that n *is* the identity. The two computations below prove that n is the identity.

$$a \star_n n = a + n - n = a.$$
$$n \star_n a = n + a - n = a.$$

We can prove the *inverse property* for (I, $\star_n$) in much the same way that we proved the identity property. To begin, we will assume that each element a has an inverse a'. Then we will use two conditions involving a', one based upon the definition of the inverse of an element and one based upon the definition of operation $\star_n$, to determine which element in (I, $\star_n$) is equal to a'. If a' is an inverse of a, then by the definition of inverse and by the fact that n is the identity, we have

$$a \star_n a' = n.$$

But, by the definition of $\star_n$,

$$a \star_n a' = a + a' - n.$$

Hence,

$$n = a + a' - n.$$

Thus,

$$a' = 2n - a.$$

We have just shown that, if the element a has an inverse a', then a' must be $2n - a$. The computations below verify that $2n - a$ is the inverse of a.

$$a \star_n (2n - a) = a + 2n - a - n = n.$$
$$(2n - a) \star_n a = 2n - a + a - n = n.$$

Now that all four of the group properties have been verified, we know that (I, $\star_n$) forms a group. For (I, $\star_n$) to be a *commutative* group, the following condition must be satisfied: For each $a, b \in$ I, $a \star_n b = b \star_n a$. The computations below show that the condition is satisfied for each a, b and each n. Hence, we can conclude that (I, $\star_n$) is an example of a commutative group.

$$a \star_n b = a + b - n.$$
$$b \star_n a = b + a - n = a + b - n.$$

Example 2 For the last example of the section, let (a, b) and (c, d) be any two elements in $(\mathfrak{R}^+ \cup \mathfrak{R}^-) \times \mathfrak{R}$. Also, let operation ☆ from $[(\mathfrak{R}^+ \cup \mathfrak{R}^-) \times \mathfrak{R}] \times [(\mathfrak{R}^+ \cup \mathfrak{R}^-) \times \mathfrak{R}]$ be defined as follows:

$$(a, b) \star (c, d) = (ac, bc + d).$$

Recall that in section 16/2 we verified that this mathematical system, denoted by (H, ☆), satisfies the four group properties. We now inquire whether or not (H ☆) is a commutative group. To show that this group is noncommutative, it is sufficient to find two ordered pairs such that the "product" of these pairs gives a different result when the order in which they occur is reversed. The following computations show that (2, 1) and (3, 4) are two such pairs.

$$(2, 1) \star (3, 4) = (2 \cdot 3, 1 \cdot 3 + 4) = (6, 7).$$

$$(3, 4) \star (2, 1) = (3 \cdot 2, 4 \cdot 2 + 1) = (6, 9).$$

Hence, the commutative property does not hold in the system (H, ☆), and we have a noncommutative group.

Exercises

1 Which of the following groups, first studied in section 17/2 and in the exercises at the end of that section, are commutative?
  a The three rotations of a triangle
  b The four rotations of a square
  c The eight motions of a square
  d The symmetric group G_2
  e The symmetric group G_3
  f The symmetric group G_4
  g The permutation group of exercise 6, page 109.

◆ 2 Prove that the set of integers modulo n under modular addition forms a commutative group. (Hint: See Theorem 17/2.)

3 Prove that any group of two elements is commutative. *Answer*

◆ 4 Prove that a group of three elements is commutative.

◆ 5 Prove that a group of four elements is commutative.

◆ 6 Prove that a group of six elements is not necessarily commutative by finding an example of a group of six elements that is not commutative.

7 Which of the following systems are commutative groups?
  a (I, ☆), where $x \star y = x + y + xy$
  b (C, ☆), where $x \star y = xy$
  c (R, ☆), where $x \star y = [x + y]$
  d ($\mathfrak{R}$, ☆), where $x \star y = \frac{1}{2}xy$
  e (G, +), where $G = \mathfrak{R} \times \mathfrak{R}$ and $(a, b) + (c, d) = (a + c, b + d)$

f (G, ☆), where $G = I \times (I^+ \cup I^-)$ and $(a, b) ☆ (c, d) = (ac, bd)$

g (G, ☆), where $G = I \times (I^+ \cup I^-)$ and $(a, b) ☆ (c, d) = (ad + bc, bd)$

h (G, ☆), where $G = \Re \times (\Re^+ \cup \Re^-)$ and $(a, b) ☆ (c, d) = (a + c, bd)$

8 Show that the powers of the full cycle of G_5 under composition form a commutative group.

9 Show that the powers of the full cycle of G_6 under composition form a commutative group.

10 From exercises 8 and 9, what conjecture would you make about the powers of the full cycle of G_n? *Answer*

◆ **11** Prove that if e is the identity of $(G, \circ)$ and if, for each $a \in G$, $a \circ a = e$, then $(G, \circ)$ is a commutative group. *Answer*

◆ **12** Prove that if $(G, \circ)$ is a group and if, for each $a, b \in G$, $(a \circ b) \circ (a \circ b) = (a \circ a) \circ (b \circ b)$, then $(G, \circ)$ is a commutative group. *Answer*

◆ **13** Prove that if e is the identity of $(G, \circ)$ and if, for each $a, b \in G$, $b' \circ a' \circ b \circ a = e$, then $(G, \circ)$ is a commutative group.

◆ **14** Prove that if $(G, \circ)$ is a group and if, for each $a \in G$, $a \circ a = a$, then $(G, \circ)$ is a commutative group.

15 Show that the group of exercise 24, page 96, is not commutative.

Subgroups of a group 19/2

Many of the examples that have been considered in this chapter show that a subset of the elements of a given group may itself form a group under a given operation. Such is the case with the permutation group $(\{P_1, P_5, P_6\}, \circ)$, which is contained in the symmetric group $(\{P_1, P_2, P_3, P_4, P_5, P_6\}, \circ)$. Even more obvious examples are those formed from subsets of the real numbers. Under the operation of addition, some examples are the integers, the rational numbers, and the integral multiples of seven. Under the operation of multiplication, such subsets as the nonzero rational numbers and the positive real numbers furnish examples. However, some care must be taken in choosing the subset, as is evidenced by the fact that the counting numbers under addition do not form a group, nor does the set of integers under multiplication. In view of these remarks it is natural to inquire: For which subsets S of the set of real numbers is it true that (S, +) or (S, •) is a group? More generally, we ask: If (G, ☆) is a group, then for which subsets S of G is it true that (S, ☆) is also a group?

That such subsets do exist in every case follows from the fact that, given any group (G, ☆), the systems ({e}, ☆), where e is the identity element of G, and (S, ☆), where S = G, are always groups. Since these subgroups exist for any group, our primary concern will be with subsets S of G for which S ≠ G and S ≠ {e}, with the further stipulation that (S, ☆) is a group.

To find an answer to the general question that has been raised, we will consider some examples that give hints as to what conditions are necessary and sufficient for (S, ☆) to be a group.

Examples 1 Recall that (I, +) is a group. One subset of I is the set of even integers. Does the set of even integers under addition form a group? The verification that ($\{2x \mid x \in I\}$, +) satisfies the properties of a group is left as an exercise for you.

2 Now consider another subset of I, the set of odd integers, under addition. One of the properties that (O_I, +) must satisfy to be a group is the closure property. Note that if $x, y \in O_I$, then we can express x and y as

$$x = 2n + 1,$$
$$y = 2m + 1,$$

with $m, n \in I$. The sum of x and y is then

$$\begin{aligned} x + y &= (2n + 1) + (2m + 1) \\ &= 2n + 2m + 2 \\ &= 2(n + m + 1), \end{aligned}$$

which is an even integer. Since the closure property is not satisfied for (O_I, +), we know that (O_I, +) is *not* a group.

3 Another subset of I is the set of whole numbers. Recall that the set of whole numbers is {0, 1, 2, . . .}. Is (W, +) an example of a group? The closure property is satisfied by the system (W, +), because the sum of two whole numbers is a whole number. The associative property is also satisfied by the system (W, +). Why? Furthermore, the system possesses an identity. What is it? However, the inverse property is not satisfied by (W, +). To demonstrate that the inverse property is not satisfied, it is sufficient to find an element $a \in W$ such that, for each $b \in W$, $a + b = 0$ is false. One such element is 3. For each $b \in W$, $3 + b = 0$ is false. Thus, the whole numbers under addition do *not* form a group.

Only three examples have been considered, but it is apparent that if (G, ☆) is a group and S is a subset of G, then for (S, ☆) to be a group, it is necessary that the closure and inverse properties be satisfied. That these two conditions are necessary should have been anticipated, but that these two conditions are also sufficient may come as a surprise to you. Theorem 28/2 establishes this fact. First, we need the following definition.

Definition 33/2 If S is a nonempty subset of G, then (S, ☆) is a *subgroup* of (G, ☆) if and only if (S, ☆) is a group. The subgroups (G, ☆) and ({e}, ☆) are called *trivial subgroups* of (G, ☆).

Note that in Definition 33/2 we have used the same symbol for the operation in (S, ☆) as in (G, ☆). The operations are technically different in these two groups since the domain in one case is S × S and, in the other, G × G.

Theorem 28/2 If S is a nonempty subset of G and the identity of (G, ☆) is e, then (S, ☆) is a subgroup of (G, ☆) if it has the following two properties:

1) *Closure*: For each $a, b \in S$, $a ☆ b \in S$.
2) *Inverse*: For each $a \in S$, there exists an $a' \in S$ such that $a' ☆ a = a ☆ a' = e$.

Proof Let S be a nonempty subset of G and let (G, ☆) be a group. Assume that (S, ☆) satisfies both the closure and the inverse properties. We will verify that (S, ☆) is a group; that is, that (S, ☆) also satisfies the associative and the identity properties.

In order to verify the associative property, let $a, b, c \in S$. The associative property holds if and only if

$$(a ☆ b) ☆ c = a ☆ (b ☆ c).$$

But because a, b, and c are elements of S, they are also elements of G and, since (G, ☆) is a group, we know that the associative property holds for all the elements of G. Therefore, the *associative property* is satisfied for (S, ☆).

It remains to show that (S, ☆) satisfies the identity property. By hypothesis, set S is not empty and, therefore, it contains at least one element. Let a be such an element and let a' be the unique inverse of a in the group (G, ☆). Also by hypothesis, we know that both a and a' are in set S and that the system (S, ☆) is closed. Therefore, $a' ☆ a$, or e, is contained in S; that is, the identity element of G is contained in S. Since e is the identity element of (G, ☆), we have $e ☆ x = x ☆ e = x$ for each $x \in G$. It follows that, because S is a subset of G, we have $e ☆ a = a ☆ e = a$ for each $a \in S$. This establishes that the system (S, ☆) satisfies the *identity property* and completes the proof of the theorem.

Theorem 28/2 is convenient for determining whether or not a particular nonempty subset, along with the group operation, is a subgroup, since the theorem shows that it is not necessary to verify all four properties of a group. Instead, we need only verify the closure and inverse properties, and we know that the associative and identity properties are necessarily satisfied.

In example 1 at the beginning of this section, we considered the system $(\{2x \mid x \in I\}, +)$, which is a subgroup of $(I, +)$. It is routine to verify that such subsets of I as the following, with the operation of addition, are also subgroups of $(I, +)$.

Examples 4 $\{7x \mid x \in I\} = \{\ldots, -14, -7, 0, 7, 14, \ldots\}$.

5 $\{10x \mid x \in I\} = \{\ldots, -20, -10, 0, 10, 20, \ldots\}$.

6 $\{5x \mid x \in I\} = \{\ldots, -10, -5, 0, 5, 10, \ldots\}$.

Notice that the subsets of I discussed in examples 1, 4, 5, and 6 are of the form $\{nx \mid n \in C \text{ and } x \in I\}$. We will now show that all subsets of I of this form are subgroups under addition of $(I, +)$.

Theorem 29/2 If $I_{nx} = \{nx \mid n \in C \text{ and } x \in I\} = \{\ldots, -2n, -n, 0, n, 2n, \ldots\}$, then I_{nx} under the operation of addition is a subgroup of the integers under addition. Symbolically, $(I_{nx}, +)$ is a subgroup of $(I, +)$.

Proof From Theorem 28/2, we know that, to prove $(I_{nx}, +)$ is a group, it is sufficient to show that the set I_{nx} under addition satisfies the closure and inverse properties.

To establish the closure property, we choose from I_{nx} elements nu and ny, whose sum is $nu + ny$. By properties of the integers, $nu + ny = n(u + y)$. Since u and $y \in I$, it follows that $u + y \in I$. Why? So by the definition of I_{nx}, it follows that $n(u + y) \in I_{nx}$. This shows that the *closure property* is satisfied.

To establish that the inverse property holds, we choose $nu \in I_{nx}$ and observe that since u is an integer, its additive inverse $-u$ is also an integer. How do you know that $n(-u) \in I_{nx}$? Since n and u are integers, $n(-u) = -(nu)$; so $-(nu) \in I_{nx}$. But, since $-(nu)$ is the additive inverse of (nu), it follows that the *inverse property* is satisfied.

We have verified the two properties necessary to show that $(I_{nx}, +)$ is a subgroup of $(I, +)$. Thus, Theorem 29/2 is proved.

Theorem 29/2 establishes that the set of integral multiples of any fixed counting number under the operation of addition is a subgroup of $(I, +)$. What we do not yet know is whether or not the converse of this statement is true. The converse can be stated as follows: If $(S, +)$ is a nontrivial subgroup of the integers, then S is the set of integral multiples of a counting number. The validity of this converse is established in the proof of Theorem 30/2.

Theorem 30/2 If (S, +) is a nontrivial subgroup of the integers under addition, then there exists a counting number n such that S is the set of all integral multiples of n, I_{nx}.

Proof The hypothesis that (S, +) is a nontrivial subgroup of (I, +) will be used to determine the counting number n whose existence is asserted in the theorem. We begin by choosing an element $a \in S$, with $a \neq 0$. By the inverse property of a group, we know that $a \in S$ implies $-a \in S$. It follows that S contains at least one positive integer, a or $-a$, and one negative integer, a or $-a$. Thus, we know that a nonempty subset of the counting numbers is included in S. By the *well-ordering property* (every nonempty subset of C has a least member), it follows that there is a least counting number contained in set S. We will denote this least element of S by n.

Now we will show that $S = I_{nx}$. This can be accomplished by showing that, first, all integral multiples of n are in set S and, second, S contains no elements other than integral multiples of n.

To establish that all integral multiples of n are contained in S, let x be any positive integer. We need to show that $nx \in S$ for each $x \in I$. Since $n \in S$, it follows from the closure property of addition that $n + n \in S$; that is, $n \cdot 2 \in S$. But by the same reasoning, $(n \cdot 2) + n$ must also be contained in S; therefore, $n \cdot 3 \in S$. After $x - 1$ applications of the closure property, we see that $nx \in S$ for any positive integer x. Now let x be a negative integer. Since n belongs to the group S, $-n$ also belongs to S by the inverse property of the group. By the closure property, it follows that $-n + (-n) = -n \cdot 2$ also belongs to S. Similarly, $-n \cdot 2 + (-n) = -n \cdot 3$ belongs to S, and, after $| x - 1 |$ applications of the closure property, it follows that $-nx \in S$. These arguments show that all positive integral multiples and all negative integral multiples of n are contained in S. The missing element is the multiple $n \cdot 0 = 0$, but, since (S, +) is a group, $0 \in S$. Why? Therefore, every integral multiple of the fixed counting number n is in set S.

It remains now to show that every element of S is an integral multiple of n. Let m be any element of S, with $m > 0$. By the division algorithm, we know that m may be expressed as $m = qn + r$ with $0 \leqq r < n$ and with q an integer. By the result of the previous paragraph, we know that $-qn \in S$. Therefore, the sum $m + (-qn)$ is also a member of S. Since $m + (-qn) = r$, it follows that $r \in S$. But the fact that $0 \leqq r < n$ and the fact that n is the least counting number in S imply that $r = 0$. If $r = 0$, then $m = qn$, and m is an integral multiple of n. This shows that any positive integer in set S is an integral multiple of n. To complete the proof of Theorem 30/2, it remains to be shown that this is the case for nonpositive integers. This is left as an exercise.

In Theorems 29/2 and 30/2, we have proved that integral multiples of a fixed counting number are subsets that form subgroups of (I, +) under addition, and, conversely, that any subgroup of (I, +) is of this type. Such theorems are examples of *classification theorems* because they serve to classify all subgroups of a particular group.

Exercises

1 Complete the proof of Theorem 30/2 by showing that, if m is any nonpositive integer in S, then m is an integral multiple of n.

2 For each of the following, determine whether the subset S under the operation of the given system G is a subgroup of G.

a G = $(\mathfrak{R}, +)$. S = E_I.

b G is the group of nonzero real numbers under multiplication. S is the set of nonzero even integers.

c G is the group of complex numbers under addition. S = R.

d G = (I, +). S = I^+.

e G = $(\mathfrak{R}, +)$. S is the set of nonzero rational numbers.

f G is the group of nonzero complex numbers under multiplication. S = $\mathfrak{R}$.

g G is the group of nonzero complex numbers under multiplication. S = $\{1, -1, i, -i\}$.

h G = $(I/6, \oplus_6)$. S = $\{\bar{0}, \bar{2}, \bar{3}\}$. *Answer*

i G = $(I/6, \oplus_6)$. S = $\{\bar{0}, \bar{1}, \bar{3}, \bar{5}\}$. *Answer*

j G = $(I/6, \oplus_6)$. S = $\{\bar{0}, \bar{3}\}$.

◆ **k** G is the set of nonzero integers under multiplication. S = $\{1, -1\}$.

l G = (I, +). S = $\{1, -1\}$.

m G = (G(i), +). S is the set of negative integers.

n G is the group of nonzero integers modulo 11 under modular multiplication. S = $\{\bar{1}, \bar{3}, \bar{4}, \bar{5}, \bar{9}\}$. *Answer*

o G is the group of nonzero integers modulo 11 under modular multiplication. S = $\{\bar{1}, \bar{3}, \overline{10}\}$.

p G is the group of nonzero integers modulo 11 under modular multiplication. S = $\{\bar{1}, \overline{10}\}$.

q G is the group of nonzero integers modulo 13 under modular multiplication. S = $\{\bar{1}, \bar{5}, \bar{8}, \overline{12}\}$.

r G is the group of nonzero integers modulo 13 under modular multiplication. S = $\{\bar{1}, \bar{3}, \bar{9}\}$.

s G is the group of nonzero integers modulo 13 under modular multiplication. S = $\{\bar{1}, \overline{12}\}$.

t G is the group of nonzero integers modulo 13 under modular multiplication. S = $\{\bar{1}, \bar{4}, \bar{9}, \overline{12}\}$. *Answer*

3 Let (G, ☆) be a group with identity e, and let (S, ☆) be a subgroup of (G, ☆) with identity x. Prove that $x = e$. *Answer*

4 Let (G, ☆) be a group with identity e, and let (S, ☆) be a subgroup of (G, ☆) with element s. Prove that if $s ☆ y = y ☆ s = e$, for $y \in S$, then $y = s'$, where s' is the inverse of s in (G, ☆).

◆ **5** Prove that if $a ☆ b' \in S$ for each $a, b \in S$, then S is a subgroup of the group (G, ☆). Also, prove that if (S, ☆) is a subgroup of the group (G, ☆), then $a ☆ b' \in S$ for each $a, b \in S$. If these two conditionals are combined, they form an alternative definition for a subgroup of a group. That is, (S, ☆) is a subgroup of (G, ☆) if and only if $a ☆ b' \in S$ for each $a, b \in S$.

6 In section 16/2 we proved that the set of all ordered pairs of real numbers (a, b), where $a \neq 0$, forms a group under the operation ☆ defined by $(a, b) ☆ (c, d) = (ac, bc + d)$. Show that the set of all ordered pairs of real numbers $(1, b)$ forms a subgroup of this group. *Answer*

If (G, ☆) is a group and (S, ☆) is a subgroup of (G, ☆), then for $x \in G$, we define a *right coset* of S as follows:

$$S ☆ x = \{s ☆ x \mid s \in S\}.$$

That is, a right coset of S is a set of elements of the form $s ☆ x$, where x is a fixed element of G and s is any element of S. Use this definition in connection with exercises 7 through 10.

7 Consider the group $(I/6, \oplus_6)$. For each of the following subsets of I/6, if the set under $\oplus_6$ forms a subgroup of $(I/6, \oplus_6)$, then find the right cosets of the subgroup.

a $\{\bar{0}, \bar{2}, \bar{4}\}$ *Answer* **b** $\{\bar{0}, \bar{2}, \bar{5}\}$ **c** $\{\bar{0}, \bar{3}\}$ **d** $\{\bar{0}, \bar{4}\}$

8 Consider the group of nonzero integers modulo 13 under modular multiplication. For each of the following subsets of I/13, if the set under $\odot_{13}$ forms a subgroup, find the right cosets of the subgroup.

a $\{\bar{1}\}$ **c** $\{\bar{1}, \bar{3}, \bar{9}\}$ *Answer* **e** $\{\bar{1}, \bar{3}, \bar{4}, \bar{9}, \overline{10}, \overline{12}\}$
b $\{\bar{1}, \overline{10}\}$ **d** $\{\bar{1}, \bar{5}, \bar{8}, \overline{12}\}$ **f** $\{\bar{1}, \bar{4}, \bar{9}, \overline{12}\}$

◆ **9** Let (S, ☆) be a subgroup of the finite group (G, ☆). Prove that if the intersection of the right cosets $S ☆ a$ and $S ☆ b$ of S is not empty, then $S ☆ a = S ☆ b$. *Answer*

10 Let (S, ☆) be a subgroup of (G, ☆). The *index* of S in G is the number of distinct right cosets of S in G. Find the index of each subgroup in exercises 7 and 8.

11 Find all subgroups of the following groups.

a $(I/3, \oplus_3)$ e $(I/8, \oplus_8)$
b $(I/4, \oplus_4)$ f $(I/9, \oplus_9)$
c $(I/5, \oplus_5)$ g $(I/10, \oplus_{10})$
d $(I/6, \oplus_6)$ h $(I/12, \oplus_{12})$

12 Find all subgroups of the symmetric group G_3 under composition. (Hint: There are subgroups of one, two, three, and six elements.)

13 Find all subgroups of the group of nonzero integers modulo 7 under modular multiplication. (Hint: There are subgroups of one, two, three, and six elements.) *Answer*

14 Find all the right cosets (see exercise 7) of each subgroup of G_3 that you determined for exercise 12.

◆ **15** A subgroup (S, ☆) of a group (G, ☆) is *normal* in G if $x ☆ s ☆ x' \in S$, where x' is the inverse of x, for each $s \in S$ and each $x \in G$. Find the normal subgroups of the symmetric group G_3 under composition.

16 Find the normal subgroups of the integers modulo 8 under modular addition.

◆ **17** Prove that every subgroup of a commutative group (G, ☆) is normal. *Answer*

◆ **18** Consider the normal subgroup $N = (\{\bar{0}, \bar{3}, \bar{6}, \bar{9}\}, \oplus_{12})$ of $(I/12, \oplus_{12})$. Compute the cosets $N \oplus_{12} \bar{x}$ of N. In this set of cosets, define a binary operation ☆ such that $(N \oplus_{12} \bar{x}) ☆ (N \oplus_{12} \bar{y}) = N \oplus_{12} (\bar{x} \oplus_{12} \bar{y})$. Show that the set of cosets of N forms a group under operation ☆.

19 Repeat exercise 18 for $N = (\{\bar{0}, \bar{4}, \bar{8}\}, \oplus_{12})$ of $(I/12, \oplus_{12})$.

◆ **20** Let (G, ☆) be a group. Also let C be the set of those elements in G that commute with all elements of G; that is, let $C = \{x \mid x \in G \text{ and } x ☆ a = a ☆ x \text{ for all } a \in G\}$. C is called the *center* of the group. Prove that C is a subgroup of G.

◆ **21** Prove that the center of any group is a normal subgroup of the group. *Answer*

◆ **22** Find all subgroups of the group of nonzero integers modulo 13 under multiplication. (Hint: There are subgroups of one, two, three, four, six, and twelve elements.)

Intersection and union of subgroups

20/2

In section 8/1 you learned that if A and B are subsets of S, then $A \cap B \subseteq S$. Therefore, if (G, ☆) is a group with subgroups (H, ☆) and (K, ☆), then set $H \cap K$ is a subset of G. But what of the system $(H \cap K, ☆)$? Is it a subgroup of (G, ☆)?

First we will look at some examples that may lead to an intelligent guess. The examples below are subgroups of (I, +).

Examples 1 $I_{3x} \cap I_{6x} =$

$$\{\ldots, -12, -9, -6, -3, 0, 3, 6, 9, 12, \ldots\} \cap$$
$$\{\ldots, -12, -6, 0, 6, 12, \ldots\} =$$
$$\{\ldots, -12, -6, 0, 6, 12, \ldots\} = I_{6x}.$$

2 $I_{3x} \cap I_{4x} =$

$$\{\ldots, -12, -9, -6, -3, 0, 3, 6, 9, 12, \ldots\} \cap$$
$$\{\ldots, -12, -8, -4, 0, 4, 8, 12, \ldots\} =$$
$$\{\ldots, -12, 0, 12, \ldots\} = I_{12x}.$$

3 $I_{6x} \cap I_{15x} =$

$$\{\ldots, -30, -24, -18, -12, -6, 0, 6, 12, 18, 24, 30, \ldots\} \cap$$
$$\{\ldots, -30, -15, 0, 15, 30, \ldots\} =$$
$$\{\ldots, -30, 0, 30, \ldots\} = I_{30x}.$$

Because each of the systems $(I_{6x}, +)$, $(I_{12x}, +)$, and $(I_{30x}, +)$ is a subgroup of (I, +), these examples would lead us to believe that the intersection of two subgroups is again a subgroup. This is in fact the case, as Theorem 31/2 establishes.

Theorem 31/2 If (H, ☆) and (K, ☆) are subgroups of (G, ☆), then (H ∩ K, ☆) is a subgroup of (G, ☆).

Proof Since H ∩ K ⊆ G, if the system (H ∩ K, ☆) is a group, then it must be a subgroup of (G, ☆). Therefore, in order to prove that (H ∩ K, ☆) is a subgroup of (G, ☆), we need only show that (H ∩ K, ☆) is a group. From Theorem 28/2, it is sufficient to show that the following statements are true:

1) H ∩ K is not empty.
2) For each $a, b \in$ H ∩ K, a ☆ $b \in$ H ∩ K.
3) For each $a \in$ H ∩ K, there exists an $a' \in$ H ∩ K such that a' ☆ $a = a$ ☆ $a' = e$.

The set H ∩ K has at least one element in it because H is a subgroup of G and the identity e of G is contained in H. Similarly, $e \in$ K. Therefore, $e \in$ H ∩ K, and H ∩ K is not empty.

To establish the closure property, let $a \in$ H ∩ K and $b \in$ H ∩ K. We will show that a ☆ $b \in$ H ∩ K. Since $a \in$ H ∩ K, it follows that $a \in$ H. Why? Similarly, $b \in$ H ∩ K implies $b \in$ H. But H is a group, so a ☆ $b \in$ H. Give an analogous argument to show that a ☆ $b \in$ K. The two conditions a ☆ $b \in$ H and a ☆ $b \in$ K imply that a ☆ $b \in$ H ∩ K. Therefore, (H ∩ K, ☆) satisfies the closure property.

To establish the inverse property we begin with an element $a \in$ H ∩ K and show that its inverse, a', is in H ∩ K. Again,

$a \in H \cap K$ implies $a \in H$. Since H is a group, the element a' is also in H. Give an analogous argument to show that $a' \in K$. The two conditions $a' \in H$ and $a' \in K$ imply that $a' \in H \cap K$. Why? It follows that $(H \cap K, \star)$ satisfies the inverse property, and Theorem 31/2 is established.

The theorem just proved establishes that the intersection of *two* subgroups is a subgroup. But what about the intersection of more than two subgroups? Just as the binary operation of intersection of sets can be extended by the associative property, the concept of intersection of subgroups can also be extended. This fact is stated in the next theorem.

Theorem 32/2 If $\mathcal{S}$ is a set of subgroups of $(G, \star)$, then the intersection of the elements of $\mathcal{S}$ under the operation $\star$ is a subgroup of $(G, \star)$.

The proof of this theorem parallels the proof for the intersection of two subgroups just given for Theorem 31/2. The steps in the argument and their justification are essentially the same.

Theorems 31/2 and 32/2 show that the intersection of any number of subgroups is a subgroup; however the only useful means they provide for constructing a subgroup is that of forming the intersection of two or more given subgroups. It is not possible to establish any general method of constructing subgroups by intersection for *every* group, but it is possible to do so for the collection of subgroups of (I, +) as a result of Theorems 29/2 and 30/2. A constructive means of determining the intersection of *any* collection of subgroups of (I, +) will now be given.

Let us again consider the examples of intersection of subgroups of the integers under addition.

H		*K*		*H* ∩ *K*
I_{3x}	∩	I_{6x}	=	I_{6x}.
I_{3x}	∩	I_{4x}	=	I_{12x}.
I_{6x}	∩	I_{15x}	=	I_{30x}.

Observe that, if we consider the factors of the counting numbers that determine the subgroups given in these examples, we have the following:

H	*K*	*H* ∩ *K*
$3 = 1 \cdot 3.$	$6 = 1 \cdot 2 \cdot 3.$	$6 = 1 \cdot 2 \cdot 3.$
$3 = 1 \cdot 3.$	$4 = 1 \cdot 2 \cdot 2.$	$12 = 1 \cdot 2 \cdot 2 \cdot 3.$
$6 = 1 \cdot 2 \cdot 3.$	$15 = 1 \cdot 3 \cdot 5.$	$30 = 1 \cdot 2 \cdot 3 \cdot 5.$

The important point to be noted is that the counting number that determines the subgroup $H \cap K$ is the *least common mul-*

tiple of the counting numbers that determine the given subgroups H and K. These examples are representative of all subgroups of (I, +), so we can generalize the idea of using the least common multiple to find the intersection of subgroups of (I, +). A definition of the least common multiple of two numbers is given below to help you recall this concept.

Definition 34/2 If a and b are counting numbers and the multiples of a and b are denoted by

$$M_a = \{a,\ 2a,\ 3a,\ 4a,\ \ldots\},$$
$$M_b = \{b,\ 2b,\ 3b,\ 4b,\ \ldots\},$$

then the *least common multiple* of a and b is the least member of $M_a \cap M_b$, which is the set of all common multiples of a and b. The least common multiple of a and b is denoted by l.c.m. (a, b) or by $[a, b]$.

Note that $M_a \cap M_b$ is not empty because $ab \in M_a$ and $ab \in M_b$. That there is a least counting number in $M_a \cap M_b$ is guaranteed by the fact that the counting numbers are well ordered. The following theorem establishes the nature of the subgroup formed by the intersection of any two subgroups of (I, +).

Theorem 33/2 If $(I_{ax}, +)$ and $(I_{bx}, +)$ are subgroups of (I, +), then their intersection is the subgroup determined by the least common multiple of the counting numbers a and b. In symbols, $I_{ax} \cap I_{bx} = I_{[a,\, b]x}$.

Proof The proof of the theorem will be established if we can show that the sets $I_{ax} \cap I_{bx}$ and $I_{[a,\, b]x}$ are equal. This can be accomplished by showing that each set is a subset of the other.

To show that $I_{ax} \cap I_{bx} \subseteq I_{[a,\, b]x}$, let $y \in I_{ax} \cap I_{bx}$. This means that y is an element of both I_{ax} and I_{bx}; that is, there exist integers m and n such that $y = am = bn$. Since $a > 0$ and $b > 0$, one of the following is true: both m and n are 0, both m and n are positive, or both m and n are negative. If $m = n = 0$, then $y = 0$, and $0 \in I_{[a,\, b]x}$, because 0 is an element of every subgroup of (I, +). Next, suppose that $m > 0$ and $n > 0$. In this case, $y \in M_a \cap M_b$, and, since l.c.m. (a, b), or $[a, b]$, is the least such element in the intersection, it follows that y is a multiple of the least common multiple, because a common multiple of two numbers is always a multiple of the least common multiple. Thus, $y \in I_{[a,\, b]x}$. For the final case in this part of the proof, both m and n negative, we see that $-y$, the additive inverse of y, is an element of $M_a \cap M_b$. The argument for the second case then proves that $-y \in I_{[a,\, b]x}$. But, since this set under addition is a group, it follows that y also belongs to the set $I_{[a,\, b]x}$. Hence, for each $y \in I_{ax} \cap I_{bx}$, it follows that $y \in I_{[a,b]x}$. Therefore, $I_{ax} \cap I_{bx} \subseteq I_{[a, b]x}$.

To show that $I_{[a, b]x} \subseteq I_{ax} \cap I_{bx}$, let $z \in I_{[a, b]x}$. We know that $[a, b] \in M_a \cap M_b$; so there exist counting numbers r and s such that $[a, b] = ar = bs$. Since $z \in I_{[a, b]x}$, there exists an integer t such that $z = [a, b]t$. Thus, we have $z = [a, b]t = art = bst$. The condition $z = art$ means that $z \in I_{ax}$, and the condition $z = bst$ means that $z \in I_{bx}$; hence, $z \in I_{ax} \cap I_{bx}$. This establishes that $I_{[a, b]x} \subseteq I_{ax} \cap I_{bx}$.

We have now shown that $I_{ax} \cap I_{bx} \subseteq I_{[a, b]x}$ and that $I_{[a, b]x} \subseteq I_{ax} \cap I_{bx}$. From these, it follows that $I_{[a, b]x} = I_{ax} \cap I_{bx}$, and the proof of Theorem 33/2 is concluded.

Now we will consider the binary operation of union of subgroups to see whether or not the union of two subgroups of $(I, +)$ is always a subgroup. It might seem that the results for the union of subgroups should be analogous to those for the intersection of subgroups.

In investigating this possibility, let us see what happens if we form the union of $(I_{3x}, +)$ and $(I_{6x}, +)$ and the union of $(I_{10x}, +)$ and $(I_{40x}, +)$.

Examples 1 $I_{3x} \cup I_{6x} =$

$$\{\ldots, -6, -3, 0, 3, 6, \ldots\} \cup \{\ldots, -12, -6, 0, 6, 12, \ldots\} =$$
$$\{\ldots, -12, -9, -6, -3, 0, 3, 6, 9, 12, \ldots\} = I_{3x}.$$

2 $I_{10x} \cup I_{40x} =$

$$\{\ldots, -40, -30, -20, -10, 0, 10, 20, 30, 40, \ldots\} \cup \{\ldots, -80, -40, 0, 40, 80, \ldots\} =$$
$$\{\ldots, -40, -30, -20, -10, 0, 10, 20, 30, 40, \ldots\} = I_{10x}.$$

Since $(I_{3x}, +)$ and $(I_{10x}, +)$ are subgroups of $(I, +)$, in these examples it is certainly the case that the union of two subgroups is a subgroup. We state a conjecture patterned after Theorem 31/2.

If $(H, \star)$ and $(K, \star)$ are subgroups of $(G, \star)$, then $(H \cup K, \star)$ is a subgroup of $(G, \star)$.

We will now investigate to determine if this conjecture is, indeed, a theorem. As a result of Theorem 28/2, it is necessary and sufficient to show that $H \cup K$ is not empty; that $H \cup K$ is closed under the operation $\star$; and that $a \in H \cup K$ implies that a', the inverse of a, is in $H \cup K$. Arguments to support these statements are given below.

Since $(H, \star)$ is a group, we know that H is not empty. Therefore, $H \cup K$ is not empty.

Let $a \in H \cup K$ and $b \in H \cup K$. If $a \in H$ and $b \in H$, then $a \star b \in H$ because $(H, \star)$ is a group; therefore, $a \star b \in H \cup K$.

If $a \in K$ and $b \in K$, then $a \star b \in K$ because K is a group; therefore, $a \star b \in H \cup K$. It follows that $(H \cup K, \star)$ satisfies the closure property.

Now let $a \in H \cup K$. It follows that a is either in H or K or in both. If $a \in H$, then $a' \in H$ because $(H, \star)$ is a group and satisfies the inverse property; therefore, $a' \in H \cup K$. If $a \in K$, then $a' \in K$ because $(K, \star)$ is a group and satisfies the inverse property; therefore, $a' \in H \cup K$. In either case, $a \in H$ or $a \in K$, it follows that $a' \in H \cup K$. Therefore, $(H \cup K, \star)$ satisfies the inverse property.

Now that arguments have been given to support the conjecture that $(H \cup K, \star)$ is a subgroup, we will consider one more example, this time choosing $(I_{3x}, +)$ and $(I_{5x}, +)$ as the subgroups of $(I, +)$.

3 $I_{3x} \cup I_{5x} =$

$$\{\ldots, -6, -3, 0, 3, 6, \ldots\} \cup \{\ldots, -10, -5, 0, 5, 10, \ldots\} = \{\ldots, -10, -6, -5, -3, 0, 3, 5, 6, 10, \ldots\}.$$

If $(I_{3x} \cup I_{5x}, +)$ is a subgroup of $(I, +)$, then it certainly must satisfy, among other properties, the closure property. In particular, the sum $-3 + 5 = 2$ must be in the union $I_{3x} \cup I_{5x}$. But 2 is not in $I_{3x} \cup I_{5x}$. Therefore, the closure property for addition does not hold for the system $(I_{3x} \cup I_{5x}, +)$. This furnishes us with a counterexample to the conjecture that the union of any two subgroups of a group is a subgroup and leads us to suspect that the argument in support of it is not valid. In fact, the conjecture is *not* a true statement; hence, there is something wrong with the supporting argument. See if you can find the fallacy.

Exercises

1 Write a proof of Theorem 32/2 on page 126.

2 In each of the following, G is a group, and S and T under the operation of G are subgroups of G. In each case, determine the subgroup $S \cap T$.

a $G = (I/6, \oplus_6)$, $S = \{\bar{0}, \bar{3}\}$, and $T = \{\bar{0}, \bar{2}, \bar{4}\}$.

b $G = (I/16, \oplus_{16})$, $S = \{\bar{0}, \bar{8}\}$, and $T = \{\bar{0}, \bar{4}, \bar{8}, \overline{12}\}$.

c $G = (I/12, \oplus_{12})$, $S = \{\bar{0}, \bar{2}, \bar{4}, \bar{6}, \bar{8}, \overline{10}\}$, and $T = \{\bar{0}, \bar{3}, \bar{6}, \bar{9}\}$. *Answer*

d G is the set of nonzero integers modulo 11 under modular multiplication, $S = \{\bar{1}, \bar{3}, \bar{4}, \bar{5}, \bar{9}\}$, and $T = \{\bar{1}, \overline{10}\}$. *Answer*

e G is the set of nonzero integers modulo 7 under modular multiplication, $S = \{\bar{1}, \bar{6}\}$, and $T = \{\bar{1}, \bar{2}, \bar{4}\}$.

f $G = (I, +)$, $S = I_{12x}$, and $T = I_{8x}$.

g $G = (\mathfrak{R}, +)$, $S = R$, and $T = I$.

h G is the set of complex numbers under addition, $S = E_I$, and $T = \Re$.

i G is the set of complex numbers under addition, S is the set of imaginary numbers, and $T = (\Re, +)$.

j $G = (I/180, \oplus_{180})$, $S = \{\overline{6n} \mid n \in I\}$, and $T = \{\overline{30n} \mid n \in I\}$.

3 In each part of exercise 2, determine $S \cup T$.

4 For each of the following, determine whether the union of the subsets A and B of I/24 forms a subgroup of the integers modulo 24 under modular addition.

a $A = \{\bar{0}, \overline{12}\}$ and $B = \{\bar{0}, \bar{6}, \overline{12}, \overline{18}\}$.

b $A = \{\bar{0}, \bar{3}, \bar{6}, \bar{9}, \overline{12}, \overline{15}, \overline{18}, \overline{21}\}$ and $B = \{\bar{0}, \bar{8}, \overline{16}\}$. *Answer*

c $A = \{\bar{0}, \bar{4}, \bar{8}, \overline{12}, \overline{16}, \overline{20}\}$ and $B = \{\bar{0}, \bar{8}, \overline{16}\}$.

d $A = \{\bar{0}, \bar{2}, \bar{4}, \bar{6}, \bar{8}, \overline{10}, \overline{12}, \overline{14}, \overline{16}, \overline{18}, \overline{20}, \overline{22}\}$ and $B = \{\bar{0}, \bar{3}, \bar{6}, \bar{9}, \overline{12}, \overline{15}, \overline{18}, \overline{21}\}$.

e $A = \{\bar{0}, \bar{2}, \bar{4}, \bar{6}, \bar{8}, \overline{10}, \overline{12}, \overline{14}, \overline{16}, \overline{18}, \overline{20}, \overline{22}\}$ and $B = \{\bar{0}, \bar{6}, \overline{12}, \overline{18}\}$. *Answer*

f $A = \{\bar{0}, \bar{6}, \overline{12}, \overline{18}\}$ and $B = \{\bar{0}, \bar{4}, \bar{8}, \overline{12}, \overline{16}, \overline{20}\}$. *Answer*

5 For each of the following, determine whether the union of sets C and D under composition forms a subgroup of the symmetric group G_4.

a $C = \left\{\begin{pmatrix}1&2&3&4\\1&2&3&4\end{pmatrix}\right\}$. $D = \left\{\begin{pmatrix}1&2&3&4\\1&2&3&4\end{pmatrix}, \begin{pmatrix}1&2&3&4\\1&2&4&3\end{pmatrix}\right\}$.

b $C = \left\{\begin{pmatrix}1&2&3&4\\1&2&3&4\end{pmatrix}, \begin{pmatrix}1&2&3&4\\1&4&2&3\end{pmatrix}, \begin{pmatrix}1&2&3&4\\1&3&4&2\end{pmatrix}\right\}$.

$D = \left\{\begin{pmatrix}1&2&3&4\\1&2&3&4\end{pmatrix}, \begin{pmatrix}1&2&3&4\\1&2&4&3\end{pmatrix}\right\}$. *Answer*

c $C = \left\{\begin{pmatrix}1&2&3&4\\1&2&3&4\end{pmatrix}, \begin{pmatrix}1&2&3&4\\1&4&2&3\end{pmatrix}, \begin{pmatrix}1&2&3&4\\1&3&4&2\end{pmatrix}, \begin{pmatrix}1&2&3&4\\1&2&4&3\end{pmatrix}, \begin{pmatrix}1&2&3&4\\1&4&3&2\end{pmatrix}, \begin{pmatrix}1&2&3&4\\1&3&2&4\end{pmatrix}\right\}$.

$D = \left\{\begin{pmatrix}1&2&3&4\\1&2&3&4\end{pmatrix}, \begin{pmatrix}1&2&3&4\\4&1&2&3\end{pmatrix}, \begin{pmatrix}1&2&3&4\\3&4&1&2\end{pmatrix}, \begin{pmatrix}1&2&3&4\\2&3&4&1\end{pmatrix}\right\}$.

d $C = \left\{\begin{pmatrix}1&2&3&4\\1&2&3&4\end{pmatrix}, \begin{pmatrix}1&2&3&4\\4&1&2&3\end{pmatrix}, \begin{pmatrix}1&2&3&4\\3&4&1&2\end{pmatrix}, \begin{pmatrix}1&2&3&4\\2&3&4&1\end{pmatrix}, \begin{pmatrix}1&2&3&4\\1&2&4&3\end{pmatrix}, \begin{pmatrix}1&2&3&4\\4&1&3&2\end{pmatrix}, \begin{pmatrix}1&2&3&4\\2&3&1&4\end{pmatrix}, \begin{pmatrix}1&2&3&4\\3&1&2&4\end{pmatrix}\right\}$.

$D = \left\{\begin{pmatrix}1&2&3&4\\1&2&3&4\end{pmatrix}, \begin{pmatrix}1&2&3&4\\2&3&4&1\end{pmatrix}, \begin{pmatrix}1&2&3&4\\4&1&2&3\end{pmatrix}, \begin{pmatrix}1&2&3&4\\3&4&1&2\end{pmatrix}\right\}$.

◆ 6 Write a criticism of the argument given on pages 128-129 to "prove" that the union of two subgroups of a group is itself a subgroup.

7 If G is the group of integers under addition, S is the subgroup of integral multiples of 6, and T is the subgroup of integral multiples of 15, is S ∪ T a subgroup? If T is the subgroup of integral multiples of 30, is S ∪ T a subgroup? *Answer*

8 If G is the group of integers under addition, S is the subgroup of integral multiples of 12, and T is the subgroup of integral multiples of 16, is S ∪ T a subgroup? If S is the subgroup of integral multiples of 24, is S ∪ T a subgroup? If S is the subgroup of integral multiples of 48, is S ∪ T a subgroup?

◆ 9 Let (G, ☆) be a group, and let S and T be subgroups of (G, ☆). Prove that S ∪ T is a subgroup of (G, ☆) if and only if S ⊆ T or T ⊆ S. (Hint: To prove the "only if," assume that S ⊈ T and T ⊈ S. Thus, there are elements *s* and *t* such that *s* ∈ S, *s* ∉ T, *t* ∈ T, and *t* ∉ S. Consider *st*, which must belong to S ∪ T. Why? Either *st* ∈ S or *st* ∈ T. Why? Show that the first alternative implies *t* ∈ S, which is a contradiction, and that the second alternative implies *s* ∈ T, which is also a contradiction.)

◆ 10 It can be proved that there is a smallest subgroup of a group (G, ☆) that contains the subgroups (S, ☆) and (T, ☆). We define the operation "subgroup—union," denoted by Ⓖ, so that S Ⓖ T is the smallest subgroup of G that contains both of the subgroups S and T of G. Determine the "subgroup—union" of S and T described in exercises 7 and 8. Also find S Ⓖ T for each part of exercise 2. This definition is often used to guarantee that the "union" of two subgroups is a subgroup.

Cyclic groups 21/2

One of the primary purposes of any theoretical course in mathematics is to prove, if possible, theorems which classify structures according to certain sets of conditions. Although the preceding statement is a very general one, you may recognize that this purpose has been achieved thus far by Theorems 29/2 and 30/2, which classify all the subgroups of the commutative group (I, +). In this section and in the one that follows, a similar kind of task will be undertaken; namely, theorems will be proven that characterize a kind of group called a *cyclic group*. Obviously, before we can categorize such groups, we must define what we mean by the term cyclic group. The group of integers under addition will serve as an example that will lead to some basic definitions.

Example The group of integers under addition can be extended to include an operation of multiplication of the elements of the group by integers. The following equalities suggest how we might define multiplication of the element 1 of (I, +) by nonnegative integers.

$$\begin{aligned} 0 \cdot 1 &= 0. \\ 1 \cdot 1 &= 0 \cdot 1 + 1. \\ 2 \cdot 1 &= 1 \cdot 1 + 1. \\ 3 \cdot 1 &= 2 \cdot 1 + 1. \\ &\vdots \\ n \cdot 1 &= (n-1) \cdot 1 + 1. \\ (n+1) \cdot 1 &= n \cdot 1 + 1. \end{aligned}$$

From the preceding, we can see that multiplication of the element 1 of the group (I, +) by nonnegative integers could be defined as $0 \cdot 1 = 0$ and $(n + 1) \cdot 1 = n \cdot 1 + 1$ for $n \geqq 1$. This definition is consistent with what is already known about multiplication of integers. But what definition should be adopted if the element of (I, +) that is chosen is different from 1? Let us now see if we can develop a definition of multiplication between the nonnegative integers and the element 2 of the group (I, +). Certainly, the following statements are true.

$$\begin{aligned} 0 \cdot 2 &= 0. \\ 1 \cdot 2 &= 0 \cdot 2 + 2. \\ 2 \cdot 2 &= 1 \cdot 2 + 2. \\ 3 \cdot 2 &= 2 \cdot 2 + 2. \\ 4 \cdot 2 &= 3 \cdot 2 + 2. \end{aligned}$$

Therefore, it seems reasonable to define multiplication of the group element 2 by nonnegative integers as follows: $0 \cdot 2 = 0$ and $(n + 1) \cdot 2 = (n \cdot 2) + 2$ for each nonnegative integer n.

Both of the fixed elements of (I, +) that have been selected for illustrative purposes have been positive. However, if the product of any nonnegative integer and a fixed element of (I, +)—positive, zero, or negative—is considered, then the results will be similar. For illustration, we will now consider -5 as the fixed element of (I, +). If we multiply -5 by each nonnegative integer in turn, we have:

$$\begin{aligned} 0 \cdot (-5) &= 0. \\ 1 \cdot (-5) &= 0 \cdot (-5) + (-5). \\ 2 \cdot (-5) &= 1 \cdot (-5) + (-5). \\ 3 \cdot (-5) &= 2 \cdot (-5) + (-5). \end{aligned}$$

These equalities suggest the definition $(n + 1) \cdot (-5) = n \cdot (-5) + (-5)$ for any integer $n \geqq 0$.

The last examples are taken from the group (I, +), but they point the way to a definition for an operation of multiplication between the elements of any group and nonnegative integers. This definition follows.

Definition 35/2 If (G, ☆) is a group, n is an integer greater than or equal to 0, e is the identity of (G, ☆), and $a \in$ G, then the product of n and a is as follows:
1) $n \cdot a = e$, for $n = 0$; that is, $0 \cdot a = e$.
2) $n \cdot a = a$, for $n = 1$; that is, $1 \cdot a = a$.
3) $(n + 1) \cdot a = (n \cdot a) \star a$, for $n \geqq 1$.
The group elements e, a, and $(n \cdot a) \star a$ are called the *products* of 0 and a, of 1 and a, and of $(n + 1)$ and a, respectively.

In Definition 35/2 meaning has been given to the product of a whole number and an element from an arbitrary group. Because the definition is based upon examples that use (I, +) as the group, it seems reasonable to use • as a symbol for the product of a whole number and a group element. If we were dealing with a modular system, the operation would be modular multiplication. For example, in (I/4, $\oplus_4$), the product of $(n + 1)$ and $\bar{a}$ would be $(\overline{n + 1}) \odot_4 \bar{a} = (\bar{n} \odot_4 \bar{a}) \oplus_4 \bar{a}$ for each nonnegative integer n and each $\bar{a} \in$ I/4 and each $n \geqq 0$.

It should be pointed out that an alternative procedure (and a procedure found in many books) is to use the whole numbers as exponents rather than as factors and to define *powers* rather than products of the group elements. Had this procedure been employed here, the following alternative definitions would have been adopted.

$$a^0 = e.$$
$$a^1 = a.$$
$$a^{n+1} = a^n \star a.$$

But the group of integers under addition naturally leads us to use the product notation rather than exponential notation in our definition of multiplication.

Definition 35/2 gives a rule for multiplying nonnegative integers and group elements. But this definition must be extended to include the product of *negative* integers and group elements. This means that the case in which n is a positive integer should be extended with a view toward defining the product of $-n$, which is the inverse of n, and any group element. Since $n > 0$, $-n < 0$. It will be helpful to continue with the example of the group of integers under addition. Addition and multiplication of integers provide a natural way of defining multiplication of the group element 1 of (I, +) by negative integers. For some specific examples, we have the following results.

$$-1 \cdot 1 = 1 \cdot (-1) = -1.$$
$$-2 \cdot 1 = 2 \cdot (-1) = -2.$$
$$-3 \cdot 1 = 3 \cdot (-1) = -3.$$
$$-4 \cdot 1 = 4 \cdot (-1) = -4.$$

In general, $-n \cdot 1 = n \cdot (-1) = -n$ for any integer n such that $n > 0$. Since there is nothing unusual about the group element 1, it seems natural to define multiplication of any group element, say 3, by a negative integer in a similar way. If the usual operations on integers are used as a guide, then we would want the following to be true.

$$-1 \cdot 3 = 1 \cdot (-3) = -3.$$
$$-2 \cdot 3 = 2 \cdot (-3) = -6.$$
$$-3 \cdot 3 = 3 \cdot (-3) = -9.$$

In general, multiplication of 3 by any negative integer $-n$ would be defined as $-n \cdot 3 = n \cdot (-3) = -(3n)$ for any integer $n > 0$. That is, the inverse of n and the group element 3 yields the same product as n and the inverse of 3 for each positive integer n. These results lead us to adopt the following definition of the product of a negative integer, thought of as the inverse of a positive integer, and any group element.

Definition 36/2 If (G, ☆) is a group, $a \in$ G, a' is the inverse of a, and n is a positive integer, then $-n \cdot a = n \cdot a'$.

Notice that Definition 36/2 can be used for computational purposes if and only if the product of the positive integer n and the group element a' is defined. But this is precisely what was done in Definition 35/2, which defines the product of a positive integer and *any* group element [since (G, ☆) is a group, $a' \in$ G for each $a \in$ G]; so, the two definitions together assure that we will always be able to compute $-n \cdot a$. We now call attention to an alternative definition for the product of a negative integer and a group element. This definition would have been used if we had adopted exponential notation and defined integral powers of the group elements rather than products of integers and group elements. For any integer $n > 0$, the definition in exponential notation would be

$$a^{-n} = (a')^n.$$

You should note that Definitions 35/2 and 36/2 require that the integer n be greater than zero. We will now prove three theorems that make Definitions 35/2 and 36/2 true for all integral replacements of n.

Theorem 34/2 If (G, ☆) is a group, n is a negative integer, and a' is the inverse of $a \in$ G, then $n \cdot a' = -n \cdot a$.

Proof Note that, for any integer n, $-(-n) = n$ and if $n < 0$, then $-n > 0$. These relations are used in the following steps.

$$\begin{aligned} n \cdot a' &= -(-n) \cdot a' \\ &= -n \cdot (a')' \\ &= -n \cdot a. \end{aligned}$$

This completes the proof of the theorem. Supply the reasons for the steps of the proof.

Theorem 35/2 If (G, ☆) is a group, $a \in$ G, and $n = -1$, then

$$(n + 1) \cdot a = (n \cdot a) \text{☆} a.$$

Proof The following steps show that $(n + 1) \cdot a = e$ and also that $(n \cdot a) \text{☆} a = e$. Hence, the steps show that $(n + 1) \cdot a = (n \cdot a) \text{☆} a$.

$$\begin{aligned} (n + 1) \cdot a &= (-1 + 1) \cdot a \\ &= 0 \cdot a \\ &= e. \\ (n \cdot a) \text{☆} a &= (-1 \cdot a) \text{☆} a \\ &= (1 \cdot a') \text{☆} a \\ &= a' \text{☆} a \\ &= e. \end{aligned}$$

You should supply the reasons for each of these steps.

Theorem 36/2 If (G, ☆) is a group, $a \in$ G, $n \in$ I, and $n < -1$, then

$$(n + 1) \cdot a = (n \cdot a) \text{☆} a.$$

Proof The following steps show how to derive $(n \cdot a) \text{☆} a$ from $(n + 1) \cdot a$.

$$\begin{aligned} (n + 1) \cdot a &= -(n + 1) \cdot a' \\ &= \big(-(n + 1) \cdot a'\big) \text{☆} e \\ &= \big(-(n + 1) \cdot a'\big) \text{☆} (a' \text{☆} a) \\ &= \big([-(n + 1) \cdot a'] \text{☆} a'\big) \text{☆} a \\ &= \big([-(n + 1) + 1] \cdot a'\big) \text{☆} a \\ &= \big((-n) \cdot a'\big) \text{☆} a \\ &= (n \cdot a) \text{☆} a. \end{aligned}$$

Notice that the expression $\big([-(n + 1) + 1] \cdot a'\big) \text{☆} a$ is obtained from $\big([-(n + 1) \cdot a'] \text{☆} a'\big) \text{☆} a$ by substituting $-(n + 1)$ for

n and a' for a in part 3 of Definition 35/2. You should supply the reasons for the other steps in the proof.

The definitions and theorems of this section show how it is possible to relate the operation of any group with a second operation (here called multiplication) involving the integers. The results achieved so far make it possible now to investigate certain interrelated properties of the group operation and the new *integral multiplication* operation. The next two theorems establish properties that exist between the two operations. These properties are easily derived from what is already known about the group (I, +).

Theorem 37/2 If (G, ☆) is a group, $a \in G$, and m and n are integers, then $(m + n) \cdot a = (m \cdot a) ☆ (n \cdot a)$.

Proof The method of proof will be to assume that m is a fixed integer and to show that the theorem holds for any integer n. Therefore, we must show that $(m + n) \cdot a = (m \cdot a) ☆ (n \cdot a)$ in each of the following cases: for $n = 0$, for $n > 0$, and for $n < 0$.

If $n = 0$, then

$$\begin{aligned}(m + n) \cdot a &= (m + 0) \cdot a \\ &= m \cdot a. \\ (m \cdot a) ☆ (n \cdot a) &= (m \cdot a) ☆ (0 \cdot a) \\ &= (m \cdot a) ☆ e \\ &= (m \cdot a).\end{aligned}$$

Hence, $(m + n) \cdot a = (m \cdot a) ☆ (n \cdot a)$ is true for $n = 0$. We will use the method of induction to prove that the theorem is true for $n > 0$. To begin the proof by induction, we first let $n = 1$. If $n = 1$, then, by Definition 35/2 and Theorems 35/2 and 36/2,

$$\begin{aligned}(m + n) \cdot a &= (m + 1) \cdot a \\ &= (m \cdot a) ☆ a. \\ (m \cdot a) ☆ (n \cdot a) &= (m \cdot a) ☆ (1 \cdot a) \\ &= (m \cdot a) ☆ a.\end{aligned}$$

Hence, $(m + n) \cdot a = (m \cdot a) ☆ (n \cdot a)$ is true for $n = 1$. Now that we have established this theorem for the first counting number, we assume that the theorem is true for any counting number n and show that it must also be true for $n + 1$. That is, we assume the hypothesis

$$(m + n) \cdot a = (m \cdot a) ☆ (n \cdot a),$$

and show that the following statement is true.

$$\big(m + (n + 1)\big) \cdot a = (m \cdot a) ☆ \big((n + 1) \cdot a\big).$$

The computation that shows that the two expressions in the preceding statement are equal is given below, along with the reason for each step.

$(m + (n + 1)) \cdot a = ((m + n) + 1) \cdot a$	Associativity of addition in I
$= ((m + n) \cdot a) \star a$	Definition 35/2 and Theorems 35/2 and 36/2
$= ((m \cdot a) \star (n \cdot a)) \star a$	Induction assumption
$= (m \cdot a) \star ((n \cdot a) \star a)$	Associativity of ☆ in G
$= (m \cdot a) \star ((n + 1) \cdot a).$	Definition 35/2

This establishes Theorem 37/2 for $n \geqq 0$. It remains now to consider the case where n is any negative integer. The following steps show that Theorem 37/2 is true for $n < 0$.

$(m + n) \cdot a = -(m + n) \cdot a'$	Definitions 35/2 and 36/2 and Theorem 34/2
$= ((-m) + (-n)) \cdot a'$	Property of the system (I, +)
$= (-m \cdot a') \star (-n \cdot a')$	Application of previous case, $-n > 0$
$= (m \cdot a) \star (n \cdot a).$	Definitions 35/2 and 36/2 and Theorem 34/2

This completes the proof of Theorem 37/2.

The proof of the following theorem, which establishes a kind of "associative" property for integral multiplication, is left as an exercise.

Theorem 38/2 If (G, ☆) is a group, $a \in$ G, and m and n are integers, then $(m \cdot n) \cdot a = m \cdot (n \cdot a)$.

As was stated in the first paragraph of this section, the primary goal of this section and of section 22/2 is the classification of cyclic groups. This section has been devoted to giving meaning to an operation of multiplication between the elements of I and the elements of any group. We now use this newly defined operation to define a cyclic group. Then, in section 22/2, we will prove classification theorems about cyclic groups.

Definition 37/2 If (G, ☆) is a group, then (G, ☆) is *cyclic* if and only if there exists an $a \in$ G such that, for each $b \in$ G, $n \cdot a = b$ for some integer n. The element a is called a *generator* of (G, ☆).

Several examples of cyclic groups are given in Display 46 on page 138. An element that generates each group, along with the integral multiples of this generator that yield each element in the group, is listed. Note that two distinct generators are shown for the group (I/3, $\oplus_3$).

Cyclic group	*Generator*	*Elements generated*
$(I/4, \oplus_4)$	$\bar{1}$	$1 \cdot \bar{1} = \bar{1}, 2 \cdot \bar{1} = \bar{2}, 3 \cdot \bar{1} = \bar{3}, 4 \cdot \bar{1} = \bar{0}$.
$(I/3, \oplus_3)$	$\bar{1}$	$1 \cdot \bar{1} = \bar{1}, 2 \cdot \bar{1} = \bar{2}, 3 \cdot \bar{1} = \bar{0}$.
$(I/3, \oplus_3)$	$\bar{2}$	$1 \cdot \bar{2} = \bar{2}, 2 \cdot \bar{2} = \bar{1}, 3 \cdot \bar{2} = \bar{0}$.
$(I, +)$	1	$\ldots, -1 \cdot 1 = -1, 0 \cdot 1 = 0, 1 \cdot 1 = 1, 2 \cdot 1 = 2, \ldots$.

Display 46

Several examples of groups are listed below that do not have a generator and, hence, are not cyclic.

Examples 1 $(G_3, \circ)$

2 $(R^+, \cdot)$

3 $(\mathfrak{R}, +)$

4 $(\{a + b\sqrt{2} \mid a, b \in R\}, +)$

In section 22/2 we will completely classify all the groups that are cyclic, somewhat in the way that we classified the subgroups of (I, +).

Exercises 1 In each of the following exercises, find, if possible, two generators of those systems that are groups.

a $(I/5, \oplus_5)$
b The set of nonzero integers modulo 3 under multiplication
c $(I/6, \oplus_6)$
d The set of nonzero integers modulo 5 under modular multiplication *Answer*
e $(I/8, \oplus_8)$
f The subset $\{\bar{1}, \overline{10}\}$ of the set of nonzero integers modulo 11 under multiplication
g $(I/9, \oplus_9)$
h The subset $\{\bar{1}, \bar{3}, \bar{4}, \bar{5}, \bar{9}\}$ of the set of nonzero integers modulo 11 under multiplication *Answer*
i $(I/10, \oplus_{10})$
j The subset $\{\bar{1}, \bar{2}, \bar{4}\}$ of the set of nonzero integers modulo 7 under multiplication
k $(I/11, \oplus_{11})$
l The subset $\{\bar{1}, \bar{5}, \bar{8}, \overline{12}\}$ of the set of nonzero integers modulo 13 under multiplication
m $(I/12, \oplus_{12})$

2 First determine if each of the following sets under composition forms a permutation group. Then find, if possible, a generator of each group.

a $\left\{\begin{pmatrix}1&2&3&4\\1&2&3&4\end{pmatrix}, \begin{pmatrix}1&2&3&4\\1&2&4&3\end{pmatrix}\right\}$

b $\left\{\begin{pmatrix}1&2&3&4\\1&2&3&4\end{pmatrix}, \begin{pmatrix}1&2&3&4\\1&4&2&3\end{pmatrix}, \begin{pmatrix}1&2&3&4\\1&3&4&2\end{pmatrix}\right\}$

c $\left\{\begin{pmatrix}1&2&3&4\\1&2&3&4\end{pmatrix}, \begin{pmatrix}1&2&3&4\\4&1&2&3\end{pmatrix}, \begin{pmatrix}1&2&3&4\\3&4&1&2\end{pmatrix}, \begin{pmatrix}1&2&3&4\\2&3&4&1\end{pmatrix}\right\}$ *Answer*

d $\left\{\begin{pmatrix}1&2&3&4\\1&2&3&4\end{pmatrix}, \begin{pmatrix}1&2&3&4\\1&4&2&3\end{pmatrix}, \begin{pmatrix}1&2&3&4\\1&3&4&2\end{pmatrix}, \begin{pmatrix}1&2&3&4\\1&2&4&3\end{pmatrix}, \begin{pmatrix}1&2&3&4\\1&4&3&2\end{pmatrix}, \begin{pmatrix}1&2&3&4\\1&3&2&4\end{pmatrix}\right\}$

e $\left\{\begin{pmatrix}1&2&3&4\\1&2&3&4\end{pmatrix}, \begin{pmatrix}1&2&3&4\\4&1&2&3\end{pmatrix}, \begin{pmatrix}1&2&3&4\\3&4&1&2\end{pmatrix}, \begin{pmatrix}1&2&3&4\\2&3&4&1\end{pmatrix}, \begin{pmatrix}1&2&3&4\\1&2&4&3\end{pmatrix}, \begin{pmatrix}1&2&3&4\\4&1&3&2\end{pmatrix}, \begin{pmatrix}1&2&3&4\\3&4&2&1\end{pmatrix}, \begin{pmatrix}1&2&3&4\\2&3&1&4\end{pmatrix}\right\}$

3 For each part of exercise 1, find, if possible, an element of the group other than the identity that does not generate the group.

4 For each part of exercise 2, find, if possible, an element of the group other than the identity that does not generate the group.

5 Which of the following groups are cyclic?

a The set of nonzero integers modulo 7 under multiplication

b The subset $\{\bar{1}, \bar{3}, \bar{5}, \bar{7}\}$ of the nonzero integers modulo 8 under multiplication *Answer*

c The subset $\{\bar{1}, \bar{2}, \bar{4}, \bar{5}, \bar{7}, \bar{8}\}$ of the set of nonzero integers modulo 9 under multiplication

d The subset $\{\bar{1}, \bar{3}, \bar{7}, \bar{9}\}$ of the set of nonzero integers modulo 10 under multiplication

◆ 6 Prove that any group of exactly three elements is a cyclic group.

7 Prove that the group $(\{1, -1, i, -i\}, \cdot)$ is cyclic. *Answer*

8 Prove that the group $(I_{2x}, +)$ is cyclic.

9 Prove that the group $(\mathfrak{R}, +)$ is not cyclic. (Hint: Consider the group elements 2 and $\sqrt{2}$. Let x be a generator of the group and deduce a contradiction.) *Answer*

10 Prove that $(I_{nx}, +)$ is cyclic.

11 Prove that the group $(\{(a, b) \mid a, b \in R\}, \star)$, where $(a, b) \star (c, d) = (a + c, b + d)$, is not cyclic. [Hint: Consider the group elements (2, 3) and (2, 4). Let (x, y) be a generator of the group and deduce a contradiction.]

12 Prove that the group $(G(i), +)$ is cyclic.

13 How many generators does each of the following groups have under modular addition?

a I/4 b I/5 c I/6 d I/7 e I/9 f I/12

14 Provide the reasons for the steps in the proof of Theorem 35/2.

15 Provide the reasons for the steps in the proof of Theorem 36/2.

◆ 16 Prove Theorem 38/2.

17 State each of the definitions and theorems of this section using exponential notation instead of multiplicative notation. *Answer*

◆ 18 Prove that every cyclic group is commutative. *Answer*

◆ 19 Prove that if (G, ☆) is a group whose identity is e, then $k \cdot e = e$ for any integer k.

20 Prove that the group $(\{1, -1\}, \cdot)$ is cyclic.

21 Prove that $\left(\left\{1, \frac{-1+i\sqrt{3}}{2}, \frac{-1-i\sqrt{3}}{2}\right\}, \cdot\right)$ is cyclic.

◆ 22 If a is a generator of a cyclic group of k elements, prove that $a, 2 \cdot a, 3 \cdot a, \ldots, k \cdot a = e$ are distinct elements of the group.

Classification of cyclic groups

22/2

In this section we will classify finite and infinite cyclic groups. We will begin by considering two groups that were first developed in section 16/2.

Example 1 Operation tables for the groups $(I/4, \oplus_4)$ and $(\{1, i, -1, -i\}, \cdot)$ are given again below.

$(I/4, \oplus_4)$

$\oplus_4$	$\bar{0}$	$\bar{1}$	$\bar{2}$	$\bar{3}$
$\bar{0}$	$\bar{0}$	$\bar{1}$	$\bar{2}$	$\bar{3}$
$\bar{1}$	$\bar{1}$	$\bar{2}$	$\bar{3}$	$\bar{0}$
$\bar{2}$	$\bar{2}$	$\bar{3}$	$\bar{0}$	$\bar{1}$
$\bar{3}$	$\bar{3}$	$\bar{0}$	$\bar{1}$	$\bar{2}$

Display 47a

$(\{1, i, -1, -i\}, \cdot)$

$\cdot$	1	i	-1	$-i$
1	1	i	-1	$-i$
i	i	-1	$-i$	1
-1	-1	$-i$	1	i
$-i$	$-i$	1	i	-1

47b

We wish to analyze and compare these two groups in some detail so that we can determine what characteristics they have in common. Since each group has four elements, it is possible to establish a one-to-one correspondence between the set of elements of (I/4, $\oplus_4$) and $\{1, i, -1, -i\}$. An illustration of one possible pairing is given below.

$$\bar{0} \leftrightarrow 1$$
$$\bar{1} \leftrightarrow i$$
$$\bar{2} \leftrightarrow -1$$
$$\bar{3} \leftrightarrow -i$$

Display 48

This pairing of elements of the two groups was chosen in such a way that the correspondence *preserves the operations* of the groups. Five examples are given below to illustrate what is meant by the preservation of the operations.

$$\begin{array}{ccccc} \bar{0} & \oplus_4 & \bar{1} & = & \bar{1}. \\ \updownarrow & & \updownarrow & & \updownarrow \\ 1 & \cdot & i & = & i. \end{array} \qquad \begin{array}{ccccc} \bar{2} & \oplus_4 & \bar{3} & = & \bar{1}. \\ \updownarrow & & \updownarrow & & \updownarrow \\ -1 & \cdot & (-i) & = & i. \end{array} \qquad \begin{array}{ccccc} \bar{1} & \oplus_4 & \bar{2} & = & \bar{3}. \\ \updownarrow & & \updownarrow & & \updownarrow \\ i & \cdot & (-1) & = & -i. \end{array}$$

Display 49a 49b 49c

$$\begin{array}{ccccc} \bar{3} & \oplus_4 & \bar{3} & = & \bar{2}. \\ \updownarrow & & \updownarrow & & \updownarrow \\ -i & \cdot & (-i) & = & -1. \end{array} \qquad \begin{array}{ccccc} \bar{1} & \oplus_4 & \bar{3} & = & \bar{0}. \\ \updownarrow & & \updownarrow & & \updownarrow \\ i & \cdot & (-i) & = & 1. \end{array}$$

49d 49e

In each of these five examples, we have chosen two elements from the group of integers modulo 4 under modular addition and the elements from the multiplicative group to which they correspond under the mapping shown in Display 48. Then the sum of the chosen elements in (I/4, $\oplus_4$) and the product of the corresponding elements in the multiplicative group are shown to correspond. For example, in Display 49a we selected $\bar{0}$ and $\bar{1}$ from I/4. From Display 48 we see that $\bar{0}$ and $\bar{1}$ correspond to 1 and i, respectively, in $\{1, i, -1, -i\}$. Next, we used the operation tables to obtain $\bar{1}$, the sum of $\bar{0}$ and $\bar{1}$, and also i, the product of 1 and i. We observe from Display 48 that $\bar{1}$ and i correspond.

Only five examples are given in Display 49, but if you were to consider all the possibilities, you would find that the sum of any two elements of I/4 corresponds to the product of the corresponding elements of $\{1, i, -1, -i\}$. Notice that, although the groups have different elements and different operations, the elements of the groups can be paired in a one-to-one fashion so that sums in the additive group correspond to products in the multiplicative group.

Example 2 As a second example, let us consider the group $(I/3, \oplus_3)$ and also the permutation group of rotations of a triangle, first discussed in section 17/2. The operation tables for these groups are shown again in Display 50.

$(I/3, \oplus_3)$

$\oplus_3$	$\bar{0}$	$\bar{1}$	$\bar{2}$
$\bar{0}$	$\bar{0}$	$\bar{1}$	$\bar{2}$
$\bar{1}$	$\bar{1}$	$\bar{2}$	$\bar{0}$
$\bar{2}$	$\bar{2}$	$\bar{0}$	$\bar{1}$

Display 50a

$$\left(\left\{P_1 = \begin{pmatrix} 1 & 2 & 3 \\ 1 & 2 & 3 \end{pmatrix}, P_5 = \begin{pmatrix} 1 & 2 & 3 \\ 2 & 3 & 1 \end{pmatrix}, P_6 = \begin{pmatrix} 1 & 2 & 3 \\ 3 & 1 & 2 \end{pmatrix}\right\}, \circ\right)$$

$\circ$	P_1	P_5	P_6
P_1	P_1	P_5	P_6
P_5	P_5	P_6	P_1
P_6	P_6	P_1	P_5

50b

As in example 1, it is possible to put the sets of elements in these two groups into one-to-one correspondence because both groups contain the same number of elements. A particular one-to-one correspondence is given below.

$\bar{0} \leftrightarrow P_1$

$\bar{1} \leftrightarrow P_5$

$\bar{2} \leftrightarrow P_6$

Display 51

This correspondence has the property that has been described as preservation of operations. To verify that this is so, we have listed all nine possible sums and compositions in Display 52.

The mapping in Display 52 illustrates that the sum of any two elements of the additive group corresponds to the composition of the corresponding elements of the permutation group. Hence, as

$$\bar{0} \oplus_3 \bar{0} = \bar{0} \leftrightarrow P_1 = P_1 \circ P_1$$
$$\bar{0} \oplus_3 \bar{1} = \bar{1} \leftrightarrow P_5 = P_1 \circ P_5$$
$$\bar{0} \oplus_3 \bar{2} = \bar{2} \leftrightarrow P_6 = P_1 \circ P_6$$
$$\bar{1} \oplus_3 \bar{0} = \bar{1} \leftrightarrow P_5 = P_5 \circ P_1$$
$$\bar{1} \oplus_3 \bar{1} = \bar{2} \leftrightarrow P_6 = P_5 \circ P_5$$
$$\bar{1} \oplus_3 \bar{2} = \bar{0} \leftrightarrow P_1 = P_5 \circ P_6$$
$$\bar{2} \oplus_3 \bar{0} = \bar{2} \leftrightarrow P_6 = P_6 \circ P_1$$
$$\bar{2} \oplus_3 \bar{1} = \bar{0} \leftrightarrow P_1 = P_6 \circ P_5$$
$$\bar{2} \oplus_3 \bar{2} = \bar{1} \leftrightarrow P_5 = P_6 \circ P_6$$

Display 52

in example 1, the correspondence preserves the operation of the groups.

Since the correspondence between group elements in each of these examples has been especially chosen, a word of warning should be given: Not all possible correspondences preserve operations. The examples were chosen to illustrate the property of preserving the operations. However, if care is not taken, then a one-to-one correspondence that might be chosen is the following:

$$\bar{0} \leftrightarrow P_5$$
$$\bar{1} \leftrightarrow P_6$$
$$\bar{2} \leftrightarrow P_1$$

If this particular correspondence is chosen, we see that $\bar{0} \oplus_3 \bar{1} = \bar{1}$ does not correspond to $P_5 \circ P_6 = P_1$ because P_1 does not correspond to $\bar{1}$. Therefore, the group operations are not preserved. Thus, there may be one-to-one correspondences between the elements of the two groups that do not have the property of preserving the operations. In the definition that follows, precise meaning is given to one-to-one correspondences that preserve the operations of the given groups.

Definition 38/2 If (G, ☆) and (H, ∘) are groups, then (G, ☆) is *isomorphic* to (H, ∘) if and only if there exists a one-to-one function f from G onto H that preserves the group operations. In symbols, if f represents a one-to-one function from G onto H, then

$$(G, \star) \cong (H, \circ)$$

if and only if, for each $g_1, g_2 \in G$,

$$(g_1 \star g_2)f = (g_1)f \circ (g_2)f.$$

Notice that we have used the symbol $\cong$ to designate the relation "is isomorphic to." The symbol $G \cong H$ is a short way of indicating the existence of a one-to-one function from G onto H that preserves the operations of the groups. This symbol is used in geometry for the congruence relation, but the context in which the symbol occurs should make clear which relation is meant.

Example 3 As another example of a pair of *isomorphic groups*, consider the set of integers under addition, (I, +), as the group (G, ☆) of Definition 38/2 and the set of even integers under addition, $(E_I, +)$, as the group (H, ∘). We now define the function f whose domain is the set of integers and whose range is included in the set of even integers by

$$(x)f = 2x \text{ for each } x \in I.$$

It is easily verified that f is a one-to-one function from I onto E_I that preserves the operations of the groups. (Note that both groups have addition as their operation.)

There are a number of steps in such a verification. First, observe that f is single-valued by definition. Second, by the definition of function f, the domain of function f is the set of integers. Further, observe that, if y is any even integer, then $y = 2x$ for some integer x. But since $(x)f = 2x$ by the definition of f, then $(x)f = y$. This shows that the function f is onto E_I. As another step toward verification of the isomorphism, we will show that the function f is one-to-one. Recall that the property of being a one-to-one function was defined in Chapter 1 (Definition 9/1). An equivalent definition is now given.

Definition 9/1 *(alternative)* If f is a function from S into T, then f is one-to-one if and only if $(x_1)f = y$ and $(x_2)f = y$ imply that $x_1 = x_2$.

To establish that function f described above is one-to-one, we let $(x_1)f = y$ and $(x_2)f = y$, and then show that $x_1 = x_2$. Now from the definition of f, we have

$$(x_1)f = y = 2x_1$$

and

$$(x_2)f = y = 2x_2.$$

Thus, $2x_1 = 2x_2$, and by the cancellation property of the integers, it follows that $x_1 = x_2$. Hence, f is a one-to-one function.

It remains to show that function f does preserve the operations of the groups. To accomplish this, we let x_1 and x_2 be integers and show that

$$(x_1 + x_2)f = (x_1)f + (x_2)f.$$

The computation below establishes this property. You should supply the reasons for the steps.

$$\begin{aligned}(x_1 + x_2)\mathrm{f} &= 2(x_1 + x_2)\\ &= 2x_1 + 2x_2\\ &= (x_1)\mathrm{f} + (x_2)\mathrm{f}.\end{aligned}$$

We are now in a position to prove two theorems that express the exact nature of finite and infinite cyclic groups. The first of these two theorems, involving finite groups, is given below.

Theorem 39/2 Let (G, ☆) be a finite cyclic group and let a be any element of G such that a is a generator of G. Then there exists a least positive integer n such that $n \cdot a = e$ and (G, ☆) is isomorphic to the group of integers modulo n under modular addition. Symbolically, if (G, ☆) is cyclic with generator a such that $n \cdot a = e$ (and n is the least such integer), then (G, ☆) $\cong$ (I/n, $\oplus_n$).

Proof Suppose that G contains a single element a. Since G is a group and, therefore, has an identity element, $a = e$. Moreover, since $a = e = 1 \cdot e$, 1 is obviously the least positive integer n such that $n \cdot a = n \cdot e = e$. Now the set of integers modulo 1 consists of the single equivalence class $\bar{0}$. Hence, ({e}, ☆) $\cong$ ({$\bar{0}$}, $\oplus_1$). That is, (G, ☆) $\cong$ (I/n, $\oplus_n$) is true when G contains only one element.

The remaining case arises when G consists of more than one element. Then there exists an element $a \neq e$ in G that is its generator. In this part of the proof, we wish to show that, given a cyclic group, with generator $a \neq e$, we can establish an isomorphism between (G, ☆) and (I/n, $\oplus_n$), where n is the least positive integer such that $n \cdot a = e$.

Recall that, if a is a generator of group G, then, for each element b of G, there exists an integer x such that $b = x \cdot a$. The integer x will be different for different elements b of G. Furthermore, for each such x, there exist unique integers q and r such that $x = qn + r$, where $0 \leqq r < n$. This, you will recall, is just a statement of the division algorithm. (Note that, if b is the identity element of G, then $q = 1$ and $r = 0$. This is so because $e = n \cdot a$ and $n = 1 \cdot n + 0$.)

We will now use the division algorithm to define a function f from the group (G, ☆) onto the group (I/n, $\oplus_n$). Function f will then be used to establish the isomorphism. If $b \in$ G and $b = x \cdot a$ with $x = qn + r$ and $0 \leqq r < n$, then the function f is defined by $(b)\mathrm{f} = \bar{r}$, where $\bar{r}$ is the equivalence class of the remainder r, modulo n. In other words, the desired isomorphism results if we map each element b of G onto the equivalence class of the remainder r that is obtained when b is divided by n. We must now present an argument in support of this assertion.

To accomplish this, we must verify the following properties about the correspondence f.

1) f has domain G.
2) f is a function.
3) f is onto the integers modulo n.
4) f is a one-to-one function.
5) f preserves the operations of the groups (G, ☆) and $(I/n, \oplus_n)$.

The formula which defines the correspondence f, that is, $(b)f = \bar{r}$, is stated for any element b of G and, hence, the domain of f is the set G. This remark establishes the first property.

The proof that f is a function (the second property) is developed step by step in exercise 1 at the end of this section.

To see that f is a mapping from G *onto* I/n [the third property immediately above], let $r \in I$ be such that $0 \leqq r < n$. Then the element $b = r \cdot a$ is in G. Since $r = 0 \cdot n + r$, it follows that $(b)f = \bar{r}$. This shows that each element $\bar{r}$ of I/n has as a pre-image the element $r \cdot a$ of G, and, hence, the mapping is onto.

To show that f is one-to-one, we let $\bar{r}$ be an element of I/n and let b and c be elements of G such that $(b)f = (c)f = \bar{r}$. We will show that $b = c$. Since $(b)f = \bar{r} = (c)f$, we have $b = x \cdot a$, with $x = q_1 n + r$, and $c = y \cdot a$, with $y = q_2 n + r$. We know that the two remainders are the same because $(b)f = (c)f = \bar{r}$. The following sequence of equalities shows that the inverse of c' is b. This is equivalent to showing that $b = c$ since the inverse of c' is c.

$$\begin{aligned} b \star c' &= (x \cdot a) \star (-y \cdot a) \\ &= \big((q_1 n + r) \cdot a\big) \star \big([-q_2 n + (-r)] \cdot a\big) \\ &= \big(q_1 n + r + (-q_2 n) + (-r)\big) \cdot a \\ &= \big(q_1 n + (-q_2 n)\big) \cdot a \\ &= \big(q_1 + (-q_2)\big) \cdot (n \cdot a) \\ &= \big(q_1 + (-q_2)\big) \cdot e \star e \\ &= e. \end{aligned}$$

Be sure that you can supply the reasons for each of the steps. This establishes that f is one-to-one.

As the final step in the proof of the theorem, we will show that the one-to-one function f preserves the operations of the groups (G, ☆) and $(I/n, \oplus_n)$. Let b and c be elements of G such that $b = t \cdot a$ and $c = s \cdot a$ where $t = q_1 n + r_1$, with $0 \leqq r_1 < n$, and $s = q_2 n + r_2$, with $0 \leqq r_2 < n$. We must show that the image of $b \star c$ is equal to the sum under modular addition of the images of b and c. That is, we must show that

$$(b \star c)\mathrm{f} = (b)\mathrm{f} \oplus_n (c)\mathrm{f}.$$

The computations below result in two expressions, one for $(b \star c)\mathrm{f}$ and the other for $(b)\mathrm{f} \oplus_n (c)\mathrm{f}$.

$$\begin{aligned}
(b \star c)\mathrm{f} &= \big((t \cdot a) \star (s \cdot a)\big)\mathrm{f} \\
&= \big((t + s) \cdot a\big)\mathrm{f} \\
&= \big((q_1 n + r_1 + q_2 n + r_2) \cdot a\big)\mathrm{f} \\
&= \big([(q_1 + q_2)n + (r_1 + r_2)] \cdot a\big)\mathrm{f} \\
&= \big([(q_1 + q_2)n \cdot a] \star [(r_1 + r_2) \cdot a]\big)\mathrm{f} \\
&= \big(e \star (r_1 + r_2) \cdot a\big)\mathrm{f} \\
&= \big((r_1 + r_2) \cdot a\big)\mathrm{f} \\
&= \overline{r_1 + r_2 - pn}.
\end{aligned}$$

$$\begin{aligned}
(b)\mathrm{f} \oplus_n (c)\mathrm{f} &= (t \cdot a)\mathrm{f} \oplus_n (s \cdot a)\mathrm{f} \\
&= \big((q_1 n + r_1) \cdot a\big)\mathrm{f} \oplus_n \big((q_2 n + r_2) \cdot a\big)\mathrm{f} \\
&= \big((q_1 n \cdot a) \star (r_1 \cdot a)\big)\mathrm{f} \oplus_n \big((q_2 n \cdot a) \star (r_2 \cdot a)\big)\mathrm{f} \\
&= \big(e \star (r_1 \cdot a)\big)\mathrm{f} \oplus_n \big(e \star (r_2 \cdot a)\big)\mathrm{f} \\
&= (r_1 \cdot a)\mathrm{f} \oplus_n (r_2 \cdot a)\mathrm{f} \\
&= \bar{r}_1 \oplus_n \bar{r}_2 \\
&= \overline{r_1 + r_2 - qn}.
\end{aligned}$$

You should supply the reasons for the preceding steps. To see that the equivalence classes $\overline{r_1 + r_2 - pn}$ and $\overline{r_1 + r_2 - qn}$ are equal, observe that, since integers p and q are such that $0 \leqq r_1 + r_2 - pn < n$ and $0 \leqq r_1 + r_2 - qn < n$, it follows that $p = q$. Hence,

$$(b \star c)\mathrm{f} = (b)\mathrm{f} \oplus_n (c)\mathrm{f},$$

and f preserves the operations of the groups. This completes the proof of the theorem.

Theorem 39/2 classifies all finite cyclic groups. Infinite cyclic groups are classified by the following theorem. Keep in mind that, if a cyclic group is infinite with generator a, then there is no integer $n \neq 0$ for which it is true that $n \cdot a = e$. The proof of Theorem 40/2 is developed in exercises 3 through 6.

Theorem 40/2 If $(\mathrm{G}, \star)$ is an infinite cyclic group and a is a generator of the group, then $(\mathrm{G}, \star)$ is isomorphic to the group of integers under addition, $(\mathrm{I}, +)$.

Exercises

1 In Theorem 39/2, a mapping from the cyclic group (G, ☆) with generator a into the group $(I/n, \oplus_n)$ has been given by

$$(b)\text{f} = \bar{r},$$

where $b \in G$, $b = x \cdot a$, $x = qn + r$, and $0 \leqq r < n$. This exercise is concerned with establishing that f is single-valued; that is, that f is a function. Another statement of the property is now given:

If $b = x \cdot a$, where $x = qn + r$ and $0 \leqq r < n$, and $b = x_1 \cdot a$, where $x_1 = q_1 n + r_1$ and $0 \leqq r_1 < n$, then $\bar{r} = \bar{r}_1$.

a Why does $b = x_1 \cdot a$ imply that $b' = -x_1 \cdot a$?

b Use part a to explain why $e = b ☆ b' = \big(x + (-x_1)\big) \cdot a$.

c How do you know that $x + (-x_1) = q_2 n + r_2$, with $0 \leqq r_2 < n$?

d Give a reason for each of the following steps.

$$\begin{aligned} e &= (q_2 n + r_2) \cdot a \\ &= (q_2 n \cdot a) ☆ (r_2 \cdot a) \\ &= \big(q_2 \cdot (n \cdot a)\big) ☆ (r_2 \cdot a) \\ &= (q_2 \cdot e) ☆ (r_2 \cdot a) \\ &= e ☆ (r_2 \cdot a) \\ &= r_2 \cdot a. \end{aligned}$$

e Why do the fact that n is the least positive integer such that $n \cdot a = e$, with $0 \leqq r_2 < n$, and the fact that $e = r_2 \cdot a$ together imply that $r_2 = 0$?

f Use parts c and e to show that $x + (-x_1) = q_2 n$.

g From the assumptions about x and x_1 and also part f, we have $(qn + r) + (-q_1 n - r_1) = q_2 n$. What properties of the integers are used in obtaining $(q_2 - q + q_1)n = r - r_1$ from the preceding equality?

h Explain why the fact that $r - r_1$ is a multiple of n implies that $\bar{r} = \bar{r}_1$. These arguments establish that f is a function.

2 Supply the reasons for the steps in the proof of Theorem 39/2 which establish that function f is one-to-one and for the steps which show that f preserves the group operation.

In the next four exercises, we will develop a proof of Theorem 40/2, which classifies infinite cyclic groups. First, we will define an appropriate function from G into I and then proceed to show that the function has the effect of establishing the isomorphism. Given the infinite cyclic group (G, ☆), with generator a, let b be any element of G. Thus, $b = t \cdot a$ for some integer t. Define the relation f as $(b)\text{f} = t$. This is the mapping that will be used to establish the isomorphism between (G, ☆) and (I, +).

◆ **3** First, we will show that f is a function, that is, a single-valued relation. Suppose that $(b, t) \in$ f and $(b, s) \in$ f, with $t \neq s$. Then $b = t \cdot a$ and $b = s \cdot a$. Why? Supply reasons for the following steps:

$$\begin{aligned} b \star b' &= (t \cdot a) \star (-s \cdot a) \\ &= \big(t + (-s)\big) \cdot a. \end{aligned}$$

Since $b \star b' = e$, this implies that $\big(t + (-s)\big) \cdot a = e$. The result is a contradiction. What is it? Thus, if $(b)\text{f} = t$ and $(b)\text{f} = s$, then $t = s$, and f is a function from G into I.

◆ **4** We will now prove that f is a function from G *onto* I. Let j be any element of I; we will show that there is a $b \in$ G such that $(b)\text{f} = j$. Further, we assert that $b = j \cdot a$. We must show that $j \cdot a \in$ G. By Definition 37/2, any integral multiple of a is an element of G. Thus, $j \cdot a \in$ G, and $(b)\text{f} = (j \cdot a)\text{f} = j$. Why does it follow from this argument that f is a function from G onto I?

◆ **5** Next we will show that f is a one-to-one function. Let $(b)\text{f} = k$ and $(c)\text{f} = k$ where $b = t \cdot a$ and $c = s \cdot a$. However, $(b)\text{f} = t$ and $(c)\text{f} = s$. Why? Thus, $k = t = s$ and f is a one-to-one function. Why?

◆ **6** Lastly, we prove that f preserves the operations of the groups (G, ☆) and (I, +) by showing that $(b \star c)\text{f} = (b)\text{f} + (c)\text{f}$, where $b, c \in$ G, $b = t \cdot a$, and $c = s \cdot a$. Supply reasons for the steps given below. *Answer*

$$\begin{aligned} (b \star c)\text{f} &= \big((t \cdot a) \star (s \cdot a)\big)\text{f} \\ &= \big((t + s) \cdot a\big)\text{f} \\ &= t + s. \\ (b)\text{f} + (c)\text{f} &= (t \cdot a)\text{f} + (s \cdot a)\text{f} \\ &= t + s. \end{aligned}$$

Thus, f preserves the operations of the groups.

In exercises 3 through 6 we have proved that f is a one-to-one function from G onto I that preserves the operations of the groups (G, ☆) and (I, +). Thus, any infinite cyclic group (G, ☆) is isomorphic to the integers under addition. This completes the proof of Theorem 40/2.

7 Find an example of a one-to-one function that is not an isomorphism from the group of integers under addition onto the group of even integers under addition. *Answer*

8 Prove that (I, +) and (I/5, $\oplus_5$) are not isomorphic.

9 Find an isomorphism other than the one given in the text on page 141 between the integers modulo 4 under addition and $(\{1, -1, i, -i\}, \cdot)$.

10 Is the relation $(x)g = -2x$ an isomorphism between the group of integers under addition and the group of even integers under addition?

11 Show explicitly how the identity elements correspond under the isomorphisms given in examples 1, 2, and 3 on pages 140 through 145.

12 Prove that, if f is an isomorphism from (G, ☆), whose identity element is e_G, onto (H, ∘), whose identity element is e_H, then $(e_G)f = e_H$. *Answer*

13 Show explicitly how pairs of inverse elements correspond under the isomorphisms of examples 1, 2, and 3 on pages 140-145.

◆ **14** Prove that, if f is an isomorphism from (G, ☆) onto (H, ∘) and x is any element of G with x' as its inverse, then $((x)f)' = (x')f$. In other words, prove that $(x)f \circ (x')f = (x')f \circ (x)f = e_H$, the identity of (H, ∘). *Answer*

15 Prove that if (G, ☆) has n elements and $G \cong H$, then (H, ∘) has n elements.

16 Are any two of the following groups isomorphic? If so, identify them. *Answer*

a The subset $\{\bar{1}, \bar{5}, \bar{8}, \overline{12}\}$ of the set of nonzero integers modulo 13 under $\odot_{13}$

b $(I/4, \oplus_4)$

c The subset $\{\bar{1}, \bar{5}, \bar{7}, \overline{11}\}$ of the set of nonzero integers modulo 12 under $\odot_{12}$

17 Prove that, if (G, ☆) has n elements and (H, ∘) has n elements, where G and H are cyclic groups, then $G \cong H$.

18 Prove that $(G(i), +)$ is isomorphic to the group $(\{2^m \cdot 5^n \mid m, n \in I\}, \cdot)$.

19 Consider the following permutation groups:

$$(A, \circ) = \left(\left\{\begin{pmatrix}1 & 2 & 3 & 4\\ 1 & 2 & 3 & 4\end{pmatrix}, \begin{pmatrix}1 & 2 & 3 & 4\\ 2 & 1 & 4 & 3\end{pmatrix}, \begin{pmatrix}1 & 2 & 3 & 4\\ 3 & 4 & 1 & 2\end{pmatrix}, \begin{pmatrix}1 & 2 & 3 & 4\\ 4 & 3 & 2 & 1\end{pmatrix}\right\}, \circ\right).$$

$$(B, \circ) = \left(\left\{\begin{pmatrix}1 & 2 & 3 & 4\\ 1 & 2 & 3 & 4\end{pmatrix}, \begin{pmatrix}1 & 2 & 3 & 4\\ 2 & 3 & 4 & 1\end{pmatrix}, \begin{pmatrix}1 & 2 & 3 & 4\\ 3 & 4 & 1 & 2\end{pmatrix}, \begin{pmatrix}1 & 2 & 3 & 4\\ 4 & 1 & 2 & 3\end{pmatrix}\right\}, \circ\right).$$

$$(C, \circ) = \left(\left\{\begin{pmatrix}1 & 2 & 3 & 4\\ 1 & 2 & 3 & 4\end{pmatrix}, \begin{pmatrix}1 & 2 & 3 & 4\\ 2 & 4 & 1 & 3\end{pmatrix}, \begin{pmatrix}1 & 2 & 3 & 4\\ 3 & 1 & 4 & 2\end{pmatrix}, \begin{pmatrix}1 & 2 & 3 & 4\\ 4 & 3 & 2 & 1\end{pmatrix}\right\}, \circ\right).$$

Each of these groups is isomorphic to one of the groups given in exercise 16. Determine the isomorphisms. Is there an isomorphism between any two of these permutation groups?

◆ **20** Show that the group of cosets you determined for exercise 18 of section 19/2, page 124, is isomorphic to $(I/3, \oplus_3)$.

◆ **21** Show that the group of cosets you determined for exercise 19, page 124, is isomorphic to $(I/4, \oplus_4)$.

22 Let $(G, \star) = (\{1, -1, i, -i\}, \cdot)$.

a Find a permutation group that is isomorphic to this group.

b Find, if possible, an isomorphism between this group and the subset $\{\bar{1}, \bar{5}, \bar{8}, \overline{12}\}$ of the nonzero integers modulo 13 under multiplication.

◆ **23** Prove that the relation of "isomorphic to" between groups is an equivalence relation.

◆ **24** An isomorphism of a group onto itself is called an *automorphism*.

a Prove that every group has at least one automorphism. *Answer*

b Prove that if $a \in (G, \star)$ is a fixed element, then f defined by $(x)f = a \star x \star a'$ is an automorphism. *Answer*

◆ **25** Determine the set of all automorphisms for each of the following groups.

a $(I/2, \oplus_2)$

b $(I/3, \oplus_3)$

c $(I/4, \oplus_4)$

d $(I/6, \oplus_6)$

e The subgroup $\{\bar{1}, \bar{5}, \bar{8}, \overline{12}\}$ of the nonzero integers modulo 13 under multiplication

f The subgroup $\{\bar{1}, \bar{5}, \bar{7}, \overline{11}\}$ of the nonzero integers modulo 12 under multiplication

g The symmetric group G_3

◆ **26** Let $(G, \star)$ be a group and let x be any element of G with inverse x'. Prove that $(x)f = x'$ is an automorphism of G if and only if G is commutative.

◆ **27** Prove that $(\mathfrak{R}, +)$ is isomorphic to the multiplicative group of positive real numbers. (Hint: Consider a function that is very useful in computational procedures.)

◆ **28** Prove that for each a, b in group $(G, \star)$, if $a \star a = e$, $b \star b \star b = e$, and $a \star b = b \star b \star a$, then $(G, \star)$ is isomorphic to the symmetric group $(G_3, \circ)$.

The Cartesian product of groups [optional]

23/2

The previous two sections dealt with cyclic groups and culminated in Theorems 39/2 and 40/2, which make it possible to categorize in a simple way all examples of cyclic groups. The results show that, for all practical purposes, the study of cyclic groups can be restricted, for finite groups, to the integers modulo n under modular addition and, for infinite groups, to the integers under addition. As noted earlier, Theorems 39/2 and 40/2 are called classification theorems because a cyclic group can be classified according to whether it can be put into one-to-one correspondence with $(I/n, \oplus_n)$, for some n, or with $(I, +)$ in such a way that the tables for the operations of the two groups are essentially the same. This statement is just a way of stating informally the isomorphic property.

This section and the next are primarily concerned with classifying finite commutative groups. This may seem redundant since we have already classified cyclic groups and all finite cyclic groups are also finite commutative groups. However, not *all* finite commutative groups are also cyclic groups. Therefore, our concern now is with *all* finite commutative groups, noncyclic as well as cyclic.

Much of the discussion that follows deals with groups that can be constructed from Cartesian products involving the integers modulo n. If $(G, \star)$ and $(H, \circ)$ are finite commutative groups, then the Cartesian product of the sets G and H is the set

$$G \times H = \{(g, h) \mid g \in G \text{ and } h \in H\}.$$

The Cartesian product $G \times H$ can be used as the set of elements for a new group. We will define an operation on the ordered pairs (g, h) of $G \times H$ so that the resulting system is a commutative group. Before we attempt to make a general definition of such an operation for any two groups, we will investigate some specific examples of Cartesian products of two groups.

Example 1 As a first example, consider the groups $(\{\bar{0}, \bar{1}, \bar{2}\}, \oplus_3)$ and $(\{\bar{0}, \bar{1}\}, \oplus_2)$ which, in notation adopted earlier, may also be designated as $(I/3, \oplus_3)$ and $(I/2, \oplus_2)$, respectively. The Cartesian product of the sets in $(I/3, \oplus_3)$ and $(I/2, \oplus_2)$ consists of six ordered pairs. These six ordered pairs are $(\bar{0}, \bar{0})$, $(\bar{0}, \bar{1})$, $(\bar{1}, \bar{0})$, $(\bar{1}, \bar{1})$, $(\bar{2}, \bar{0})$, $(\bar{2}, \bar{1})$, where the first component is in the set $I/3$ and the second component is in $I/2$. Keep in mind that, although the symbol $\bar{1}$ appears as both a first and second component, it has different meanings, depending upon its position in the ordered pair. That is, if it appears as a first component of an ordered pair, it symbolizes the equivalence class $\bar{1}$, modulo 3; if it appears as a second component, it represents the equivalence class $\bar{1}$, modulo 2.

For this set of six elements, we define an operation, which we will refer to as addition. We will add two ordered pairs in the set by using the operation of $(I/3, \oplus_3)$ to add corresponding first components and the operation of $(I/2, \oplus_2)$ to add corresponding second components. To be specific, we define the sum of $(\bar{a}, \bar{b})$ and $(\bar{c}, \bar{d})$ as follows:

$$(\bar{a}, \bar{b}) + (\bar{c}, \bar{d}) = (\bar{a} \oplus_3 \bar{c}, \bar{b} \oplus_2 \bar{d}).$$

(Note that we have used "+" to denote the operation just defined.)

Some of the sums that result from this operation from the set $(I/3 \times I/2) \times (I/3 \times I/2)$ are shown below.

$$(\bar{0}, \bar{0}) + (\bar{0}, \bar{1}) = (\bar{0}, \bar{1}).$$
$$(\bar{1}, \bar{1}) + (\bar{1}, \bar{0}) = (\bar{2}, \bar{1}).$$
$$(\bar{2}, \bar{1}) + (\bar{1}, \bar{1}) = (\bar{0}, \bar{0}).$$
$$(\bar{1}, \bar{1}) + (\bar{1}, \bar{1}) = (\bar{2}, \bar{0}).$$

It is routine to check that the Cartesian product of the integers modulo 3 and the integers modulo 2, under the operation of addition as defined above, forms a group. As a first step in verifying that $(I/3 \times I/2, +)$ is a group, note that the binary operation of addition has as its domain the Cartesian product $(I/3 \times I/2) \times (I/3 \times I/2)$ and has its range in $I/3 \times I/2$. This observation leads to the conclusion that addition is *closed.*

The verification of the *associative property* is left as an exercise. The *identity* element is $(\bar{0}, \bar{0})$. You should verify that this is the case.

Each of the six elements has an additive *inverse*. Each element, along with its inverse, is listed below.

The inverse of $(\bar{0}, \bar{0})$ is $(\bar{0}, \bar{0})$.
The inverse of $(\bar{1}, \bar{0})$ is $(\bar{2}, \bar{0})$.
The inverse of $(\bar{2}, \bar{0})$ is $(\bar{1}, \bar{0})$.
The inverse of $(\bar{0}, \bar{1})$ is $(\bar{0}, \bar{1})$.
The inverse of $(\bar{1}, \bar{1})$ is $(\bar{2}, \bar{1})$.
The inverse of $(\bar{2}, \bar{1})$ is $(\bar{1}, \bar{1})$.

These remarks establish that $(I/3 \times I/2, +)$ is a group. In the exercises, you are asked to show that the group is commutative. Notice that this group is also cyclic and the element $(\bar{1}, \bar{1})$ is one particular generator of the group. The six integral multiples shown below confirm that $(\bar{1}, \bar{1})$ is a generator.

$$1 \cdot (\bar{1}, \bar{1}) = (\bar{1}, \bar{1}).$$
$$2 \cdot (\bar{1}, \bar{1}) = (\bar{2}, \bar{0}).$$
$$3 \cdot (\bar{1}, \bar{1}) = (\bar{0}, \bar{1}).$$
$$4 \cdot (\bar{1}, \bar{1}) = (\bar{1}, \bar{0}).$$
$$5 \cdot (\bar{1}, \bar{1}) = (\bar{2}, \bar{1}).$$
$$6 \cdot (\bar{1}, \bar{1}) = (\bar{0}, \bar{0}).$$

Since the group we have constructed is a cyclic group with six elements, we know by Theorem 39/2 that it is isomorphic to the integers modulo 6 under addition. There are two isomorphisms that can be established; one such isomorphism is shown in Display 53.

$$
\begin{array}{l}
I/3 \times I/2 \overset{f}{\longleftrightarrow} I/6 \\
\quad (\bar{0}, \bar{0}) \leftrightarrow \bar{0} \\
\quad (\bar{1}, \bar{1}) \leftrightarrow \bar{1} \\
\quad (\bar{2}, \bar{0}) \leftrightarrow \bar{2} \\
\quad (\bar{0}, \bar{1}) \leftrightarrow \bar{3} \\
\quad (\bar{1}, \bar{0}) \leftrightarrow \bar{4} \\
\quad (\bar{2}, \bar{1}) \leftrightarrow \bar{5}
\end{array}
$$

Display **53**

You should verify that the operations of the two groups are preserved by correspondence f.

The group that we have formed from $(I/3, \oplus_3)$ and $(I/2, \oplus_2)$ contains a subgroup isomorphic to the integers modulo 2 under modular addition, the subgroup $(\{(\bar{0}, \bar{0}), (\bar{0}, \bar{1})\}, +)$. Remember that, by Theorem 28/2, if $(G, \star)$ is a group and $H \subset G$, then to show that $(H, \star)$ is a subgroup of $(G, \star)$ it is necessary to verify only the closure and inverse properties. It is routine to verify that the set $\{(\bar{0}, \bar{0}), (\bar{0}, \bar{1})\}$ does satisfy the closure and inverse properties under addition. An isomorphism between $(\{(\bar{0}, \bar{0}), (\bar{0}, \bar{1})\}, +)$ and $(I/2, \oplus_2)$ is given by the correspondence

$$
\begin{array}{l}
(\bar{0}, \bar{0}) \leftrightarrow \bar{0} \\
(\bar{0}, \bar{1}) \leftrightarrow \bar{1}.
\end{array}
$$

Notice that the *first* component of each element of $I/3 \times I/2$ that is used in the isomorphism is the identity element of $(I/3, \oplus_3)$. Determine whether or not there is another isomorphism of these two groups.

The group $(I/3 \times I/2, +)$ has a subgroup that is isomorphic to the integers modulo 3 under modular addition, the subgroup $(\{(\bar{0}, \bar{0}), (\bar{1}, \bar{0}), (\bar{2}, \bar{0})\}, +)$. An isomorphism between this subgroup and $(I/3, \oplus_3)$ is given by the correspondence

$$
\begin{array}{l}
(\bar{0}, \bar{0}) \leftrightarrow \bar{0} \\
(\bar{1}, \bar{0}) \leftrightarrow \bar{1} \\
(\bar{2}, \bar{0}) \leftrightarrow \bar{2}.
\end{array}
$$

Verify that the correspondence satisfies all the properties of an isomorphism. Notice that, this time, the *second* component of each element of $I/3 \times I/2$ that is used in the isomorphism is the identity element of $(I/2, \oplus_2)$. Are there any other isomorphisms between the two groups?

To summarize what was done in this example, we used the integers modulo 3 and the integers modulo 2 to construct a set of ordered pairs containing six elements. We then defined a binary operation on pairs of these elements so that the resulting system is a group. This group, $(I/3 \times I/2, +)$, is isomorphic to $(I/6, \oplus_6)$, and contains subgroups isomorphic to each of the groups used in constructing it. Specifically, $\big(\{(\bar{0}, \bar{0}), (\bar{0}, \bar{1})\}, +\big) \cong (I/2, \oplus_2)$ and $\big(\{(\bar{0}, \bar{0}), (\bar{1}, \bar{0}), (\bar{2}, \bar{0})\}, +\big) \cong (I/3, \oplus_3)$.

Example 2 Now consider the groups $(\{\bar{0}, \bar{1}\}, \oplus_2)$ and $(\{\bar{0}, \bar{1}, \bar{2}, \bar{3}\}, \oplus_4)$ or, more simply, $(I/2, \oplus_2)$ and $(I/4, \oplus_4)$. The Cartesian product of I/2 and I/4 is the set consisting of the following eight ordered pairs.

$$\begin{array}{ll} (\bar{0}, \bar{0}) & (\bar{1}, \bar{0}) \\ (\bar{0}, \bar{1}) & (\bar{1}, \bar{1}) \\ (\bar{0}, \bar{2}) & (\bar{1}, \bar{2}) \\ (\bar{0}, \bar{3}) & (\bar{1}, \bar{3}) \end{array}$$

We define an operation, which we will call addition, as follows: For each $(\bar{a}, \bar{b}), (\bar{c}, \bar{d}) \in I/2 \times I/4$,

$$(\bar{a}, \bar{b}) + (\bar{c}, \bar{d}) = (\bar{a} \oplus_2 \bar{c}, \bar{b} \oplus_4 \bar{d}).$$

To verify that $(I/2 \times I/4, +)$ is a group, we can give arguments analogous to those given for example 1. First note that the operation is from the Cartesian product $(I/2 \times I/4) \times (I/2 \times I/4)$ and is into $I/2 \times I/4$; hence, operation + is *closed*. The *associative property* can be verified by computation. The *identity* element is the ordered pair $(\bar{0}, \bar{0})$. Each of the elements has an *inverse* as indicated below.

The inverse of $(\bar{0}, \bar{0})$ is $(\bar{0}, \bar{0})$.
The inverse of $(\bar{0}, \bar{1})$ is $(\bar{0}, \bar{3})$.
The inverse of $(\bar{0}, \bar{2})$ is $(\bar{0}, \bar{2})$.
The inverse of $(\bar{0}, \bar{3})$ is $(\bar{0}, \bar{1})$.
The inverse of $(\bar{1}, \bar{0})$ is $(\bar{1}, \bar{0})$.
The inverse of $(\bar{1}, \bar{1})$ is $(\bar{1}, \bar{3})$.
The inverse of $(\bar{1}, \bar{2})$ is $(\bar{1}, \bar{2})$.
The inverse of $(\bar{1}, \bar{3})$ is $(\bar{1}, \bar{1})$.

These arguments establish that the system $(I/2 \times I/4, +)$ is a group with eight elements. This group is commutative. However, unlike the group of the first example, it is *not* cyclic. One way to verify that the group is not cyclic is to show that none of the eight elements can serve as a generator of the group. Because $(I/2 \times I/4, +)$ is not cyclic, it follows that this group is not isomorphic to the integers modulo 8. It is true, however, that $(I/2 \times I/4, +)$ contains two cyclic subgroups, one which is isomorphic to $(I/2, \oplus_2)$ and another which is isomorphic to $(I/4, \oplus_4)$.

The first example of this section showed how to set up "natural" isomorphisms between subgroups of the constructed group and the groups used in the construction. The isomorphisms are "natural" in the sense that the nonzero components of the ordered pairs in the subgroups correspond to the elements onto which the pairs are mapped. Since the situation here is so nearly the same, we list only the subgroups and the correspondences without discussing them in great detail. It is left as an exercise to show that these correspondences are isomorphisms.

Groups: $(\{(\bar{0}, \bar{0}), (\bar{1}, \bar{0})\}, +) \cong (I/2, \oplus_2)$.

Corresponding elements:
$(\bar{0}, \bar{0}) \leftrightarrow \bar{0}$
$(\bar{1}, \bar{0}) \leftrightarrow \bar{1}$

Display 54a

Groups: $(\{(\bar{0}, \bar{0}), (\bar{0}, \bar{1}), (\bar{0}, \bar{2}), (\bar{0}, \bar{3})\}, +) \cong (I/4, \oplus_4)$.

Corresponding elements:
$(\bar{0}, \bar{0}) \leftrightarrow \bar{0}$
$(\bar{0}, \bar{1}) \leftrightarrow \bar{1}$
$(\bar{0}, \bar{2}) \leftrightarrow \bar{2}$
$(\bar{0}, \bar{3}) \leftrightarrow \bar{3}$

54b

Examples 1 and 2 show, first of all, how it is possible to define an operation on the Cartesian set of the elements of the two groups —in a manner that is natural and dependent only on the operations of the given groups—so that the resulting system is a group. In these examples, we used the symbol for addition to designate the operation of the constructed group because each group used in the construction involved modular addition. The following theorem generalizes this procedure; here, we use the symbol $\triangle$ to denote the operation of the constructed group.

Theorem 41/2 If $(G, \star)$ and $(H, \circ)$ are groups, with $(a, b), (c, d) \in G \times H$ and the operation $\triangle$ is defined by

$$(a, b) \triangle (c, d) = (a \star c, b \circ d),$$

then the system $(G \times H, \triangle)$ is a group.

Proof There are four properties to be verified for the system $(G \times H, \triangle)$. The first property to be verified is *closure*. Observe that the operation $\triangle$ as defined in Theorem 41/2 has as its domain the Cartesian product $(G \times H) \times (G \times H)$ and has as its range a subset of $G \times H$; hence, the operation $\triangle$ is closed.

The *associative property* can be verified as follows.

For each $(a, b), (c, d), (e, f) \in G \times H$,

$\big((a, b) \triangle (c, d)\big) \triangle (e, f) = \big((a \star c, b \circ d)\big) \triangle (e, f)$	Definition of $\triangle$
$= \big((a \star c) \star e, (b \circ d) \circ f\big)$	Definition of $\triangle$
$= \big(a \star (c \star e), b \circ (d \circ f)\big)$	Associative properties of $(G, \star)$ and $(H, \circ)$
$= (a, b) \triangle (c \star e, d \circ f)$	Definition of $\triangle$
$= (a, b) \triangle \big((c, d) \triangle (e, f)\big).$	Definition of $\triangle$

The next property to be verified is the existence of an *identity*. If we denote by θ the identity of the group $(G, \star)$, and denote by ϕ the identity of the group $(H, \circ)$, then (θ, ϕ) is the identity of the system $(G \times H, \triangle)$. That the ordered pair (θ, ϕ) is the identity of the system constructed can be verified as follows. If $(a, b) \in G \times H$, then

$(\theta, \phi) \triangle (a, b) = (\theta \star a, \phi \circ b)$	Definition of $\triangle$
$= (a, b).$	Identity properties of $(G, \star)$ and $(H, \circ)$
$(a, b) \triangle (\theta, \phi) = (a \star \theta, b \circ \phi)$	Definition of $\triangle$
$= (a, b).$	Identity properties of $(G, \star)$ and $(H, \circ)$

To verify the *inverse property*, observe that if $(a, b) \in G \times H$, then the inverse of the element (a, b) is (a', b'), with a' the inverse of a in G, and b' the inverse of b in H. The following steps establish this fact.

$$(a', b') \triangle (a, b) = (a' \star a, b' \circ b) = (\theta, \phi).$$

$$(a, b) \triangle (a', b') = (a \star a', b \circ b') = (\theta, \phi).$$

This concludes the proof of Theorem 41/2.

In the two examples considered in this section, the group constructed contains subgroups that are isomorphic to the groups used in the construction. These examples typify the general situation, as Theorem 42/2 establishes.

Theorem 42/2 If (G, ☆) and (H, ∘) are groups, the operation △ in the system (G × H, △) is defined as the group operation on corresponding components, and $\overline{G}$ is the set of elements $\{(g, \phi) \mid g \in G\}$ with ϕ the identity of (H, ∘), then
1) ($\overline{G}$, △) is a subgroup of (G × H, △).
2) ($\overline{G}$, △) is isomorphic to (G, ☆).

Proof To show that ($\overline{G}$, △) is a subgroup of the group (G × H, △), it is necessary and sufficient to show that $\overline{G}$ is a nonempty subset of G × H and that ($\overline{G}$, △) satisfies the closure and inverse properties. Note that, since $\overline{G}$ contains (θ, ϕ), it is not empty.

To establish the *closure property*, let (g_1, ϕ) and (g_2, ϕ) be elements of $\overline{G}$. Then $(g_1, \phi) \triangle (g_2, \phi) = (g_1 \star g_2, \phi)$. But $g_1 \star g_2 \in G$. Why does it follow from this that $(g_1 \star g_2, \phi) \in \overline{G}$?

To establish the *inverse property*, let $(g, \phi) \in \overline{G}$. The element (g', ϕ), where g' is the inverse of g in (G, ☆), is also in set $\overline{G}$. Why? Therefore, $(g, \phi) \triangle (g', \phi) = (g \star g', \phi \circ \phi) = (\theta, \phi)$. Also, $(g', \phi) \triangle (g, \phi) = (g' \star g, \phi) = (\theta, \phi)$. Hence, (g', ϕ) is the inverse of (g, ϕ). This concludes the proof of the first part of the theorem by establishing that ($\overline{G}$, △) is a subgroup of (G × H, △).

Now consider the second part of the theorem, which asserts that ($\overline{G}$, △) is isomorphic to (G, ☆). To show that ($\overline{G}$, △) is isomorphic to the group (G, ☆), it is necessary and sufficient to exhibit a one-to-one function from ($\overline{G}$, △) onto (G, ☆) that preserves the operations of these two groups. The mapping of an arbitrary element (g, ϕ) of ($\overline{G}$, △) onto an element $g \in$ (G, ☆),

$$(g, \phi) \leftrightarrow g,$$

is such a correspondence. The proof that this function is an isomorphism is given as an exercise.

Notice that Theorem 42/2 asserts only that ($\overline{G}$, △) is a subgroup of (G × H, △) which is isomorphic to (G, ☆). In the exercises at the end of this section, you are asked to show that if $\overline{H} = \{(\phi, h) \mid h \in H\}$, then ($\overline{H}$, △) is a subgroup of (G × H, △) which is isomorphic to (H, ∘).

The examples and the theorems of this section have been restricted to the question of constructing from two groups a group whose set is the Cartesian product of the two groups. But the same basic concepts can be extended to the cross product of three or more groups. Thus, if $(G_1, \star)$, $(G_2, \circ)$ and $(G_3, \square)$ are three finite groups, then the set $G_1 \times G_2 \times G_3$ that is defined as

$\{(x, y, z) \mid x \in G_1, y \in G_2, \text{ and } z \in G_3\}$ is the set of elements in a group. The group operation is defined as: $(x, y, z) \triangle (u, v, w) = ((x \star u), (y \circ v), (z \square w))$. It is easy to see how to define the operation for a cross product that involves the elements of four groups, of five groups, and so on. Some of the following exercises extend these concepts to more than two groups.

Exercises

1 Find a generator other than $(\bar{1}, \bar{1})$ for $(I/3 \times I/2, +)$. *Answer*

2 Let $(\bar{a}, \bar{b})$, $(\bar{c}, \bar{d})$, and $(\bar{e}, \bar{f})$ be elements of $(I/3 \times I/2, +)$. Give reasons for the following steps:

$$\begin{aligned}((\bar{a}, \bar{b}) + (\bar{c}, \bar{d})) + (\bar{e}, \bar{f}) &= (\bar{a} \oplus_3 \bar{c}, \bar{b} \oplus_2 \bar{d}) + (\bar{e}, \bar{f}) \\ &= ((\bar{a} \oplus_3 \bar{c}) \oplus_3 \bar{e}, (\bar{b} \oplus_2 \bar{d}) \oplus_2 \bar{f}) \\ &= (\bar{a} \oplus_3 (\bar{c} \oplus_3 \bar{e}), \bar{b} \oplus_2 (\bar{d} \oplus_2 \bar{f})) \\ &= (\bar{a}, \bar{b}) + (\bar{c} \oplus_3 \bar{e}, \bar{d} \oplus_2 \bar{f}) \\ &= (\bar{a}, \bar{b}) + ((\bar{c}, \bar{d}) + (\bar{e}, \bar{f})).\end{aligned}$$

What result is established with regard to $(I/3 \times I/2, +)$?

3 Show that $(I/3 \times I/2, +)$ is a commutative group.

4 Verify that the correspondence given in the text between $(I/3 \times I/2, +)$ and $(I/6, \oplus_6)$ is an isomorphism. Is there another isomorphism between these groups?

5 Verify that the correspondences given in the text between $(\{(\bar{0}, \bar{0}), (\bar{0}, \bar{1})\}, +)$ and $(I/2, \oplus_2)$ and between $(\{(\bar{0}, \bar{0}), (\bar{1}, \bar{0}), (\bar{2}, \bar{0})\}, +)$ and $(I/3, \oplus_3)$ are isomorphisms.

6 Verify the associative property for $(I/2 \times I/4, +)$.

7 Verify that $(\bar{0}, \bar{0})$ is the identity element of $(I/2 \times I/4, +)$.

8 Show that none of the eight elements of $I/2 \times I/4$ is a generator of the group $(I/2 \times I/4, +)$.

9 Verify that the following subgroups of $(I/2 \times I/4, +)$ are isomorphic to the integers modulo 2 and modulo 4, respectively, as indicated.

a $(\{(\bar{0}, \bar{0}), (\bar{1}, \bar{0})\}, +) \cong (I/2, \oplus_2)$.

b $(\{(\bar{0}, \bar{0}), (\bar{0}, \bar{1}), (\bar{0}, \bar{2}), (\bar{0}, \bar{3})\}, +) \cong (I/4, \oplus_4)$.

10 For Theorem 41/2, supply reasons for the steps of the proof of the inverse property.

11 In Theorem 42/2, verify that the mapping $\overline{(g, \phi)} \to g$ is an isomorphism between $(G, \star)$ and $(\overline{G}, \triangle)$.

◆ 12 Let $\overline{H}$ denote the set $\{(\theta, h) \mid h \in H\}$ where θ is the identity of $(G, \star)$ in Theorem 42/2. Prove that $\overline{H}$ is a subgroup under $\triangle$ of the group $(G \times H, \triangle)$. Also prove that $(\overline{H}, \triangle)$ is isomorphic to $(H, \circ)$.

◆ **13** Let (G, ☆), (H, ∘), and (K, □) be groups with identities θ, ϕ, and ψ, respectively. State and prove a theorem about these three groups that is analogous to Theorem 41/2. *Answer*

◆ **14** Let (G, ☆), (H, ∘), and (K, □) be groups with identities θ, ϕ, and ψ, respectively. Use these groups to state and prove a theorem analogous to Theorem 42/2.

15 Form the group $(I/3 \times I/3, +) = G$. Is G cyclic? Is $G \cong (I/9, \oplus_9)$? Is there a subgroup of G that is isomorphic to $(I/3, \oplus_3)$?

16 Form the group $(I/6 \times I/3, +) = G$. Is G cyclic? Is $G \cong (I/18, \oplus_{18})$? Is there a subgroup of G that is isomorphic to $(I/6, \oplus_6)$? To $(I/3, \oplus_3)$? To $(I/9, \oplus_9)$? To $(I/2, \oplus_2)$? *Answer*

17 Form the group $(I/2 \times I/9, +) = G$. Is G cyclic? Is $G \cong (I/18, \oplus_{18})$? Is there a subgroup of G that is isomorphic to $(I/2, \oplus_2)$? To $(I/9, \oplus_9)$? To $(I/3, \oplus_3)$? To $(I/6, \oplus_6)$? *Answer*

18 Form the group $(I/2 \times I/3 \times I/3, +) = G$. Is G cyclic? Is $G \cong (I/18, \oplus_{18})$? Is there a subgroup of G that is isomorphic to $(I/2, \oplus_2)$? To $(I/3, \oplus_3)$? To $(I/9, \oplus_9)$? To $(I/6, \oplus_6)$?

19 Form the group $(I/2 \times I/2 \times I/2, +) = G$. Is G cyclic? Is $G \cong (I/8, \oplus_8)$? Is there a subgroup of G that is isomorphic to $(I/2, \oplus_2)$? To $(I/4, \oplus_4)$?

◆ **20** Prove that if (G, ☆) and (H, ∘) are finite commutative groups, then $(G \times H, \triangle)$ is a finite commutative group. The operation $\triangle$ from $(G \times H) \times (G \times H)$ is defined as follows:
For each $(a, b), (c, d) \in G \times H$, $(a, b) \triangle (c, d) = (a ☆ c, b \circ d)$.

24/2 Construction of finite commutative groups

[optional]

In this section we will be concerned with determining the answers to two questions. First, for any counting number n, is there a commutative group with exactly n elements? Second, for any counting number n, if there exist finite commutative groups with exactly n elements, how many such distinct, in the sense of *non-isomorphic*, groups are there?

The answer to the first question is obvious. For any counting number n, there exists a finite commutative group with exactly n elements; namely, the integers modulo n under addition.

The second question is more important and is harder to answer completely. As a start toward an answer, we have just seen that there exists at least one finite commutative group with exactly n elements for any counting number n. The other part of the answer is concerned with determining how many finite commutative groups with n elements there are and deciding which of the groups are distinct in the sense that they are not isomorphic. We will now consider some examples that should help us find a partial answer to our question.

Example 1 The set of integers modulo 12 under modular addition forms a finite commutative group with exactly 12 elements, as you know; but there are other finite commutative groups with exactly 12 elements, as we will establish. Consider, for example, the set of ordered triples with first components contained in the set of integers modulo 2, with second components contained in the set of integers modulo 2, and with third components contained in the set of integers modulo 3. The 12 elements of $(I/2 \times I/2 \times I/3)$ are listed below.

$$\begin{array}{ll} (\bar{0}, \bar{0}, \bar{0}) & (\bar{1}, \bar{0}, \bar{0}) \\ (\bar{0}, \bar{0}, \bar{1}) & (\bar{1}, \bar{0}, \bar{1}) \\ (\bar{0}, \bar{0}, \bar{2}) & (\bar{1}, \bar{0}, \bar{2}) \\ (\bar{0}, \bar{1}, \bar{0}) & (\bar{1}, \bar{1}, \bar{0}) \\ (\bar{0}, \bar{1}, \bar{1}) & (\bar{1}, \bar{1}, \bar{1}) \\ (\bar{0}, \bar{1}, \bar{2}) & (\bar{1}, \bar{1}, \bar{2}) \end{array}$$

We will designate the set $I/2 \times I/2 \times I/3$ by the letter S and use the 12 ordered triples contained in S to construct a commutative group. The operation for the group will be defined in terms of the operations of the cyclic groups that were used in forming set S. In section 23/2 we defined such an operation on the Cartesian product of two groups and showed how the definition could be extended to three or more groups. The definition of the binary operation for the three groups of this example is as follows: If $(\bar{a}, \bar{b}, \bar{c})$ and $(\bar{f}, \bar{g}, \bar{h}) \in I/2 \times I/2 \times I/3$, then

$$(\bar{a}, \bar{b}, \bar{c}) + (\bar{f}, \bar{g}, \bar{h}) = (\bar{a} \oplus_2 \bar{f}, \bar{b} \oplus_2 \bar{g}, \bar{c} \oplus_3 \bar{h}).$$

The verification that $(I/2 \times I/2 \times I/3, +)$ is a commutative group is given as an exercise at the end of the section.

Before deciding whether or not the groups $(I/12, \oplus_{12})$ and $(I/2 \times I/2 \times I/3, +)$ are isomorphic, we need a new definition and a theorem.

Definition 39/2 If $(G, \star)$ is a group whose identity is e, $a \in G$, and there exists a positive integer n such that $n \cdot a = e$, then the least such positive integer n is the *order* of a. Symbolically, $o(a) = n$.

As particular examples, in $I/12$ the element $\bar{1}$ has order 12; $\bar{2}$ has order 6; $\bar{3}$ has order 4; $\bar{4}$ has order 3, $\bar{5}$ has order 12, $\bar{6}$ has order 2; and so on.

Now we will prove a theorem which shows that corresponding elements under an isomorphism must have the same order. A property like the preservation of order under an isomorphism is called an *invariant* property.

Theorem 43/2 If (G, ☆) and (H, ∘) are isomorphic under the mapping f and if $a \in G$, $b \in H$ are such that $(a)f = b$, then $o(a) = o(b)$.

Proof In exercise 12 on page 150, you proved that if f is an isomorphism from (G, ☆) onto (H, ∘) and if e_G and e_H are the identities of (G, ☆) and (H, ∘), respectively, then $(e_G)f = e_H$. This result will be used in the proof of Theorem 43/2.

We must establish that if $a \in G$, $o(a) = n$, $b \in H$, $o(b) = m$, and $(a)f = b$, then $o(a) = o(b)$; that is, $n = m$. Since $(a)f = b$, $2 \cdot ((a)f) = 2 \cdot b$, $3 \cdot ((a)f) = 3 \cdot b$, and so on, it follows that

$$\begin{aligned} m \cdot (a)f &= m \cdot b \\ &= e_H \\ &= (e_G)f. \end{aligned}$$

By induction, it can be shown that $m \cdot (a)f = (m \cdot a)f$; hence, it follows that $m \cdot a = e_G$. But, since the order of a is n, where n is the least positive integer such that $n \cdot a = e_G$, it follows that $n \leqq m$. A similar argument, beginning with the statement $n \cdot b = n \cdot (a)f$, leads to the conclusion that $n \geqq m$. But, $n \geqq m$ and $n \leqq m$ imply that $n = m$. This completes the proof of Theorem 43/2.

Since an isomorphism preserves the order of elements, to prove that two groups are not isomorphic, it is sufficient to show that there is an element of one group whose order is different from the order of each element of the other group. Consider again the two groups $(I/12, \oplus_{12})$ and $(I/2 \times I/2 \times I/3, +)$. The element $\bar{1}$ of $(I/12, \oplus_{12})$ has order 12; but, no element of $(I/2 \times I/2 \times I/3, +)$ has order 12. Hence, $(I/12, \oplus_{12})$ and $(I/2 \times I/2 \times I/3, +)$ are *not* isomorphic.

Examples 2 Still another way to construct a finite commutative group with exactly 12 elements is to use the elements of the group of integers modulo 4 and the group of integers modulo 3 under modular addition. The 12 ordered pairs in the Cartesian product $I/4 \times I/3$ are listed below.

$(\bar{0}, \bar{0})$	$(\bar{1}, \bar{0})$	$(\bar{2}, \bar{0})$	$(\bar{3}, \bar{0})$
$(\bar{0}, \bar{1})$	$(\bar{1}, \bar{1})$	$(\bar{2}, \bar{1})$	$(\bar{3}, \bar{1})$
$(\bar{0}, \bar{2})$	$(\bar{1}, \bar{2})$	$(\bar{2}, \bar{2})$	$(\bar{3}, \bar{2})$

Using the operations of the cyclic groups $(I/4, \oplus_4)$ and $(I/3, \oplus_3)$, we can define an operation for each $(\bar{a}, \bar{b})$, $(\bar{c}, \bar{d}) \in I/4 \times I/3$ as follows:

$$(\bar{a}, \bar{b}) + (\bar{c}, \bar{d}) = (\bar{a} \oplus_4 \bar{c}, \bar{b} \oplus_3 \bar{d}).$$

This is just a special case of Theorem 41/2 and, hence, the resulting system is a finite commutative group.

Now we wish to decide if this group of 12 elements is isomorphic to the group of example 1, to the group of integers modulo 12 under addition, or to neither of these groups. First we note that the group $(I/4 \times I/3, +)$ contains an element of order 4. One element with order 4 is the element $(\bar{1}, \bar{0})$ since 4 is the least positive integer n such that $n \cdot (\bar{1}, \bar{0}) = (\bar{0}, \bar{0})$. However, no element of $(I/2 \times I/2 \times I/3, +)$ has order 4. Therefore, $(I/4 \times I/3, +)$ is *not* isomorphic to the group of example 1 because an isomorphism preserves the order of elements.

However, the group $(I/4 \times I/3, +)$ *is* isomorphic to the integers modulo 12 under modular addition. A function f that establishes an isomorphism between $(I/4 \times I/3, +)$ and $(I/12, \oplus_{12})$ is:

$(\bar{0}, \bar{0})f = \bar{0}$.	$(\bar{1}, \bar{0})f = \bar{9}$.	$(\bar{2}, \bar{0})f = \bar{6}$.	$(\bar{3}, \bar{0})f = \bar{3}$.
$(\bar{0}, \bar{1})f = \bar{4}$.	$(\bar{1}, \bar{1})f = \bar{1}$.	$(\bar{2}, \bar{1})f = \overline{10}$.	$(\bar{3}, \bar{1})f = \bar{7}$.
$(\bar{0}, \bar{2})f = \bar{8}$.	$(\bar{1}, \bar{2})f = \bar{5}$.	$(\bar{2}, \bar{2})f = \bar{2}$.	$(\bar{3}, \bar{2})f = \overline{11}$.

The verification that f is an isomorphism is left as an exercise.

The two examples presented in this section show that, for any counting number n, there may exist finite commutative groups with exactly n elements that are not isomorphic.

Examples 1 and 2 dealt with groups containing 12 elements. Now let us consider cases in which the counting number $n = 60$ is given. We know that there exists at least one finite commutative group with exactly 60 elements—namely, the integers modulo 60. We will investigate to see if there are other groups with 60 elements that are not isomorphic to $I/60$.

3 Let us first consider the group consisting of the set of ordered triples $I/4 \times I/3 \times I/5$ under an operation + patterned after the operation between ordered triples given for example 1 of this section. Some of the 60 elements of this set of ordered triples are:

$(\bar{0}, \bar{0}, \bar{0})$	$(\bar{0}, \bar{1}, \bar{0})$	$(\bar{0}, \bar{2}, \bar{0})$	$(\bar{1}, \bar{0}, \bar{0})$	$(\bar{1}, \bar{1}, \bar{0})$	...
$(\bar{0}, \bar{0}, \bar{1})$	$(\bar{0}, \bar{1}, \bar{1})$	$(\bar{0}, \bar{2}, \bar{1})$	$(\bar{1}, \bar{0}, \bar{1})$	$(\bar{1}, \bar{1}, \bar{1})$	...
$(\bar{0}, \bar{0}, \bar{2})$	$(\bar{0}, \bar{1}, \bar{2})$	$(\bar{0}, \bar{2}, \bar{2})$	$(\bar{1}, \bar{0}, \bar{2})$	$(\bar{1}, \bar{1}, \bar{2})$	...
$(\bar{0}, \bar{0}, \bar{3})$	$(\bar{0}, \bar{1}, \bar{3})$	$(\bar{0}, \bar{2}, \bar{3})$	$(\bar{1}, \bar{0}, \bar{3})$	$(\bar{1}, \bar{1}, \bar{3})$	...
$(\bar{0}, \bar{0}, \bar{4})$	$(\bar{0}, \bar{1}, \bar{4})$	$(\bar{0}, \bar{2}, \bar{4})$	$(\bar{1}, \bar{0}, \bar{4})$	$(\bar{1}, \bar{1}, \bar{4})$	...

By an extension of Theorem 41/2, we know that the system (I/4 × I/3 × I/5, +) is a group. Furthermore, it is a cyclic group, and one generator of the group is the element $(\bar{1}, \bar{1}, \bar{1})$. The order of the element $(\bar{1}, \bar{1}, \bar{1})$ is 60. Why? By Theorem 39/2, it follows that the group (I/4 × I/3 × I/5, +) is isomorphic to (I/60, $\oplus_{60}$). You should exhibit a function that establishes an isomorphism between the two groups.

Example 4 As another example of a finite commutative group with exactly 60 elements, the set of ordered 4-tuples I/2 × I/2 × I/3 × I/5 under an operation patterned after previous examples is a group. Some of the 60 elements in this group are listed below.

$(\bar{0}, \bar{0}, \bar{0}, \bar{0})$	$(\bar{0}, \bar{0}, \bar{1}, \bar{0})$	$(\bar{0}, \bar{0}, \bar{2}, \bar{0})$	$(\bar{0}, \bar{1}, \bar{0}, \bar{0})$	...
$(\bar{0}, \bar{0}, \bar{0}, \bar{1})$	$(\bar{0}, \bar{0}, \bar{1}, \bar{1})$	$(\bar{0}, \bar{0}, \bar{2}, \bar{1})$	$(\bar{0}, \bar{1}, \bar{0}, \bar{1})$	...
$(\bar{0}, \bar{0}, \bar{0}, \bar{2})$	$(\bar{0}, \bar{0}, \bar{1}, \bar{2})$	$(\bar{0}, \bar{0}, \bar{2}, \bar{2})$	$(\bar{0}, \bar{1}, \bar{0}, \bar{2})$	...
$(\bar{0}, \bar{0}, \bar{0}, \bar{3})$	$(\bar{0}, \bar{0}, \bar{1}, \bar{3})$	$(\bar{0}, \bar{0}, \bar{2}, \bar{3})$	$(\bar{0}, \bar{1}, \bar{0}, \bar{3})$	...
$(\bar{0}, \bar{0}, \bar{0}, \bar{4})$	$(\bar{0}, \bar{0}, \bar{1}, \bar{4})$	$(\bar{0}, \bar{0}, \bar{2}, \bar{4})$	$(\bar{0}, \bar{1}, \bar{0}, \bar{4})$	...

This group is not isomorphic to the integers modulo 60 because the orders of the elements in the group are 2, 3, 6, 15, and 30. Since there is no element in this group of order 60, we have constructed a finite commutative group with 60 elements that is not isomorphic to the integers modulo 60.

From the foregoing examples, we can make some generalizations about the construction of finite commutative groups. If n is a counting number and $n = a_1a_2 \ldots a_r$, then set $S = I/a_1 \times I/a_2 \times \ldots \times I/a_r$ can be used to construct a commutative group by defining an operation $\triangle$ on the components. The operation $\triangle$ is defined in terms of the operations of the cyclic groups I/a_i for $i = 1, 2, \ldots, r$. The group $(S, \triangle)$ contains $a_1a_2 \ldots a_r = n$ elements; it may or may not be isomorphic to the group $(I/n, \oplus_n)$. The answer to this question depends upon whether the factors $a_1, a_2, \ldots, a_r$ have n as their least common multiple or some integral divisor of n as their least common multiple. A complete answer to this question will not be developed here, but we have given a clue to the answer, and some of the following exercises will carry this idea a bit further.

Exercises

1 Verify that (I/2 × I/2 × I/3, +) is a commutative group.

2 Determine the order of each element in (I/4 × I/3, +). *Answer*

3 Verify that the correspondence given in the text between (I/4 × I/3, +) and (I/12, $\oplus_{12}$) is an isomorphism.

4 Verify that 60 is the order of the element $(\bar{1}, \bar{1}, \bar{1})$ of the group $(I/4 \times I/3 \times I/5, +)$.

5 Find elements of the group $(I/2 \times I/2 \times I/3 \times I/5, +)$ with orders 1, 2, 3, 6, 15, and 30.

6 Consider the isomorphism f given in the text between $(I/4 \times I/3, +)$ and $(I/12, \oplus_{12})$. By Theorem 42/2, we know that $(I/4 \times I/3, +)$ contains a subgroup isomorphic to $(I/4, \oplus_4)$ and a subgroup isomorphic to $(I/3, \oplus_3)$. What do you notice about the images of the elements of these subgroups under the isomorphism f? Determine another isomorphism between $(I/4 \times I/3, +)$ and $(I/12, \oplus_{12})$. What features do the two isomorphisms have in common?

7 Form the group G with elements in $I/2 \times I/6$. What subgroup of G is isomorphic to $(I/2, \oplus_2)$? What subgroup is isomorphic to $(I/6, \oplus_6)$? Attempt to determine an isomorphism between G and $(I/12, \oplus_{12})$ by using corresponding subgroups. What difficulty occurs? Is $G \cong (I/12, \oplus_{12})$? *Answer*

8 Neither $(I/2 \times I/2 \times I/3, +)$ nor $(I/2 \times I/6, +)$ is isomorphic to $(I/12, \oplus_{12})$. Is $(I/2 \times I/2 \times I/3, +) \cong (I/2 \times I/6, +)$? Use corresponding subgroups to find an isomorphism, if it exists, between these two groups. *Answer*

9 We have shown that $(I/4 \times I/3, +) \cong (I/12, \oplus_{12})$ and that $(I/2 \times I/2 \times I/3, +) \cong (I/2 \times I/6, +)$. Are there any other ways to build a commutative group of 12 elements from groups of integers modulo *n* under modular addition? How many distinct commutative groups of 12 elements can be constructed from these groups of integers modulo *n* in the sense of isomorphism? That is, if you regard isomorphic groups as nondistinct, how many distinct commutative groups of 12 elements can be formed in this way?

10 A commutative group of 18 elements may be constructed from $I/18$, $I/2 \times I/3 \times I/3$, $I/2 \times I/9$, and $I/3 \times I/6$. Using corresponding subgroups, find an isomorphism between $(I/18, \oplus_{18})$ and $(I/2 \times I/9, +)$. Using the same technique, try to find an isomorphism between $(I/18, \oplus_{18})$ and $(I/3 \times I/6, +)$.

11 Find an isomorphism between the groups $(I/3 \times I/6, +)$ and $(I/2 \times I/3 \times I/3, +)$. *Answer*

12 A commutative group with 16 elements can be built from groups of integers modulo *n* under modular addition in 5 possible ways. List these ways.

13 Find an isomorphism from $(I/3 \times I/8, +)$ onto $(I/24, \oplus_{24})$. Is $(I/3 \times I/8, +)$ cyclic? Find a generator of $(I/3 \times I/8, +)$.

14 Find an isomorphism from $(I/2 \times I/2 \times I/2 \times I/3, +)$ onto $(I/2 \times I/2 \times I/6, +)$. *Answer*

15 Find an isomorphism from $(I/2 \times I/3 \times I/4, +)$ onto $(I/2 \times I/12, +)$.

16 Find an isomorphism from $(I/2 \times I/3 \times I/4, +)$ onto $(I/4 \times I/6, +)$.

17 From exercises 15 and 16, is there an isomorphism from $(I/2 \times I/12, +)$ onto $(I/4 \times I/6, +)$? If so, how is it defined?

18 From exercises 13 through 17, how many commutative groups, in the sense of isomorphism, of 24 elements can be constructed from groups of integers modulo n? *Answer*

19 Determine the order of each element in the groups given in exercise 25 of section 22/2 (page 151).

20 Show how example 2 of this section illustrates that an isomorphism preserves the order of the elements of the groups $(I/12, \oplus_{12})$ and $(I/4 \times I/3, +)$. *Answer*

◆ **21** Let $(G, \star)$ be a group with $a \in G$, $a \neq e_G$. Prove that if the order of a in $(G, \star)$ is n, and m is a positive integral multiple of n, then $m \cdot a = e_G$.

◆ **22** Let $(G, \star)$ be a group with $a \in G$, $a \neq e_G$. Prove that if the order of a in $(G, \star)$ is n and m is a positive integer which is not an integral multiple of n, then $m \cdot a \neq e_G$. (Hint: Consider $m = kn + r$.)

◆ **23** Let $(G, \star)$ and $(H, \circ)$ be groups with $x \in G$ and $y \in H$. Prove that if the order of x in $(G, \star)$ is m and the order of y in $(H, \circ)$ is n, then the order of (x, y) in $(G \times H, +)$ is the least common multiple of m and n. *Answer*

24 List three possible ways in which a commutative group of 20 elements can be built from groups of integers modulo n under modular addition.

25 Which element of $(I/20, \oplus_{20})$ has the greatest order? What is its order? Which element of $(I/2 \times I/10, +)$ has the greatest order? What is its order? Could $(I/20, \oplus_{20})$ be isomorphic to $(I/2 \times I/10, +)$? *Answer*

26 Which element of $(I/2 \times I/2 \times I/5, +)$ has the greatest order? What is its order? Could $(I/20, \oplus_{20})$ be isomorphic to $(I/2 \times I/2 \times I/5, +)$?

27 Which element of $(I/4 \times I/5, +)$ has the greatest order? What is its order? Could $(I/20, \oplus_{20})$ be isomorphic to $(I/4 \times I/5, +)$?

28 Could $(I/2 \times I/10, +)$ be isomorphic to $(I/2 \times I/2 \times I/5, +)$? If so, find an isomorphism.

For the following exercises, determine the element of each group that has the greatest order and give the order. Then tell whether or not the two groups *could* be isomorphic.

29 $(I/36, \oplus_{36})$ and $(I/2 \times I/18, +)$
30 $(I/36, \oplus_{36})$ and $(I/3 \times I/12, +)$
31 $(I/36, \oplus_{36})$ and $(I/4 \times I/9, +)$
32 $(I/36, \oplus_{36})$ and $(I/6 \times I/6, +)$
33 $(I/12 \times I/3, +)$ and $(I/18 \times I/2, +)$
34 $(I/3 \times I/12, +)$ and $(I/6 \times I/6, +)$
35 $(I/2 \times I/18, +)$ and $(I/6 \times I/6, +)$
36 $(I/36, \oplus_{36})$ and $(I/2 \times I/2 \times I/9, +)$
37 $(I/36, \oplus_{36})$ and $(I/2 \times I/3 \times I/6, +)$
38 $(I/36, \oplus_{36})$ and $(I/3 \times I/3 \times I/4, +)$
39 $(I/36, \oplus_{36})$ and $(I/2 \times I/2 \times I/3 \times I/3, +)$
40 $(I/2 \times I/2 \times I/9, +)$ and $(I/3 \times I/3 \times I/4, +)$ *Answer*
41 $(I/2 \times I/2 \times I/3 \times I/3, +)$ and $(I/3 \times I/3 \times I/4, +)$
42 $(I/2 \times I/2 \times I/3 \times I/3, +)$ and $(I/2 \times I/2 \times I/9, +)$ *Answer*
43 List eight possible ways in which a commutative group of 36 elements can be built from groups of integers modulo n under modular addition.

Chapter review

1 Let the function $E_I \times E_I \xrightarrow{\star} E_I$ be defined by $a \star b = \frac{1}{2}(a + b)$ for each $a, b \in E_I$. Is $\star$ a binary operation? Is $(E_I, \star)$ a semi-group?

2 Let the function $R^+ \times R^+ \xrightarrow{\star} R^+$ be defined by $a \star b = \frac{1}{2}(a \div b)$ for each $a, b \in R^+$. Is $\star$ a binary operation? Is $(R^+, \star)$ a semi-group?

3 Let $G = \{a_0, a_1, \ldots, a_6\}$. Let $a_i \star a_j = a_{i+j}$ if $i + j < 7$ and $a_i \star a_j = a_{i+j-7}$ if $i + j \geqq 7$. Is $(G, \star)$ a group? If so, what is the identity element?

4 In the symmetric group on $S_3 = \{1, 2, 3\}$, $(G_3, \circ)$, find two elements P_i and P_j such that $(P_i \circ P_j)^2 \neq P_i^2 \circ P_j^2$.

* 5 If G is a group with an even number of elements, prove that it must have an element $a \neq e$ of order 2, where e is the identity element of the group.

6 Show that if a group G has three elements, it must be commutative. Find all groups with three elements.

* 7 Form the Cartesian product $I/4 \times I/4$ and define addition in terms of modular addition of corresponding components. Is

*Exercises marked with an asterisk in the "reviews" pertain to optional sections in the book.

this system a group? If multiplication from $I/4 \times I/4$ is defined in terms of modular multiplication of corresponding components, is the resulting system a group?

8 Find all the subgroups of the group of symmetries of the square.

9 Find the inverse of each member of $(G_3, \circ)$, the symmetric group on $\{1, 2, 3\}$.

10 Determine all the subgroups of $(I/36, \oplus_{36})$. What do you observe about the number of elements in a subgroup as compared to the number of elements in the original group?

11 If $(G, \star)$ is a cyclic group containing 8 elements, how many generators does it have?

12 For what replacements of n does $(I_{nx}, +) = (I, +)$?

13 Is $(I_{12x} \cup I_{8x}, +)$ a subgroup of $(I, +)$? If so, what subgroup is it equal to?

14 Under what circumstances is the intersection of two subgroups of $(I, +)$ a trivial subgroup?

15 Let G and H be groups and let function f be an isomorphism from G onto H. Show that $(e_G)f = e_H$.

16 Let f, G, and H be as described in exercise 15. Let $a \in G$. Show that $(a')f = ((a)f)'$.

*17 Let $G = (I/3 \times I/3, +)$, where $+$ is defined as addition modulo 3 of corresponding components. Determine mappings f and g from G onto G such that $(a, b)f \circ g = (0, 0)$ for all $(a, b) \in G$.

*18 List all possible ways of constructing a group with 24 elements from groups of integers modulo n under modular addition.

Cumulative review

1 Suppose that $N(A) = n$ and $N(B) = n - 1$. What is $N(A \times B)$?

2 Describe a domain and a range in the set of real numbers so that $(x)f = \sqrt{x}$ is a function. Is this function one-to-one?

3 Is $O_I \times O_I \xrightarrow{-} E_I$ a closed binary operation? Explain.

4 Is "greater than or equal to" an equivalence relation in $\mathfrak{R}$? Give reasons to support your answer.

5 How many elements are in $(G_n, \circ)$, the symmetric group on n elements?

6 Determine a nontrivial commutative subgroup of $(G_3, \circ)$.

7 Show that if $(G, \star)$ is a group in which every element is its own inverse, then G is commutative.

8 Let $S = \{20n \mid n \in I\}$ and $T = \{15n \mid n \in I\}$. Find the groups $S \cap T$ and $S \cup T$ under addition.

9 Show that $(I/4, \oplus_4)$ and $(\{1, -1, i, -i\}, \cdot)$ are isomorphic. Show that two isomorphisms exist between these groups.

10 Which elements of $(I/15, \oplus_{15})$ are generators of the elements of this group?

11 Prove that $(I, +)$ and $(I/5, \oplus_5)$ are not isomorphic.

12 Define the function f_n from I into I by $(x)f_n = nx$, where $n \in I$. Let $G = \{f_n \mid n \in I\}$. Define the mapping $G \times G \xrightarrow{+} G$ by $f_n + f_m = f_{n+m}$. Is $(G, +)$ a group? If so, prove it.

13 Let $S = \{a, b\}$. Let $\mathbb{S}$ be the set of subsets of S. Define the operation $+$ on $\mathbb{S}$ by $A + B = \{x \mid x \in A \cup B \text{ and } x \notin A \cap B\}$ for each $A, B \in \mathbb{S}$. Show that $(\mathbb{S}, +)$ is a group and construct the addition table.

14 Find a group $(H, \star)$ that is isomorphic to the group of exercise 13 and exhibit an appropriate correspondence between the elements of the two groups.

15 Let $S = \{a, b, c\}$ and let $\mathbb{S}$ be the set of all subsets of S. Define $\mathbb{S} \times \mathbb{S} \xrightarrow{+} \mathbb{S}$ by $A + B = A \cap B$ for all $A, B \in \mathbb{S}$. Is $(\mathbb{S}, +)$ a group? If so, prove it. If not, show why, and decide if $(\mathbb{S}, +)$ is a semi-group. Does $(\mathbb{S}, +)$ have an identity?

* **16** Let group G be the set of all nonzero integers modulo 5 under modular multiplication and let group H be the set of all nonzero integers modulo 3 under modular multiplication. Construct $G \times H$ and define an appropriate multiplication so that $(G \times H, \cdot)$ is a group.

* **17** Exhibit an isomorphism between a subgroup of $(G \times H, \cdot)$ and group G of exercise 16. Exhibit an isomorphism between a subgroup of $(G \times H, \cdot)$ and group H.

Chapter **3**
Rings and integral domains

25 *Rings*
26 *Commutative rings with identity*
27 *Elementary properties of a ring*
28 *Subrings*
29* *Ideals*
30* *Homomorphisms*
31 *Polynomial rings*
32 *Integral domains*

Introduction The mathematical systems discussed in Chapter 2 each consisted of a set of elements and one binary operation. In this and the next chapter, mathematical systems with two, rather than one, binary operations will be discussed. The method of developing these new systems will closely parallel the method used in developing examples of groups. Just as with groups, we will begin with the simplest kinds of examples of rings, but as we proceed, we will "add" other properties so that the systems become more complex and, therefore, more interesting.

Rings 25/3

As indicated in the introduction, a ring is a mathematical system that consists of a set of elements under two binary operations that satisfy certain properties. We will say a great deal about these properties in the pages that follow.

Many familiar subsets of the real numbers under the operations of addition and multiplication, such as the set of integers, the set of even integers, the set of rational numbers, and the set of real numbers, form examples of rings. If we use notation patterned after the group notation (G, ☆), then the systems

$$(I, +, \cdot) \qquad (R, +, \cdot)$$
$$(E_I, +, \cdot) \qquad (\mathfrak{R}, +, \cdot)$$

are examples of rings. Since we have not yet defined a ring, this assertion obviously cannot be verified now. These examples are given so that you will have some specific examples in mind as you consider the abstract definition of a ring.

Not only does a ring involve a set and two operations, usually denoted by + and $\cdot$, but it is also required that the operations be connected by a distributive property. Later in this chapter we will see how other requirements yield more complex algebraic systems. The properties of a ring are summarized in the following definition.

Definition **40/3** Suppose that S is a set and that + and $\cdot$ are two binary operations defined on S; that is, + is a function from S × S into S and $\cdot$ is a function from S × S into S. Then (S, +, $\cdot$) is a *ring* if and only if (S, +) is a commutative group and the following properties also hold:

Closure for $\cdot$ **6** For each $a, b \in S$, $a \cdot b \in S$.

Associativity for $\cdot$ **7** For each $a, b, c \in S$,
$(a \cdot b) \cdot c = a \cdot (b \cdot c)$.

Distributive **8** For each $a, b, c \in S$,
1) $a \cdot (b + c) = (a \cdot b) + (a \cdot c)$ and
2) $(a + b) \cdot c = (a \cdot c) + (b \cdot c)$.

Notice that, because the commutative group (S, +) has five properties, the ring (S, +, $\cdot$) has a total of eight properties. We will usually denote the mathematical system called a ring by (S, +, $\cdot$), but we may sometimes refer to set S as a ring without mentioning specifically the two operations. When we do this, you must keep in mind that there are two binary operations defined on S that satisfy the eight properties of Definition 40/3.

Since we are using the symbol + to represent the operation of the commutative group, we will usually designate the additive identity by 0. Again, because we are using the additive notation, we will usually represent the additive inverse of an element a in S by $-a$.

In keeping with the idea that as little notation as possible should be used when no confusion can arise, we will often omit the symbol $\cdot$ for multiplication and denote $a \cdot b$ by ab. We will refer to ab as the *product* of a and b.

The eight properties of a ring are summarized in the following chart. We have labeled them with the numerals 1 through 8 so that we will be able to refer to property 1, property 2, and so on.

Properties of a ring $(S, +, \cdot)$

Closure for $+$	1	For each $a, b \in S$, $a + b \in S$.
Associativity for $+$	2	For each $a, b, c \in S$, $(a + b) + c = a + (b + c)$.
Identity for $+$	3	There exists an identity in S, denoted by 0, such that, for each $a \in S$, $0 + a = a + 0 = a$.
Inverse for $+$	4	For each $a \in S$, there exists an inverse in S, denoted by $-a$, such that $-a + a = a + (-a) = 0$.
Commutativity for $+$	5	For each $a, b \in S$, $a + b = b + a$.
Closure for $\cdot$	6	For each $a, b \in S$, $ab \in S$.
Associativity for $\cdot$	7	For each $a, b, c \in S$, $(ab)c = a(bc)$.
Distributive property	8	For each $a, b, c \in S$, 1) $a(b + c) = ab + ac$, and 2) $(a + b)c = ac + bc$.

Remember that in the definition of a group we require only that the binary operation be an into function, but that it is actually onto. Similarly, in our definition of a ring we require only that the functions $+$ and $\cdot$ be into. Is the function $\cdot$ necessarily an "onto" function? To answer this question, consider the ring of even integers under addition and multiplication. Is every even integer in the range of the operation of multiplication?

Most of the examples of rings that we mentioned on page 171 were subsets of the real numbers. We will now develop another example of a ring whose elements do not form a subset of the real numbers. In developing this example, first we will need to define a *matrix*, and the set of elements in the ring will be a set of matrices. Since matrices are useful in solving systems of linear conditions and also in the study of linear transformations in geometry, you may have been exposed to the concept of a matrix in your previous studies. In Definition 41/3, we have defined the particular type of matrix to be used in our example. No previous knowledge of matrices is assumed in the development that follows.

Definition 41/3 Let $M_{2 \times 2}$ be the set of all *arrays* A of the form

$$A = \begin{pmatrix} a_{11} & a_{12} \\ a_{21} & a_{22} \end{pmatrix},$$

where a_{11}, a_{12}, a_{21}, and a_{22} are real numbers. An element of the set $M_{2 \times 2}$ is a *2 × 2 real matrix*. The numbers that occur in the matrix are the *entries* of the matrix. In a 2 × 2 matrix, the real numbers a_{i1} and a_{i2} are the entries in the *i*th row for $i = 1, 2$; and the real numbers a_{1j} and a_{2j} are the entries in the *j*th column for $j = 1, 2$.

The numerals in the symbols a_{11}, a_{12}, and so on, are called *subscripts*. These subscripts were not chosen arbitrarily. The first digit in the subscript indicates the row in which an entry occurs, and the second digit indicates the column. For example, entry a_{21} occurs in the second row and the first column of the matrix. Thus, the subscript of a_{21} should be read as "two, one," not as "twenty-one," to indicate the row and column.

Some examples of 2 × 2 real matrices are listed below. Note that every 2 × 2 real matrix has exactly two rows and two columns and that any real number may occur as an entry in such a matrix.

Examples 1 $\begin{pmatrix} \frac{\sqrt{5}}{3} & \pi \\ 0 & -1 \end{pmatrix}$

2 $\begin{pmatrix} \sqrt{51} & 0 \\ 0 & -3 \end{pmatrix}$

3 $\begin{pmatrix} 0 & 0 \\ 4 & -8 \end{pmatrix}$

4 $\begin{pmatrix} -5 & 0 \\ \frac{13}{4} & 0 \end{pmatrix}$

5 $\begin{pmatrix} \sqrt[3]{2} & \sqrt[4]{2} \\ \sqrt[5]{2} & \sqrt[6]{2} \end{pmatrix}$

By definition, two matrices are *equal* if and only if the corresponding entries are equal. That is, two matrices A and B are equal if and only if the *ij*th entry of A is equal to the *ij*th entry of B for each *i*, *j*.

In exercise 2 at the end of this section, you are asked to verify that the relation "equals" on the set of 2 × 2 real matrices satisfies the reflexive, symmetric, and transitive properties of an equivalence relation.

Now that we have a set of elements and an equality relation between the elements of the set, we will define two operations on the set so that the resulting system satisfies the properties of a ring. First, we define a binary operation of addition for 2×2 real matrices.

Definition 42/3 If A and B are elements of $M_{2 \times 2}$, then the *sum* of A and B is the 2×2 real matrix whose entry in the *ij*th position is the sum of the entries in the *ij*th position of A and in the *ij*th position of B.

That is, if $A = \begin{pmatrix} a_{11} & a_{12} \\ a_{21} & a_{22} \end{pmatrix}$ and $B = \begin{pmatrix} b_{11} & b_{12} \\ b_{21} & b_{22} \end{pmatrix}$, then

$$A + B = \begin{pmatrix} a_{11} & a_{12} \\ a_{21} & a_{22} \end{pmatrix} + \begin{pmatrix} b_{11} & b_{12} \\ b_{21} & b_{22} \end{pmatrix} = \begin{pmatrix} a_{11} + b_{11} & a_{12} + b_{12} \\ a_{21} + b_{21} & a_{22} + b_{22} \end{pmatrix}.$$

An informal statement of this definition is that we add two matrices simply by adding their corresponding entries. Specific examples of the sum of two 2×2 real matrices are given below.

Examples 1 $$\begin{pmatrix} 2 & -3 \\ 5 & 0 \end{pmatrix} + \begin{pmatrix} 6 & \frac{2}{3} \\ 4 & -5 \end{pmatrix} = \begin{pmatrix} 8 & -\frac{7}{3} \\ 9 & -5 \end{pmatrix}.$$

2 $$\begin{pmatrix} 6 & 4 \\ -2 & 0 \end{pmatrix} + \begin{pmatrix} 4 & \frac{3}{2} \\ 2 & -5 \end{pmatrix} = \begin{pmatrix} 10 & \frac{11}{2} \\ 0 & -5 \end{pmatrix}.$$

We will now define a multiplication operation on the set of all 2×2 real matrices. Because addition of matrices is defined as addition of corresponding entries of the matrices, it might seem reasonable to define multiplication of matrices so that the product is a matrix whose entries are the products of corresponding entries. Indeed, such a definition is possible, but, perhaps surprisingly, such a definition would not be so useful in solving practical problems as the one we will adopt. The following example, which will serve to motivate the definition, shows how matrices and their products can be used to interpret a physical situation.

Example John's father is concerned about how much money John spends on dates. He is also concerned about how much John uses the family car. To allay his father's fears, John decides to keep a record of his expenses and mileage for two months. He knows how much he spends and how far he drives with each girl friend. John tabulates this information as follows:

	Peggy	*Patricia*
Amount spent each date	\$1.50	\$5.00
Miles driven each date	6	12

During the months of September and October, John has the following number of dates.

	September	*October*
Peggy	3	2
Patricia	2	2

To compute the cost for September, John multiplies the entries in row 1 of the first chart by the entries in column 1 of the second chart to obtain

$$(1.50)3 + (5.00)2 = 4.50 + 10.00 = \$14.50.$$

For October, the first row in the first chart multiplied by the second column in the second chart yields

$$(1.50)2 + (5.00)2 = 3.00 + 10.00 = \$13.00.$$

Similar computations involving the second row in the first chart and the columns in the second chart give the monthly mileage as follows:

$$(6)3 + (12)2 = 18 + 24 = 42.$$
$$(6)2 + (12)2 = 12 + 24 = 36.$$

These results are summarized in the matrices shown below.

$$\begin{array}{c} \\ \text{Cost} \\ \text{Miles} \end{array} \begin{array}{c} \textit{Peggy} \quad \textit{Patricia} \\ \begin{pmatrix} 1.50 & 5.00 \\ 6 & 12 \end{pmatrix} \end{array} \times \begin{array}{c} \\ \text{Peggy} \\ \text{Patricia} \end{array} \begin{array}{c} \textit{Sept.} \quad \textit{Oct.} \\ \begin{pmatrix} 3 & 2 \\ 2 & 2 \end{pmatrix} \end{array} = \begin{array}{c} \\ \text{Cost} \\ \text{Miles} \end{array} \begin{array}{c} \textit{Sept.} \quad \textit{Oct.} \\ \begin{pmatrix} 14.50 & 13.00 \\ 42 & 36 \end{pmatrix} \end{array}.$$

The cost-mileage-girl matrix multiplied by the girl-month matrix gives John the figures to present to his father, the cost-mileage-month matrix. Note that the product of these 2 × 2 real matrices is again a 2 × 2 real matrix.

The preceding, somewhat frivolous, example should help you understand the following definition of the product of two 2 × 2 real matrices.

Definition **43/3** If

$$A = \begin{pmatrix} a_{11} & a_{12} \\ a_{21} & a_{22} \end{pmatrix} \text{ and } B = \begin{pmatrix} b_{11} & b_{12} \\ b_{21} & b_{22} \end{pmatrix}$$

are 2 × 2 real matrices, then the *product* of A and B, denoted by A • B, is as follows:

$$A \cdot B = \begin{pmatrix} a_{11} & a_{12} \\ a_{21} & a_{22} \end{pmatrix} \cdot \begin{pmatrix} b_{11} & b_{12} \\ b_{21} & b_{22} \end{pmatrix} = \begin{pmatrix} a_{11}b_{11} + a_{12}b_{21} & a_{11}b_{12} + a_{12}b_{22} \\ a_{21}b_{11} + a_{22}b_{21} & a_{21}b_{12} + a_{22}b_{22} \end{pmatrix}.$$

Notice that the *ij*th entry of A • B is $a_{i1}b_{1j} + a_{i2}b_{2j}$. That is, the *ij*th entry of A • B is the sum of the following two terms: the product of the first entry of A in the *i*th row and the first entry of B in the *j*th column and the product of the second entry of A in the *i*th row and the second entry of B in the *j*th column.

Some examples of the products of 2 × 2 real matrices are given below.

Examples 1

$$\begin{pmatrix} \sqrt{2} & 4 \\ -3 & \frac{3}{2} \end{pmatrix} \cdot \begin{pmatrix} \frac{8}{5} & -3 \\ 0 & -2 \end{pmatrix} = \begin{pmatrix} \frac{8\sqrt{2}}{5} + 4 \cdot 0 & -3\sqrt{2} + 4(-2) \\ -\frac{24}{5} + \frac{3}{2} \cdot 0 & -3(-3) + \frac{3}{2}(-2) \end{pmatrix}$$

$$= \begin{pmatrix} \frac{8\sqrt{2}}{5} & -3\sqrt{2} - 8 \\ -\frac{24}{5} & 6 \end{pmatrix}.$$

2

$$\begin{pmatrix} 3 & -1 \\ 0 & \frac{2}{5} \end{pmatrix} \cdot \begin{pmatrix} 6 & -3 \\ 4 & 0 \end{pmatrix} = \begin{pmatrix} 3 \cdot 6 + (-1) \cdot 4 & 3(-3) + (-1) \cdot 0 \\ 0 \cdot 6 + \frac{2}{5} \cdot 4 & 0(-3) + \frac{2}{5} \cdot 0 \end{pmatrix}$$

$$= \begin{pmatrix} 14 & -9 \\ \frac{8}{5} & 0 \end{pmatrix}.$$

Our primary purpose in defining the operations of addition and multiplication of 2 × 2 real matrices is to show that $(M_{2 \times 2}, +, \cdot)$ is a ring. To simplify the computation in the remainder of this section, we will limit the set of matrices to a subset of $M_{2 \times 2}$. The subset we will consider is the set of matrices that have even integers as entries. Later we will give another reason, aside from simplifying the computation, for making such a restriction. A definition of the subset of $M_{2 \times 2}$ with which we will be working follows.

Definition 44/3 If A is a 2 × 2 real matrix, then A is a 2 × 2 *even matrix* if and only if each entry of A is an even integer. We denote the set of 2 × 2 even matrices by $E_{2 \times 2}$. Symbolically, if $A \in M_{2 \times 2}$, then $A \in E_{2 \times 2}$ if and only if each entry a_{ij} in A implies that $a_{ij} \in E_I$ for each $i = 1, 2$ and each $j = 1, 2$.

We have defined the binary operations of addition and multiplication on the set of all 2 × 2 real matrices (Definitions 42/3 and 43/3). Since each 2 × 2 even matrix is also a 2 × 2 real matrix, we know that these definitions apply to $E_{2 \times 2}$. Consequently, we have two binary operations from $E_{2 \times 2}$, addition and multiplication. We will now verify that the system $(E_{2 \times 2}, +, \cdot)$ is a ring by showing that this system satisfies the eight properties given in the chart on page 172.

Theorem 44/3 The mathematical system $(E_{2 \times 2}, +, \cdot)$ is a ring.

Proof To show that the sum of two even matrices is an even matrix, it is necessary and sufficient to show that each entry in the sum of two even matrices is an even integer. This is an immediate consequence of the fact that the sum of two even integers is an even integer. The details follow. Let A, B ϵ $E_{2 \times 2}$. That is, let

$$A = \begin{pmatrix} 2a_{11} & 2a_{12} \\ 2a_{21} & 2a_{22} \end{pmatrix} \text{ and } B = \begin{pmatrix} 2b_{11} & 2b_{12} \\ 2b_{21} & 2b_{22} \end{pmatrix},$$

with a_{ij}, b_{ij} ϵ I. Why is it possible to use $2a_{ij}$ to denote any entry of A?

Applying the definition of the binary operation of addition of matrices and the distributive property for integers [assuming here that (I, +, •) is a ring], we have

$$A + B = \begin{pmatrix} 2a_{11} + 2b_{11} & 2a_{12} + 2b_{12} \\ 2a_{21} + 2b_{21} & 2a_{22} + 2b_{22} \end{pmatrix} = \begin{pmatrix} 2(a_{11} + b_{11}) & 2(a_{12} + b_{12}) \\ 2(a_{21} + b_{21}) & 2(a_{22} + b_{22}) \end{pmatrix}.$$

Since a_{ij} and b_{ij} are integers, $a_{ij} + b_{ij}$ is also an integer. Why? Therefore, $2(a_{ij} + b_{ij})$ is an even integer. It follows that the sum of two even matrices is an even matrix. This verifies the *closure property of addition* for 2 × 2 even matrices.

We can use properties of E_I to show that the *associative property of addition* is valid for 2 × 2 even matrices, that is, to show that if A, B, C ϵ $E_{2 \times 2}$, then (A + B) + C = A + (B + C). The proof of this property, which is based upon the analogous property of addition of even integers, is given as an exercise at the end of the section.

The *additive identity* of this mathematical system is the even matrix

$$\theta = \begin{pmatrix} 2 \cdot 0 & 2 \cdot 0 \\ 2 \cdot 0 & 2 \cdot 0 \end{pmatrix} = \begin{pmatrix} 0 & 0 \\ 0 & 0 \end{pmatrix}.$$

To show that the matrix with each entry 0 is an additive identity of $E_{2 \times 2}$, it is necessary and sufficient to show that, for each A ϵ $E_{2 \times 2}$,

$$\theta + A = A + \theta = A.$$

But

$$\theta + A = \begin{pmatrix} 0 & 0 \\ 0 & 0 \end{pmatrix} + \begin{pmatrix} a_{11} & a_{12} \\ a_{21} & a_{22} \end{pmatrix} = \begin{pmatrix} 0 + a_{11} & 0 + a_{12} \\ 0 + a_{21} & 0 + a_{22} \end{pmatrix} = \begin{pmatrix} a_{11} & a_{12} \\ a_{21} & a_{22} \end{pmatrix} = A,$$

and

$$A + \theta = \begin{pmatrix} a_{11} & a_{12} \\ a_{21} & a_{22} \end{pmatrix} + \begin{pmatrix} 0 & 0 \\ 0 & 0 \end{pmatrix} = \begin{pmatrix} a_{11} + 0 & a_{12} + 0 \\ a_{21} + 0 & a_{22} + 0 \end{pmatrix} = \begin{pmatrix} a_{11} & a_{12} \\ a_{21} & a_{22} \end{pmatrix} = A.$$

This verifies that the 2×2 matrix with each entry 0 is an additive identity.

Now that it has been established that the mathematical system $(E_{2 \times 2}, +, \cdot)$ has an additive identity, it can be shown that each element A of $E_{2 \times 2}$ has an *additive inverse.* Let

$$A = \begin{pmatrix} a_{11} & a_{12} \\ a_{21} & a_{22} \end{pmatrix}.$$

Also let $-A$ denote the matrix

$$\begin{pmatrix} -a_{11} & -a_{12} \\ -a_{21} & -a_{22} \end{pmatrix},$$

with $-a_{ij}$ the additive inverse of a_{ij} in the set of even integers. How do you know that $-A \in E_{2 \times 2}$? The following computation shows that $-A$ is the additive inverse of A.

$$-A + A = \begin{pmatrix} -a_{11} & -a_{12} \\ -a_{21} & -a_{22} \end{pmatrix} + \begin{pmatrix} a_{11} & a_{12} \\ a_{21} & a_{22} \end{pmatrix} =$$

$$\begin{pmatrix} -a_{11} + a_{11} & -a_{12} + a_{12} \\ -a_{21} + a_{21} & -a_{22} + a_{22} \end{pmatrix} = \begin{pmatrix} 0 & 0 \\ 0 & 0 \end{pmatrix} = \theta.$$

$$A + (-A) = \begin{pmatrix} a_{11} & a_{12} \\ a_{21} & a_{22} \end{pmatrix} + \begin{pmatrix} -a_{11} & -a_{12} \\ -a_{21} & -a_{22} \end{pmatrix} =$$

$$\begin{pmatrix} a_{11} + (-a_{11}) & a_{12} + (-a_{12}) \\ a_{21} + (-a_{21}) & a_{22} + (-a_{22}) \end{pmatrix} = \begin{pmatrix} 0 & 0 \\ 0 & 0 \end{pmatrix} = \theta.$$

It is easy to show that the *commutative property of addition* is also satisfied in $E_{2 \times 2}$. The proof is left as an exercise at the end of this section.

As you know, the five properties mentioned above for addition of even matrices are the distinguishing properties of a commutative group. Hence, the arguments given thus far show that the set of 2×2 even matrices under the operation of addition is a *commutative group.*

It follows from the definition of matrix multiplication and various properties of the even integers that $E_{2 \times 2}$ is closed under multiplication. To see this, we let A and B be even matrices. Then the entry in the *ij*th position of $A \cdot B$ is $(a_{i1}b_{1j} + a_{i2}b_{2j}) = c_{ij}$. In exercise 8 at the end of this section, you are asked to verify the fact that c_{ij} is an even integer.

The *associative property of multiplication* and the *distributive properties,* properties 7 and 8 of a ring, are also satisfied in the system ($E_{2 \times 2}$, +, •). You are asked to verify these properties in exercises 9 and 10 on page 180. These exercises will complete the proof of the theorem. (In this proof, we have sometimes used $2a_{ij}$, with $a \in I$, and sometimes a_{ij}, with $a \in E_I$, to represent entries in a matrix A of $E_{2 \times 2}$. These notations are equivalent.)

In proving Theorem 44/3, we have constructed a proof that is very much like the proof that ($M_{2 \times 2}$, +, •) is a ring. In fact, every argument we used to establish a property for elements of $E_{2 \times 2}$ could also be used for $M_{2 \times 2}$, with the proper substitutions of real numbers for even integers. Hence, we can assume, without giving all details of the proof, that ($M_{2 \times 2}$, +, •) is a ring.

In the next section, we will consider properties of certain rings besides the eight defining properties. The system ($M_{2 \times 2}$, +, •) has at least one of these additional properties—the identity property of multiplication, but ($E_{2 \times 2}$, +, •) does not. This is why we chose to consider only the set of 2 × 2 even matrices in developing an example of a ring with just the eight basic properties.

Exercises

1 Consider the ring (E_I, +, •). Prove or disprove that the operation • is onto E_I.

2 Show that the relation "equals" on the set of 2 × 2 real matrices is an equivalence relation.

3 For each of the following pairs of matrices, find, if possible, replacements for x, y, and z such that A = B.

a $A = \begin{pmatrix} 1 & 2 \\ -1 & 0 \end{pmatrix}$. $B = \begin{pmatrix} 1 & x \\ y & -5 \end{pmatrix}$. *Answer*

b $A = \begin{pmatrix} 1 & 2 \\ -1 & z \end{pmatrix}$. $B = \begin{pmatrix} 1 & x \\ y & -5 \end{pmatrix}$.

c $A = \begin{pmatrix} x+2 & 2-y \\ z+4 & 1-x \end{pmatrix}$. $B = \begin{pmatrix} -3 & 0 \\ 3z & 6 \end{pmatrix}$.

d $A = \begin{pmatrix} 2x-1 & z \\ y+5 & 1-x \end{pmatrix}$. $B = \begin{pmatrix} -3 & 0 \\ 5 & 3 \end{pmatrix}$.

4 For each pair of matrices in exercise 3, find the 2 × 2 real matrices A • B and B • A. *Answer*

5 For each pair of matrices in exercise 3, find, if possible, replacements for x, y, and z so that

$$A \cdot B = \begin{pmatrix} 1 & 0 \\ 0 & 1 \end{pmatrix}.$$ *Answer*

6 Verify the associative property for addition of even 2×2 matrices. That is, let

$$A = \begin{pmatrix} a_{11} & a_{12} \\ a_{21} & a_{22} \end{pmatrix}, B = \begin{pmatrix} b_{11} & -b_{12} \\ b_{21} & b_{22} \end{pmatrix}, \text{ and } C = \begin{pmatrix} c_{11} & c_{12} \\ c_{21} & c_{22} \end{pmatrix}$$

be elements of $E_{2 \times 2}$, and show that $(A + B) + C = A + (B + C)$.

7 Verify the commutative property for addition of 2×2 even matrices. *Answer*

8 Complete the verification, begun on page 178, of the closure property for multiplication of 2×2 even matrices.

9 Verify the associative property for multiplication of 2×2 even matrices.

10 Verify the distributive property for 2×2 even matrices.

◆ 11 Give an example to show that multiplication of 2×2 even matrices is not commutative.

12 Determine which of the following mathematical systems are rings.

a $(\{6x \mid x \in I\}, +, \cdot)$

b $(I, +, -)$ *Answer*

c $(I^+, +, \div)$

d $(O_I, +, \cdot)$

e $(\{2x \mid x \in I\}, +, -)$

f $(G(i), +, \cdot)$

g $(\{a + b\sqrt{2} \mid a, b \in I\}, +, \cdot)$

h $(\{a + b\sqrt{2} \mid a, b \in R\}, +, \cdot)$

i $(I/4, \oplus_4, \odot_4)$ *Answer*

j $(I/3, \oplus_3, \odot_3)$

k $(\{0, 1, -1\}, +, \cdot)$

l $(\{x \mid x \in R \text{ and } x \geqq 0\}, +, \cdot)$

m $(\{i, -1, -i, 1\}, +, \cdot)$

n $(\{nx \mid n \in C \text{ and } x \in I\}, +, \cdot)$

o $(\{a + b\sqrt[3]{2} \mid a, b \in R\}, +, \cdot)$ *Answer*

p $(\{a + b\sqrt[3]{2} + c\sqrt[3]{4} \mid a, b, c \in R\}, +, \cdot)$ *Answer*

q $(\{a + bi \mid a, b \in \Re \text{ and } i^2 = -1\}, +, \cdot)$

13 Let $I_{2 \times 2}$ be the set of all 2×2 matrices with entries in I. Assuming that $(M_{2 \times 2}, +, \cdot)$ is a ring, prove that $(I_{2 \times 2}, +, \cdot)$ is a ring. *Answer*

◆ 14 Assume that $(I/6, \oplus_6, \odot_6)$ is a ring. Let $I/6_{2 \times 2}$ be the set of all 2×2 matrices with entries in $I/6$. Prove that $I/6_{2 \times 2}$ under matrix addition and matrix multiplication forms a ring.

15 Is $(\{\bar{0}, \bar{2}, \bar{4}\}, \oplus_6, \odot_6)$ a ring?

16 Consider the subset S of $I/6_{2 \times 2}$ with entries chosen from $\{\bar{0}, \bar{2}, \bar{4}\}$. Is $(S, +, \cdot)$ a ring?

17 Consider the set $I/6_{2\times 2}$ of 2×2 matrices with integers modulo 6 as entries; that is, the set of all matrices of the form

$$\begin{pmatrix} \bar{a} & \bar{c} \\ \bar{b} & \bar{d} \end{pmatrix}$$

where $\bar{a}, \bar{b}, \bar{c}, \bar{d} \in I/6$. Let T be the subset of $I/6_{2\times 2}$ such that $\bar{a} \odot_6 \bar{b} \odot_6 \bar{c} \odot_6 \bar{d} \neq \bar{0}$. Show that $(T, \oplus_6, \odot_6)$ is a ring.

◆ 18 Let S be any set. Let $\mathbb{S}$ be the collection of all subsets of S. For A, B $\in \mathbb{S}$, define

$$A + B = \{x \mid x \in A \cup B \text{ and } x \notin A \cap B\} \text{ and}$$
$$A \cdot B = \{x \mid x \in A \cap B\}.$$

Prove that $(\mathbb{S}, +, \cdot)$ is a ring.

◆ 19 Let $\mathcal{I}$ be the set of all functions whose domain is the set of integers and whose range is in the set of integers. For f, g $\in \mathcal{I}$ define $(x)(f + g) = (x)f + (x)g$ and $(x)(f \cdot g) = (x)f \cdot (x)g$. Is $(\mathcal{I}, +, \cdot)$ a ring? *Answer*

◆ 20 Let $\mathcal{I}$ be as described in exercise 19. For f, g, $\in \mathcal{I}$, define $(x)(f + g) = (x)f + (x)g$ and $(x)(f \circ g) = ((x)f)g$, the composition of f and g. Is $(\mathcal{I}, +, \circ)$ a ring?

Commutative rings with identity

26/3

This section is concerned with rings that satisfy either the identity property or the commutative property of multiplication or both of these properties, along with the eight basic ring properties. Each of these kinds of rings is a new type of mathematical system, and each has a special name to distinguish it. First, we define a ring with identity.

Definition 45/3 If $(S, +, \cdot)$ is a ring then S is a *ring with identity* if and only if there exists an element e in S such that, for each $a \in S$,

Identity for $\cdot$ 9 $e \cdot a = a \cdot e = a.$

Even though a ring has two operations, observe that a ring that satisfies the identity property of multiplication is called simply a ring with identity rather than a ring with a multiplicative identity. Since all rings satisfy the additive-identity property, it is obvious that "ring with identity" must mean a ring that satisfies the multiplicative-identity property.

Notice that we have labeled the identity property of multiplication with the numeral 9. We do this for convenience in referring to the identity property and to indicate that, along with the eight properties of a ring expressed in the chart on page 172, a ring with identity satisfies nine properties in all.

We now define a commutative ring. Note that we have labeled the commutative property of multiplication as the tenth ring property. Also keep in mind that the word *commutative* in *commutative ring* refers to a property of multiplication since addition is already assumed to be commutative in a ring.

Definition **46/3** If (S, +, •) is a ring, then S is a *commutative ring* if and only if, for each $a, b \in S$,

Commutativity for • **10** $a \cdot b = b \cdot a.$

If both properties 9 and 10 are satisfied by a ring (S, +, •), then (S, +, •) is a *commutative ring with identity.*

The ten properties of a commutative ring with identity are summarized in the following chart.

Properties of a commutative ring (S, +, •) with identity

Closure for +	1	For each $a, b \in S$, $a + b \in S$.
Associativity for +	2	For each $a, b, c \in S$, $(a + b) + c = a + (b + c)$.
Identity for +	3	There exists an additive identity in S, denoted by 0, such that, for each $a \in S$, $0 + a = a + 0 = a$.
Inverse for +	4	For each $a \in S$, there exists an inverse in S, denoted by $-a$, such that $-a + a = a + (-a) = 0$.
Commutativity for +	5	For each $a, b \in S$, $a + b = b + a$.
Closure for •	6	For each $a, b \in S$, $ab \in S$.
Associativity for •	7	For each $a, b, c \in S$, $(ab)c = a(bc)$.
Distributive property	8	For each $a, b, c \in S$, 1) $a(b + c) = ab + ac$ and 2) $(a + b)c = ac + bc$.
Identity for •	9	There exists a multiplicative identity in S, denoted by e, such that, for each $a \in S$, $e \cdot a = a \cdot e = a$.
Commutativity for •	10	For each $a, b \in S$, $ab = ba$.

Examples 1 There are examples of rings that satisfy one but not both of properties 9 and 10. One such example is the set of even integers under addition and multiplication. The mathematical system $(\{2x \mid x \in I\}, +, \cdot)$ does not have a multiplicative identity because there does not exist an element e in the set of even integers such that for each $a \in E_I$, $e \cdot a = a \cdot e = a$. Observe, however, that the ring $(\{2x \mid x \in I\}, +, \cdot)$ is a commutative ring because, for each $a, b \in E_I$, $a \cdot b = b \cdot a$. Hence, $(\{2x \mid x \in I\}, +, \cdot)$ is a commutative ring that does not have a multiplicative identity.

2 The system $(M_{2 \times 2}, +, \cdot)$ is an example of a ring that has a multiplicative identity, but that is not commutative. In the previous section we stated that $(M_{2 \times 2}, +, \cdot)$ is a ring and that the eight properties established for $(E_{2 \times 2}, +, \cdot)$ could easily be verified for $(M_{2 \times 2}, +, \cdot)$. Now we claim the multiplicative identity for $(M_{2 \times 2}, +, \cdot)$ is

$$e = \begin{pmatrix} 1 & 0 \\ 0 & 1 \end{pmatrix}.$$

The computation below shows that the matrix e is an identity for multiplication. If $A \in M_{2 \times 2}$, then

$$e \cdot A = \begin{pmatrix} 1 & 0 \\ 0 & 1 \end{pmatrix} \cdot \begin{pmatrix} a_{11} & a_{12} \\ a_{21} & a_{22} \end{pmatrix} = \begin{pmatrix} 1 \cdot a_{11} + 0 \cdot a_{21} & 1 \cdot a_{12} + 0 \cdot a_{22} \\ 0 \cdot a_{11} + 1 \cdot a_{21} & 0 \cdot a_{12} + 1 \cdot a_{22} \end{pmatrix}$$

$$= \begin{pmatrix} a_{11} & a_{12} \\ a_{21} & a_{22} \end{pmatrix} = A;$$

$$A \cdot e = \begin{pmatrix} a_{11} & a_{12} \\ a_{21} & a_{22} \end{pmatrix} \cdot \begin{pmatrix} 1 & 0 \\ 0 & 1 \end{pmatrix} = \begin{pmatrix} a_{11} \cdot 1 + a_{12} \cdot 0 & a_{11} \cdot 0 + a_{12} \cdot 1 \\ a_{21} \cdot 1 + a_{22} \cdot 0 & a_{21} \cdot 0 + a_{22} \cdot 1 \end{pmatrix}$$

$$= \begin{pmatrix} a_{11} & a_{12} \\ a_{21} & a_{22} \end{pmatrix} = A.$$

We will now show that the ring $(M_{2 \times 2}, +, \cdot)$ does not have the commutative property of multiplication. Remember that, in order to show that a mathematical system is *not* commutative, it is sufficient to find two elements in the system whose product is not the same when the order of the factors is changed. Two such elements and the resulting products are given below.

$$\begin{pmatrix} 2 & 2 \\ 0 & 0 \end{pmatrix} \cdot \begin{pmatrix} 0 & 2 \\ 0 & 2 \end{pmatrix} = \begin{pmatrix} 0 & 8 \\ 0 & 0 \end{pmatrix}.$$

$$\begin{pmatrix} 0 & 2 \\ 0 & 2 \end{pmatrix} \cdot \begin{pmatrix} 2 & 2 \\ 0 & 0 \end{pmatrix} = \begin{pmatrix} 0 & 0 \\ 0 & 0 \end{pmatrix}.$$

Since these two products are not equal, the operation of multiplication in $M_{2 \times 2}$ is not commutative.

Example 1 shows that a ring may have property 10 without having property 9 and, hence, may be a commutative ring without identity. Example 2 shows that a ring may have property 9 without having property 10 and, hence, may be a noncommutative ring with identity. The following example shows that a ring need not satisfy either property 9 or 10.

Examples 3 In example 2, we also showed that multiplication of 2×2 even matrices is not commutative because the two matrices chosen are elements of $E_{2 \times 2}$. Hence, we know that $(E_{2 \times 2}, +, \cdot)$ is not a commutative ring. We will use an indirect proof to show that the ring $(E_{2 \times 2}, +, \cdot)$ does not have a multiplicative identity. Assume that the set of all 2×2 even matrices does possess an identity and denote it by

$$e = \begin{pmatrix} a & b \\ c & d \end{pmatrix}.$$

If the matrix e is in fact a multiplicative identity of the system $(E_{2 \times 2}, +, \cdot)$, then the product of e and A is A for each $A \in E_{2 \times 2}$. In particular, let A be the matrix

$$\begin{pmatrix} 2 & 0 \\ 0 & 0 \end{pmatrix}.$$

Then it must follow that

$$\begin{pmatrix} a & b \\ c & d \end{pmatrix} \cdot \begin{pmatrix} 2 & 0 \\ 0 & 0 \end{pmatrix} = \begin{pmatrix} 2a & 0 \\ 2c & 0 \end{pmatrix} = \begin{pmatrix} 2 & 0 \\ 0 & 0 \end{pmatrix}.$$

But, because two matrices are equal if and only if their entries are equal, we have $2a = 2$ and $2c = 0$. It follows that $a = 1$ and $c = 0$ and, thus,

$$e = \begin{pmatrix} 1 & b \\ 0 & d \end{pmatrix}.$$

Even without determining possible replacements for b and d, we know that this matrix does not belong to the ring $(E_{2 \times 2}, +, \cdot)$. Why? The assumption that

$$e = \begin{pmatrix} a & b \\ c & d \end{pmatrix}$$

is the multiplicative identity of $(E_{2 \times 2}, +, \cdot)$ has led us to a contradiction. Consequently, we conclude that the system $(E_{2 \times 2}, +, \cdot)$ has no multiplicative identity.

Such systems as (I, +, ·) and ($\mathfrak{R}$, +, ·) are examples of commutative rings with identity. In each of these systems, the set of elements is infinite; however, there are commutative rings with identity that have a finite number of elements. A commutative ring with identity that has a finite number of elements is the set of integers modulo n. We will now show that this is so.

4 In Chapter 2, we saw that (I/n, $\oplus_n$) is a commutative group. Therefore, (I/n, $\oplus_n$, $\odot_n$) satisfies properties 1 through 5 of a commutative ring with identity. For (I/n, $\odot_n$), the closure property was established in Theorem 14/2; the associative property was verified in exercise 4 of section 13/2; and the identity property was established in Theorem 20/2. Thus, we know that (I/n, $\oplus_n$, $\odot_n$) satisfies properties 6, 7, and 9 of a commutative ring with identity. The other properties of a commutative ring with identity are the distributive properties and commutativity for $\odot_n$. These two properties, properties 8 and 10, can be established by computation. Their verification is left as an exercise at the end of this section.

Assuming, as we shall, that the operation of multiplication on the set of integers modulo n does satisfy properties 8 and 10, we can exhibit tables of sums and products for a commutative ring with identity having *any* finite number of elements. Display 55 shows addition and multiplication tables for I/4 and I/5.

$\oplus_4$	$\bar{0}$	$\bar{1}$	$\bar{2}$	$\bar{3}$
$\bar{0}$	$\bar{0}$	$\bar{1}$	$\bar{2}$	$\bar{3}$
$\bar{1}$	$\bar{1}$	$\bar{2}$	$\bar{3}$	$\bar{0}$
$\bar{2}$	$\bar{2}$	$\bar{3}$	$\bar{0}$	$\bar{1}$
$\bar{3}$	$\bar{3}$	$\bar{0}$	$\bar{1}$	$\bar{2}$

Display 55a

$\odot_4$	$\bar{0}$	$\bar{1}$	$\bar{2}$	$\bar{3}$
$\bar{0}$	$\bar{0}$	$\bar{0}$	$\bar{0}$	$\bar{0}$
$\bar{1}$	$\bar{0}$	$\bar{1}$	$\bar{2}$	$\bar{3}$
$\bar{2}$	$\bar{0}$	$\bar{2}$	$\bar{0}$	$\bar{2}$
$\bar{3}$	$\bar{0}$	$\bar{3}$	$\bar{2}$	$\bar{1}$

55b

$\oplus_5$	$\bar{0}$	$\bar{1}$	$\bar{2}$	$\bar{3}$	$\bar{4}$
$\bar{0}$	$\bar{0}$	$\bar{1}$	$\bar{2}$	$\bar{3}$	$\bar{4}$
$\bar{1}$	$\bar{1}$	$\bar{2}$	$\bar{3}$	$\bar{4}$	$\bar{0}$
$\bar{2}$	$\bar{2}$	$\bar{3}$	$\bar{4}$	$\bar{0}$	$\bar{1}$
$\bar{3}$	$\bar{3}$	$\bar{4}$	$\bar{0}$	$\bar{1}$	$\bar{2}$
$\bar{4}$	$\bar{4}$	$\bar{0}$	$\bar{1}$	$\bar{2}$	$\bar{3}$

55c

$\odot_5$	$\bar{0}$	$\bar{1}$	$\bar{2}$	$\bar{3}$	$\bar{4}$
$\bar{0}$	$\bar{0}$	$\bar{0}$	$\bar{0}$	$\bar{0}$	$\bar{0}$
$\bar{1}$	$\bar{0}$	$\bar{1}$	$\bar{2}$	$\bar{3}$	$\bar{4}$
$\bar{2}$	$\bar{0}$	$\bar{2}$	$\bar{4}$	$\bar{1}$	$\bar{3}$
$\bar{3}$	$\bar{0}$	$\bar{3}$	$\bar{1}$	$\bar{4}$	$\bar{2}$
$\bar{4}$	$\bar{0}$	$\bar{4}$	$\bar{3}$	$\bar{2}$	$\bar{1}$

55d

In this section we have studied examples of rings with identity, commutative rings, commutative rings with identity, and rings that satisfy neither the commutative nor the identity property for multiplication. Observe that if (T, +, •) is a ring which does not satisfy the commutative property, then there cannot exist a "larger" ring, say (S, +, •), such that $T \subset S$ and (S, +, •) satisfies the commutative property. To see why this is true, we note that, if (T, +, •) is not commutative, there exist elements $a, b \in T$ such that $a \cdot b \neq b \cdot a$. If $T \subset S$, then $a, b \in S$. Since $a \cdot b \neq b \cdot a$, it follows that (S, +, •) is not commutative. Therefore, a noncommutative ring cannot be included or "embedded" in a commutative ring. We cannot be so definite about the converse of this statement, however. That is, if the ring T satisfies the commutative property, then the ring S, where $T \subset S$, may or may not satisfy the commutative property. To see why this is so, let us consider some examples.

First, the ring of even integers is a commutative ring whose elements are a subset of the elements of (I, +, •), also a commutative ring. Other examples of commutative rings contained in commutative rings are the ring of integers in the ring of rational numbers, the ring of integers in the ring of real numbers, and the ring of rational numbers in the ring of real numbers. There are many such examples. To exhibit an example of a commutative ring (T, +, •) contained in a noncommutative ring (S, +, •) is more difficult. Such an example is given in exercise 14 on page 188.

In the previous paragraph, we have seen that if a ring is not commutative, then its containing ring is not commutative. But if a ring is commutative, its containing ring may be either commutative or noncommutative. The situation is different with respect to the existence of a multiplicative identity. There are rings without identity contained in rings with identity. For example, the ring of even integers (E_I, +, •), which does not have an identity, is contained in the ring of integers (I, +, •), which does have an identity. Furthermore, ($\{4x \mid x \in I\}$, +, •) has no identity and is contained in (E_I, +, •), which also has no identity. Hence, we see that rings without identity are contained in rings that may or may not satisfy the identity property.

It is important to note that it is always possible to embed a ring without identity in a ring with identity. This is done by means of an *isomorphism* between the set of elements of the ring without identity and a subset of the set of elements in the ring with identity. You will see how to do this for one example in exercises 5 through 10 at the end of the section. A definition of isomorphism for rings is given next.

Definition 47/3 If $(T, +, \cdot)$ and $(S, \oplus, \odot)$ are rings, then $(T, +, \cdot)$ and $(S, \oplus, \odot)$ are *isomorphic* if and only if there exists a one-to-one function f from set T onto set S such that, for each $a, b \in T$,

1) $(a + b)f = (a)f \oplus (b)f$ and
2) $(a \cdot b)f = (a)f \odot (b)f$.

Notice that this definition provides a natural extension of Definition 38/2 for isomorphic groups. That is, this definition insures that multiplication, as well as addition, will be preserved by an isomorphism between two rings.

Exercises

1 Determine which of the following rings satisfy the multiplicative-identity property. Also determine those that satisfy the commutative property of multiplication. *Answer*

a $(I/5_{2 \times 2}, +, \cdot)$
b $(G(i), +, \cdot)$
c $(I/4_{2 \times 2}, +, \cdot)$
d $(I/4, \oplus_4, \odot_4)$
e $(\{6x \mid x \in I\}, +, \cdot)$
f $(\{a + b\sqrt{3} \mid a, b \in I\}, +, \cdot)$
g $(\{a + b\sqrt[3]{2} + c\sqrt[3]{4} \mid a, b, c \in R\}, +, \cdot)$

2 For the following exercises in section 25/3, pages 180-181, determine which rings described in the exercises are commutative rings with identity.

a Exercise 13 *Answer*
b Exercise 14
c Exercise 16
d Exercise 17
e Exercise 18 *Answer*
f Exercise 19 *Answer*

◆ 3 Prove that, if $\bar{a}, \bar{b}, \bar{c} \in I/n$, then
$\bar{a} \odot_n (\bar{b} \oplus_n \bar{c}) = (\bar{a} \odot_n \bar{b}) \oplus_n (\bar{a} \odot_n \bar{c})$ and
$(\bar{a} \oplus_n \bar{b}) \odot_n \bar{c} = (\bar{a} \odot_n \bar{c}) \oplus_n (\bar{b} \odot_n \bar{c})$. *Answer*

4 Prove that, if $\bar{a}, \bar{b} \in I/n$, then $\bar{a} \odot_n \bar{b} = \bar{b} \odot_n \bar{a}$.

Consider the Cartesian product $E_I \times I$. We define addition and multiplication on the elements of $E_I \times I$ as follows:

$$(x, a) + (y, b) = (x + y, a + b),$$
$$(x, a) \cdot (y, b) = (xy + bx + ay, ab),$$

for each $(x, a), (y, b) \in E_I \times I$. Use this information in connection with exercises 5 through 11.

◆ 5 Show that $(E_I \times I, +, \cdot)$ is a ring.

◆ 6 Show that $(E_I \times I, +, \cdot)$ is a commutative ring with an identity element. *Answer*

◆ 7 Consider the subset $E_I \times \{0\}$ of $E_I \times I$. Show that the system $(E_I \times \{0\}, +, \cdot)$ is a ring.

◆ **8** Show that $(E_I \times \{0\}, +, \cdot)$ is a commutative ring. Does this ring have a multiplicative identity? *Answer*

◆ **9** Is $(E_I, +, \cdot)$ a commutative ring? Does this ring have a multiplicative identity?

◆ **10** Consider the mapping f from E_I into $E_I \times \{0\}$ given by $(x)f = (x, 0)$ for $x \in E_I$. Show that f is an isomorphism between the rings E_I and $E_I \times \{0\}$. *Answer*

By the procedure in exercises 5 through 10, we have shown that the ring $(E_I \times \{0\}, +, \cdot)$ is contained in the ring $(E_I \times I, +, \cdot)$ and that $(E_I, +, \cdot)$ is isomorphic to $(E_I \times \{0\}, +, \cdot)$. Hence, we say that we have *embedded* $(E_I, +, \cdot)$, which does not have an identity, in $(E_I \times I, +, \cdot)$, which does have an identity.

◆ **11** If we had defined multiplication as $(x, a) \cdot (y, b) = (xy, ab)$, what would be your answers to exercises 5 through 10?

12 Consider the group of integers under addition, $(I, +)$ and also those functions f from I into I such that, for each $x, y \in I$, $(x)f + (y)f = (x + y)f$. Which of the following functions satisfy this property?

a $(x)f = 0$. **c** $(x)f = x$. **e** $(x)f = 2x$.
b $(x)f = 1$. **d** $(x)f = -x$. **f** $(x)f = x + 1$.

13 Which of the functions in exercise 12 satisfy the property that for each $x, y \in I$, $(x)f \cdot (y)f = (x \cdot y)f$?

14 We have established that $(E_{2 \times 2}, +, \cdot)$ is a noncommutative ring. In this exercise we will consider a subset S of $E_{2 \times 2}$ defined by

$$S = \left\{ A \mid A \in E_{2 \times 2} \text{ and } A = \begin{pmatrix} a & 0 \\ 0 & 0 \end{pmatrix} \right\}.$$

Let the operations of $E_{2 \times 2}$ apply to elements of S.

a Show that $(S, +)$ is closed under addition.

b Why is $(S, +)$ associative? Commutative?

c For what replacement of a is $A = \begin{pmatrix} 0 & 0 \\ 0 & 0 \end{pmatrix}$?

d Does each element A have an additive inverse in S? What replacement must be made for a in each case?

e Show that S is closed under multiplication.

f Why is $(S, \cdot)$ associative?

g Verify that $(S, +, \cdot)$ satisfies the distributive properties.

h Is $(S, +, \cdot)$ a ring?

i We will now verify that $(S, +, \cdot)$ is commutative. Supply reasons for the following computations.

$$A \cdot B = \begin{pmatrix} a & 0 \\ 0 & 0 \end{pmatrix} \cdot \begin{pmatrix} b & 0 \\ 0 & 0 \end{pmatrix} = \begin{pmatrix} ab & 0 \\ 0 & 0 \end{pmatrix}.$$

$$B \cdot A = \begin{pmatrix} b & 0 \\ 0 & 0 \end{pmatrix} \cdot \begin{pmatrix} a & 0 \\ 0 & 0 \end{pmatrix} = \begin{pmatrix} ba & 0 \\ 0 & 0 \end{pmatrix}.$$

Thus, $A \cdot B = B \cdot A$.

These steps show that there does exist a commutative ring whose elements are contained in a ring that is not commutative.

Elementary properties of a ring

27/3

One of the important reasons for studying algebra from the standpoint of generalized or abstract systems is that theorems proved about such systems hold for any specific examples of the abstract system. In this section we will use the eight basic properties of a ring to prove some theorems. By proving these theorems for rings in general, we know, of course, that they will apply to all particular examples of rings.

Theorem 45/3 If $(S, +, \cdot)$ is a ring whose additive identity is denoted by 0, then, for each $a \in S$,

$$a \cdot 0 = 0 = 0 \cdot a.$$

Proof Because 0 is the additive identity, we have

$$\begin{aligned} a \cdot a &= a \cdot (a + 0) \\ &= (a \cdot a) + (a \cdot 0). \end{aligned}$$

This shows that $a \cdot 0$ must be an identity element for addition. But the additive identity of a group is unique. Therefore, it must be the case that $a \cdot 0 = 0$. You should supply the reasons for the above steps. It is left as an exercise to show that $0 \cdot a = 0$.

Theorem 45/3 shows that, if a mathematical system is a ring, then it necessarily follows that the product of the additive identity 0 and any ring element is 0. Thus, it is not necessary to prove a theorem to this effect for any particular example of a ring. As a particular example of a ring, consider the ring of real numbers. From Theorem 45/3, we know that the product of 0 and any real number is 0 without having to prove a theorem specifically for the ring of real numbers.

In the definition of a ring, we stated the distributive property that is satisfied by a ring. The two parts of this property can be generalized for a ring as follows. The proof is left as an exercise.

Theorem 46/3 If $(S, +, \cdot)$ is a ring and $a_1, a_2, b_1, b_2 \in S$, then

$$(a_1 + a_2) \cdot (b_1 + b_2) = (a_1b_1 + a_1b_2) + (a_2b_1 + a_2b_2).$$

As you know, the operations of a ring are usually called addition and multiplication and are so denoted. We can, however, use the inverse property of addition in defining an operation of *subtraction* for a ring. Since many of the computations that are normally performed on ring elements often involve the additive inverse of an element, we will find such an operation useful.

Definition 48/3 If $(S, +, \cdot)$ is a ring and $a, b \in S$, then the *difference* of a and b, denoted by $a - b$, is the sum of a and the additive inverse of b. Symbolically, for each $a, b \in S$, $a - b = a + (-b)$.

The next theorem expresses some relations between products that should appear familiar to you since you no doubt learned of them in connection with real numbers.

Theorem 47/3 If $(S, +, \cdot)$ is a ring and $a, b \in S$, then
1) $(-a)b = -(ab)$,
2) $a(-b) = -(ab)$,
3) $(-a)b = a(-b)$.

Proof The proof of each part of Theorem 47/3 is given below.

PART I

$0 = 0 \cdot b$	Theorem 45/3
$= \big(a + (-a)\big) \cdot b$	Additive-inverse property
$= ab + (-a)b.$	Distributive property
$(-a)b = -(ab).$	Uniqueness of additive inverse of ab

PART II

$0 = a \cdot 0$	Theorem 45/3
$= a \cdot \big(b + (-b)\big)$	Additive-inverse property
$= (ab) + a(-b).$	Distributive property
$a(-b) = -(ab).$	Uniqueness of additive inverse of ab

PART III

$(-a)b = -(ab).$	Part 1 of theorem
$-(ab) = a(-b).$	Part 2 of theorem and symmetric property of equality
$(-a)b = a(-b).$	Transitive property of equality

Recall that one property of the real-number system is that the product of two negative real numbers is a positive real number. Although not stated in precisely these terms, it is easily recognized that this property is generalized in Theorem 48/3.

Theorem 48/3 If $(S, +, \cdot)$ is a ring and x and y are elements of S whose additive inverses are $-x$ and $-y$, respectively, then $(-x)(-y) = xy$.

Proof $(-x)(-y) = -\big(x(-y)\big)$ Part 1 of Theorem 47/3 with a replaced by x and b replaced by $-y$

$= -\big(-(xy)\big)$ Part 2 of Theorem 47/3 with a replaced by x and b replaced by y

$= xy.$ Exercise 12 of section 16/2

There are several other elementary properties concerning additive inverses and subtraction that can be proved much as Theorems 47/3 and 48/3 have been proved. Some of these are given in the exercises at the end of the section.

In section 21 of Chapter 2 we defined a multiplication of group elements by integers as follows: If a is an element of the group $(G, \star)$ with identity e and n is a nonnegative integer, then the product of n and a is as follows: (1) $n \cdot a = e$, for $n = 0$; (2) $n \cdot a = a$, for $n = 1$; and (3) $(n + 1) \cdot a = (n \cdot a) \star a$, for $n \geqq 1$. We now extend this definition to the multiplication of ring elements by integers.

Definition 49/3 If $(S, +, \cdot)$ is a ring with additive identity 0, $a \in S$, and n is a nonnegative integer, then the product of n and a is as follows:
1) $n \cdot a = 0$, for $n = 0$; that is, $0 \cdot a = 0$.
2) $n \cdot a = a$, for $n = 1$; that is, $1 \cdot a = a$.
3) $(n + 1) \cdot a = (n \cdot a) + a$, for $n \geqq 1$.

Note that the multiplication of ring elements by integers is denoted by the symbol that also represents the operation of multiplication in $(S, +, \cdot)$. The ring elements 0, a, and $(n \cdot a) + a$ are called the *products* of 0 and a, 1 and a, and $n + 1$ and a, respectively.

Exercises

1 Prove that if $(S, +, \cdot)$ is a ring, $a \in S$, and 0 is the group identity, then $0 \cdot a = 0$.
2 Give a proof of Theorem 46/3.
3 Which of the theorems proved in this section require that the given ring be commutative?
4 Which of the theorems of this section require that the ring be a ring with identity?

5 Prove that if $(S, +, \cdot)$ is a ring and $a, b, c \in S$, then $a(b - c) = ab - ac$. *Answer*

6 Prove that if $(S, +, \cdot)$ is a ring and $a, b \in S$, then $-(a + b) = -a - b$.

7 Prove that if $(S, +, \cdot)$ is a ring and $a, b, c \in S$, then $(a - b) + (b - c) = a - c$.

8 Prove that if $(S, +, \cdot)$ is a ring and $a, b \in S$, then $-(a - b) = -a + b$.

9 Prove that if $(S, +, \cdot)$ is a ring and $a, b, c \in S$, then $(a - b) - c = a - (b + c)$ and $a - (b - c) = (a - b) + c$.

◆ 10 Prove that if $(S, +, \cdot)$ is a ring and $a \cdot a = a$ for each $a \in S$, then $a + a = 0$ for each $a \in S$. *Answer*

◆ 11 Prove that if $(S, +, \cdot)$ is a ring and $a \cdot a = a$ for each $a \in S$, then $(S, +, \cdot)$ is a commutative ring. [Hint: Consider $(a + b) \cdot (a + b)$.]

◆ 12 Let $(S, +, \cdot)$ be a ring with identity containing more than one element. Prove that the additive identity 0 and the multiplicative identity 1 are not the same element. *Answer*

◆ 13 Let $(S, +, \cdot)$ be a system that has been shown to satisfy all properties of a ring except commutativity of addition. Further, let S contain an element x such that for each $a, b \in S$, $xa = xb$ implies that $a = b$. Prove that $(S, +, \cdot)$ is a ring. That is, if $xa = xb$ implies that $a = b$, show that the commutative property of addition must hold. [Hint: Show that $x\big(a + b + (-a) + (-b)\big) = 0$.]

14 How should the product of the integer -1 and a be defined in order to be consistent with Definition 49/3?

Subrings 28/3

Just as the study of subgroups gave us more information about groups, the analysis of various subsystems of a ring should be helpful in learning more about the structure of a ring. In this section we will discuss the subsystems of a ring that are called subrings.

Recall that, if $(G, \star)$ is a group and S is a subset of G, then the system $(S, \star)$ is a subgroup of $(G, \star)$ if and only if $(S, \star)$ is a group. The definition for a subring of a ring is patterned after the definition of a subgroup.

Definition 50/3 If (S, +, •) is a ring and T is a nonempty subset of S, then the system (T, +, •) is a *subring* of (S, +, •) if and only if (T, +, •) is a ring. If (T, +, •) is a subring of (S, +, •), then (S, +, •) is the *containing ring*.

On occasion, we have proved a theorem that gives conditions equivalent to those given earlier in a definition. We proved such a theorem, for example, about the subgroups of a group. First we defined a subgroup in somewhat the same way that we have just defined a subring, and then we proved a theorem (Theorem 28/2) establishing conditions necessary and sufficient to verify that a subset of a group is a subgroup. Specifically, if (G, ☆) is a group and S is a subset of G, then (S, ☆) is a subgroup of (G, ☆) if and only if the closure and inverse properties are satisfied in (S, ☆). We will now prove a similar theorem for a subring of a ring.

Theorem 49/3 If (S, +, •) is a ring and T is a nonempty subset of S, then (T, +, •) is a subring of (S, +, •) if and only if, for each $a, b \in$ T,
1) the difference $a - b \in$ T, and
2) the product $ab \in$ T.

We can, of course, show that if T ⊂ S, then (T, +, •) is a subring of (S, +, •) by verifying the eight properties of a ring for (T, +, •). That is just what we must do to prove this theorem. However, once we have established Theorem 49/3, to determine if a subset T is a subring of S we need only verify two properties for T: *closure under subtraction* and *closure under multiplication*.

Proof To establish the theorem, we must show that, if a system (T, +, •) is a subring, then conditions 1 and 2 of the theorem are satisfied; and conversely, if conditions 1 and 2 of the theorem are satisfied by the system (T, +, •), then the system is a ring.

First let us show that if the system (T, +, •) is a subring, then conditions 1 and 2 of the theorem are satisfied. To establish property 1 when T is a subring, let $a, b \in$ T. Since T is a ring, we know that $b \in$ T implies that the additive inverse of b, or $-b$, is in T. But, again, since T is a ring, T is closed under addition. Thus, it follows that $a + (-b) \in$ T. From Definition 48/3 we know that $a + (-b) = a - b$. Therefore, $a - b \in$ T. This argument shows that T is closed under subtraction.

To verify that T is closed under multiplication observe that, since T is a ring, it satisfies the eight properties of a ring. In particular, T satisfies the sixth property, which is closure under multiplication.

Now let us show that if (T, +, •) satisfies conditions 1 and 2 of the theorem, then the system (T, +, •) is a subring.

First we will verify properties 1 through 5 of a ring, but, because certain properties follow immediately from the fact that T is a subset of S, we will proceed in a different order.

Since the *associative property of addition* holds for (S, +, •), and because T is a subset of S, we know that the associative property holds for (T, +, •).

Similarly, the *commutative property of addition* for T follows from the commutative property of addition for S.

If $a \in T$, then, because T is assumed to be closed under subtraction, the difference $a - a$ is contained in set T. But $a - a = 0$, the additive identity of S, and it follows that $0 \in T$. This shows that the *additive identity* of the ring S is contained in T. How do you know that 0 is also the additive identity for T?

Now that we have verified that the additive identity of S is contained in T, we can verify that the system (T, +, •) satisfies the *inverse* property. Since T is closed under subtraction, for each $a \in T, 0 - a \in T$. But $0 - a = 0 + (-a) = -a$; so $-a \in T$. This shows that, for each $a \in T$, the additive inverse $-a$ is in T.

To verify the *closure* property of addition we must show that if $a, b \in T$, then $a + b \in T$. By the inverse property, just verified for T, the element $-b \in T$. By condition 1 of the theorem, the difference $a - (-b) \in T$. But $a - (-b) = a + (-(-b)) = a + b$, so the closure property of addition holds.

With regard to properties 6 through 8 for a ring, observe that property 6, the closure property, holds because of the hypothesis, condition 2 of the theorem. Properties 7 and 8, the associative and distributive properties, hold for T since they hold for S. This concludes the proof of Theorem 49/3.

We will now apply this theorem to some subsets of certain rings to determine if they are subrings.

Examples 1 The integers under addition and multiplication form a subring of the ring of rational numbers under addition and multiplication. The verification of this is left as an exercise.

2 The system (E_I, +, •) is a subring of the ring (I, +, •) because the even integers are closed under subtraction and multiplication.

3 We will now determine if the subsystem (O_I, +, •) is a subring of (I, +, •). To show that this set is closed under subtraction, we must show that, for any two odd integers a and b, the difference $a - b$ is an odd integer. But 5 and 3 are odd integers and $5 - 3 = 2$. Since $2 \notin O_I$, the set is not closed under subtraction. This shows that (O_I, +, •) is *not* a subring of (I, +, •). Therefore, we need not even consider the closure property of multiplication.

Another way of reaching the same conclusion is to notice that the set of odd integers is not a subgroup of (I, +). Since subrings must also be subgroups under addition, it follows that $(O_I, +, \cdot)$ is not a subring.

4 As another example, we will show that $(E_{2\times 2}, +, \cdot)$ is a subring of the ring of all 2×2 matrices whose entries are integers, $(I_{2\times 2}, +, \cdot)$. We have already shown that $(E_{2\times 2}, +, \cdot)$ is a ring, and, because the set of 2×2 even matrices is a subset of the set of all 2×2 integral matrices, it automatically follows that $(E_{2\times 2}, +, \cdot)$ is a subring of the ring of all 2×2 integral matrices. [We have never proved that the system $(I_{2\times 2}, +, \cdot)$ is a ring, but the proof is analogous to the one given for the ring of 2×2 even matrices.] However, to illustrate Theorem 49/3, we will show that the conditions of the theorem are fulfilled. If $A, B \in E_{2\times 2}$, then the difference of A and B is

$$A - B = \begin{pmatrix} 2a_{11} & 2a_{12} \\ 2a_{21} & 2a_{22} \end{pmatrix} - \begin{pmatrix} 2b_{11} & 2b_{12} \\ 2b_{21} & 2b_{22} \end{pmatrix} = \begin{pmatrix} 2a_{11} - 2b_{11} & 2a_{12} - 2b_{12} \\ 2a_{21} - 2b_{21} & 2a_{22} - 2b_{22} \end{pmatrix}$$
$$= \begin{pmatrix} 2(a_{11} - b_{11}) & 2(a_{12} - b_{12}) \\ 2(a_{21} - b_{21}) & 2(a_{22} - b_{22}) \end{pmatrix}.$$

Since the difference of any two even matrices is an even matrix, we have shown that this set, $E_{2\times 2}$, is closed under subtraction. In exercise 8, page 180, you were asked to verify that the set of all 2×2 even matrices is closed under multiplication. Thus, by Theorem 49/3, $(E_{2\times 2}, +, \cdot)$ is a subring of $(I_{2\times 2}, +, \cdot)$.

5 Let us again consider the example of the ring of all 2×2 matrices whose entries are integers, $(I_{2\times 2}, +, \cdot)$. Let T be a subset of $I_{2\times 2}$ such that, if $A \in T$, then

$$A = \begin{pmatrix} a & 0 \\ 0 & 0 \end{pmatrix},$$

where $a \in I$. Another way to express the condition that matrix A is in set T is to say that S is the set of all matrices with zero entries except for a_{11}, where the entry is an integer. We will now verify that the subsystem $(T, +, \cdot)$ is a subring of the ring $(I_{2\times 2}, +, \cdot)$. If A and B are any elements of T, then the difference of A and B is

$$A - B = \begin{pmatrix} a_{11} & 0 \\ 0 & 0 \end{pmatrix} - \begin{pmatrix} b_{11} & 0 \\ 0 & 0 \end{pmatrix} = \begin{pmatrix} a_{11} - b_{11} & 0 \\ 0 & 0 \end{pmatrix}.$$

Why is $A - B \in T$? The product of A and B is

$$A \cdot B = \begin{pmatrix} a_{11} & 0 \\ 0 & 0 \end{pmatrix} \begin{pmatrix} b_{11} & 0 \\ 0 & 0 \end{pmatrix} = \begin{pmatrix} a_{11}b_{11} & 0 \\ 0 & 0 \end{pmatrix}.$$

Why is $A \cdot B \in T$? Since the difference and the product of any two matrices A and B of T are contained in T, we have another example of a subring of a ring.

Recall that, if (G, +) is a subgroup of (I, +), then there exists a positive integer n such that $G = \{nx \mid x \in I\}$. That is, the set of elements in the subgroup is the set of all integral multiples of a given positive integer n. Conversely, for a positive integer n, the set $G = \{nx \mid x \in I\}$ is such that (G, +) is a subgroup of (I, +). These assertions were proved in Theorems 30/2 and 29/2, respectively. We will now establish an analogous property for subrings of the ring of integers (I, +, •).

Theorem **50/3** If (I, +, •) is the ring of integers and S is a subset of I, then the subsystem (S, +, •) is a subring of (I, +, •) if and only if there exists a positive integer n such that $S = \{nx \mid x \in I\}$.

Proof First, let us assume that (S, +, •) is a subring of the ring of integers, (I, +, •). Since (S, +, •) is a ring, it satisfies the eight properties of a ring. This means that (S, +) is a group, and by the definition of a subgroup, it is a subgroup of the group (I, +). But under these circumstances, Theorem 30/2 applies and it is possible to conclude that a positive integer n does exist such that $S = \{nx \mid x \in I\}$.

Second, suppose that set S is given such that $S = \{nx \mid x \in I\}$ for some particular positive integer n. We will show that the subsystem (S, +, •) is a subring of (I, +, •). We already know that (S, +) is a subgroup of (I, +). Why? It remains to show that properties 6, 7, and 8 of a ring are satisfied. Since all of the elements of S are integers, we are assured that the associative and distributive properties are satisfied. It remains to show that S is closed under the operation of multiplication. So, let $y, z \in S$; then, by hypothesis, there exist integers u and v such that $y = un$ and $z = vn$. The product of the integers y and z can be expressed as

$$\begin{aligned} y \cdot z &= (un) \cdot (vn) \\ &= n(uvn). \end{aligned}$$

But this product is of the form nx with $x \in I$. Why is the product uvn an integer? This demonstrates that set S is closed under multiplication, and the second part of the theorem is established.

It follows from these arguments that (S, +, •) is a subring of

(I, +, •). Thus, every subring of the integers is a system (S, +, •) where $S = \{nx \mid x \in I\}$ and n is a positive integer.

Exercises

1 Prove that (I, +, •) is a subring of the ring of rational numbers.

2 Prove that $\{a + 0\sqrt{2} \mid a \in I\}$ under addition and multiplication is a subring of $(I(\sqrt{2}), +, \cdot)$. *Answer*

3 Prove that $\{a + 0\sqrt{3} \mid a \in R\}$ under addition and multiplication is a subring of $(R(\sqrt{3}), +, \cdot)$.

4 Prove that $\{a + 0i \mid a \in I \text{ and } i^2 = -1\}$ under addition and multiplication is a subring of $(G(i), +, \cdot)$.

5 Prove that $\{A \mid A \in M_{2\times 2}, a_{ij} = 8k, \text{ and } k \in I\}$ under matrix addition and matrix multiplication is a subring of $(M_{2\times 2}, +, \cdot)$.

6 Prove that $\{A \mid A \in I_{2\times 2}, a_{21} = 0, \text{ and } a_{11}, a_{12}, a_{22} \in I\}$ under matrix addition and multiplication is a subring of the ring $(I_{2\times 2}, +, \cdot)$. *Answer*

7 Prove that $\{A \mid A \in I_{2\times 2} \text{ and } a_{21} = a_{22} = 0, \text{ and } a_{12}, a_{11} \in I\}$ under matrix addition and multiplication is a subring of $(I_{2\times 2}, +, \cdot)$.

8 Consider the ring $\mathcal{J}$ of all functions with domain the integers and range in the integers where $(x)(f + g) = (x)f + (x)g$ and $(x)(f \cdot g) = (x)f \cdot (x)g$. Let the set $\mathcal{T} = \{f \mid f \in \mathcal{J}$ and, for each $x \in I$, $(x)f = k$, where k is a fixed integer$\}$. Show that $(\mathcal{T}, +, \cdot)$ is a subring of $(\mathcal{J}, +, \cdot)$.

9 Repeat exercise 8 with the ring operation of multiplication defined as composition of functions, that is, as $(x)(f \circ g) = ((x)f)g$. *Answer*

10 Find all subrings of the following rings:

a $(I/3, \oplus_3, \odot_3)$
b $(I/4, \oplus_4, \odot_4)$
c $(I/6, \oplus_6, \odot_6)$ *Answer*
d $(I/12, \oplus_{12}, \odot_{12})$
e $(I/15, \oplus_{15}, \odot_{15})$
f $(I/24, \oplus_{24}, \odot_{24})$
g $(I/7, \oplus_7, \odot_7)$
h $(I/13, \oplus_{13}, \odot_{13})$

11 Let (S, +, •) be a ring. Prove that, if (T, +) is a subgroup of (S, +) such that T is closed under multiplication, then (T, +, •) is a subring of S.

◆ 12 Let $\mathcal{J}$ be the set of all functions with domain the set of integers and range in the set of integers. For each f, g $\in \mathcal{J}$, $(x)(f + g) = (x)f + (x)g$ and $(x)(f \cdot g) = (x)f \cdot (x)g$. Determine whether or not each of the following subsets of $\mathcal{J}$ is a subring of the ring $(\mathcal{J}, +, \cdot)$.

a $\{f \mid (0)f = 0\}$ *Answer*
b $\{f \mid (0)f \neq 0\}$
c $\{f \mid (0)f = 1\}$
d $\{f \mid (0)f = (1)f\}$
e $\{f \mid -1 \leqq (x)f \leqq 1\}$
f $\{f \mid (x + 1)f = (x)f\}$

13 Prove that $\{A \mid A \in M_{2\times 2}, a_{12} = a_{21} = a_{22} = 0, \text{ and } a_{11} \in I\}$ under + and • is a subring of $(M_{2\times 2}, +, \cdot)$.

14 Let R_2 be the set of rational numbers of the form $\frac{m}{n}$, where $m, n \in I$ and $n \neq 0$, such that m and n are relatively prime and 2 is not a factor of n. Show that $(R_2, +, \cdot)$ is a subring of $(R, +, \cdot)$. *Answer*

15 By analogy with R_2 defined in exercise 14, define R_3. Prove or disprove that $(R_3, +, \cdot)$ is a subring of $(R, +, \cdot)$.

16 Use exercise 14 to define R_6. Prove or disprove that $(R_6, +, \cdot)$ is a subring of $(R, +, \cdot)$. *Answer*

17 Let V be the set of rational numbers of the form $\frac{1}{2}x$ where $x = \frac{m}{n}$, $m, n \in I$, $n \neq 0$, and m and 2 are relatively prime. Find an example to show that $(V, +, \cdot)$ is not a subring of $(R, +, \cdot)$. (Hint: Is V closed under addition?)

18 Prove that $\{A \mid A \in M_{2 \times 2}$ and $a_{12} = a_{21} = 0\}$ under matrix addition and multiplication is a subring of $(M_{2 \times 2}, +, \cdot)$.

19 Let A_2 be the set of rational numbers of the form $\frac{a}{2^n}$, where $a, n \in I$. Show that $(A_2, +, \cdot)$ is a subring of $(R, +, \cdot)$. *Answer*

20 By analogy with A_2 defined in exercise 19, define A_3 and show that $(A_3, +, \cdot)$ is a subring of $(R, +, \cdot)$.

◆21 Use exercise 19 to define A_6 and show that $(A_6, +, \cdot)$ is a subring of $(R, +, \cdot)$.

Ideals 29/3

[optional]

We have seen that if the subsystem $(T, +, \cdot)$ is to be a subring of a ring $(S, +, \cdot)$, then the set T must be closed under multiplication. When we extend the notion of closure under multiplication so that set T of the subsystem $(T, +, \cdot)$ is closed under multiplication by each element of S in the containing ring $(S, +, \cdot)$, we have a mathematical system called an *ideal*. A definition of an ideal is given below.

Definition 51/3 Let $(S, +, \cdot)$ be a ring and let T be a nonempty subset of S. Then the system $(T, +, \cdot)$ is an *ideal* of $(S, +, \cdot)$ if and only if for each $a, b \in T$ and for each $s \in S$, each of the following is true:
1) The difference $a - b \in T$,
2) the product $s \cdot a \in T$, and
3) the product $a \cdot s \in T$.

By comparing Theorem 49/3 and Definition 51/3, we see that the distinction between an ideal and a subring is that, in the case of an ideal, closure of multiplication in T between the elements of subset T and the elements of set S is required; whereas, in the case of a subring, closure of multiplication in T is required between the elements of the subset T.

It should be obvious from this discussion that an ideal of a ring is also a subring. But is a subring necessarily an ideal? To answer this question, let us reconsider some of the examples of subrings given in the preceding section to determine whether they are examples of ideals.

Examples 1 The subring $(E_{2 \times 2}, +, \cdot)$ is an ideal of the ring $(I_{2 \times 2}, +, \cdot)$. To verify this statement, we must show that the conditions of Definition 51/3 are satisfied. We have already observed that $E_{2 \times 2}$ is closed under subtraction. Hence, condition 1 of the definition is fulfilled. For condition 2, we form the product of any matrix A of $I_{2 \times 2}$ and any matrix B of $E_{2 \times 2}$. Let

$$A = \begin{pmatrix} a_{11} & a_{12} \\ a_{21} & a_{22} \end{pmatrix}, \quad B = \begin{pmatrix} 2b_{11} & 2b_{12} \\ 2b_{21} & 2b_{22} \end{pmatrix},$$

with $a_{ij} \in I$ and $2b_{ij} \in E_I$. Applying the definition of multiplication of 2×2 matrices, we have the product

$$A \cdot B = \begin{pmatrix} 2a_{11}b_{11} + 2a_{12}b_{21} & 2a_{11}b_{12} + 2a_{12}b_{22} \\ 2a_{21}b_{11} + 2a_{22}b_{21} & 2a_{21}b_{12} + 2a_{22}b_{22} \end{pmatrix}.$$

We must determine if the product $A \cdot B$ is in $E_{2 \times 2}$. Since the product of 2 and any integer $a_{ij}b_{ij}$ is an even integer and since the sum of two even integers is again an even integer, the entries in the product $A \cdot B$ are even integers. Hence, $A \cdot B \in E_{2 \times 2}$.

In a similar manner, we can show that the product $B \cdot A$ is in $E_{2 \times 2}$. Hence, condition 3 is satisfied. Therefore, the ring of 2×2 even matrices is an ideal of the ring of 2×2 matrices whose entries are in I.

2 In section 28/3 we proved that the set of all integral multiples of a fixed positive integer under addition and multiplication forms a subring of $(I, +, \cdot)$. Remember that we earlier adopted the notation I_{nx} for the set of integral multiples of a fixed integer n, with $n, x \in I, n > 0$. We will show that $(I_{nx}, +, \cdot)$ is an ideal of the ring $(I, +, \cdot)$. Let $m \in I$ and $nu \in I_{nx}$. Why is the product $m \cdot (nu)$ an element of the set of multiples of n? Why is the product $(nu) \cdot m \in I_{nx}$? It follows that the subsystem $(I_{nx}, +, \cdot)$ is an ideal of $(I, +, \cdot)$.

3 We have just seen that the subring $(E_{2 \times 2}, +, \cdot)$ is an ideal of $(I_{2 \times 2}, +, \cdot)$ and that the subring $(I_{nx}, +, \cdot)$ is an ideal of

(I, +, •). So that you do not reach a false conclusion, we now consider a subring that is *not* an ideal. In exercise 1 of section 28/3, you were asked to prove that (I, +, •) is a subring of (R, +, •). The following theorem establishes that this subring is not an ideal.

Theorem 51/3 The subring (I, +, •) is not an ideal of the ring (R, +, •).

Proof We will show that (I, +, •) is not an ideal of (R, +, •) by showing that I is not closed under multiplication by elements in the ring of rational numbers. It is sufficient to exhibit one example of an element in I and an element in R whose product is not in I. One such product is $1 \cdot \frac{1}{2} = \frac{1}{2}$. Thus, the subring (I, +, •) is not an ideal of the ring of rational numbers.

Exercises

1 Show that the subring of rational numbers is not an ideal of the ring of real numbers.

2 Show that the subring of integers is not an ideal of the ring $(\{a + b\sqrt{2} \mid a, b \in I\}, +, \cdot)$.

3 Show that the subring of integers is not an ideal of the ring of Gaussian integers, $\{a + bi \mid a, b \in I \text{ and } i^2 = -1\}$. *Answer*

4 Show that the set A of exercise 5, page 197, in section 28/3 is an ideal under matrix addition and multiplication of $(I_{2 \times 2}, +, \cdot)$. Is this system an ideal of $(M_{2 \times 2}, +, \cdot)$? *Answer*

5 Show specifically that $(\{3x \mid x \in I\}, +, \cdot)$ is an ideal of (I, +, •).

◆ 6 Prove that every subring of the ring of integers is an ideal.

◆ 7 Determine which of the subrings of exercise 10, page 197, of section 28/3 are ideals.

8 Determine whether the systems described in the following exercises of section 28/3, pages 197 and 198, are ideals.

a Exercise 3	g Exercise 15 *Answer*
b Exercise 6	h Exercise 16
c Exercise 7	i Exercise 18
d Exercise 8	j Exercise 19 *Answer*
e Exercise 9 *Answer*	k Exercise 20
f Exercise 14	l Exercise 21

9 Let (T, +, •) be an ideal of the ring (S, +, •). Prove or disprove that (T, +, •) is a subring of ring S.

10 Let (T, +, •) be an arbitrary subring of the ring (S, +, •). Prove or disprove that (T, +, •) is an ideal of ring S.

◆ 11 Consider the ring $(I/6, \oplus_6, \odot_6)$, and in this ring let S be the ideal $(\{\bar{0}, \bar{2}, \bar{4}\}, \oplus_6, \odot_6)$. Compute the cosets $S \oplus_6 \bar{a}$ of S, where $\bar{a} \in \{\bar{0}, \bar{2}, \bar{4}\}$, in I/6. Define two binary operations ☆ and ∘ on cosets such that $(S \oplus_6 \bar{a}) ☆ (S \oplus_6 \bar{b}) = S \oplus_6 (\bar{a} \oplus_6 \bar{b})$

and $(S \oplus_6 \bar{a}) \circ (S \oplus_6 \bar{b}) = S \oplus_6 (\bar{a} \odot_6 \bar{b})$. Show that this set of cosets under ☆ and ∘ forms a ring.

12 Repeat exercise 11 with $S = (\{\bar{0}, \bar{3}\}, \oplus_6, \odot_6)$.

13 Which subsets of exercise 12, page 197, of section 28/3 are ideals?

14 Is the subring of exercise 13 of section 28/3 an ideal? *Answer*

◆ **15** Let $(A, +, \cdot)$ and $(B, +, \cdot)$ be ideals of a ring $(S, +, \cdot)$. Prove that $(A \cap B, +, \cdot)$ is an ideal of $(S, +, \cdot)$. *Answer*

◆ **16** Find the intersections of the following ideals of $(I, +, \cdot)$.

a $A = (I_{2x}, +, \cdot)$ and $B = (I_{3x}, +, \cdot)$. *Answer*
b $A = (I_{4x}, +, \cdot)$ and $B = (I_{6x}, +, \cdot)$. *Answer*
c $A = (I_{3x}, +, \cdot)$ and $B = (I_{15x}, +, \cdot)$.
d $A = (I_{8x}, +, \cdot)$ and $B = (I_{20x}, +, \cdot)$.
e $A = (I_{7x}, +, \cdot)$ and $B = (I_{4x}, +, \cdot)$.
f $A = (I_{36x}, +, \cdot)$ and $B = (I_{10x}, +, \cdot)$.

◆ **17** Let $(A, +, \cdot)$ and $(B, +, \cdot)$ be ideals of a ring $(S, +, \cdot)$. Then the *ideal sum* of A and B is the set of all sums $a + b$, where $a \in A$ and $b \in B$. Symbolically, $A + B = \{a + b \mid a \in A \text{ and } b \in B\}$. In this exercise we will find the ideal sum of the ideals $A = (I_{8x}, +, \cdot)$ and $B = (I_{12x}, +, \cdot)$ of the ring $(I, +, \cdot)$. Let $d \in A + B$. Give reasons for the following steps.

a $d = a + b$, where $a \in A$ and $b \in B$.
b $d = 8x + 12y$, where $x, y \in I$.
c $d = 4(2x + 3y)$.
d $d = 4z, z \in I$.
e $A + B \subseteq I_{4x}$.
f If $j \in I_{4x}$, then $j = 4k, k \in I$.
g $j = 4k(2(-1) + 3(1))$.
h $j = 8(-k) + 12k$.
i $j \in A + B$.
j $I_{4x} \subseteq A + B$.
k $A + B = I_{4x}$.

◆ **18** Find the ideal sums of the following ideals of $(I, +, \cdot)$.

a $(I_{4x}, +, \cdot)$ and $(I_{6x}, +, \cdot)$ *Answer*
b $(I_{3x}, +, \cdot)$ and $(I_{15x}, +, \cdot)$ *Answer*
c $(I_{2x}, +, \cdot)$ and $(I_{3x}, +, \cdot)$
d $(I_{8x}, +, \cdot)$ and $(I_{20x}, +, \cdot)$
e $(I_{36x}, +, \cdot)$ and $(I_{24x}, +, \cdot)$
f $(I_{21x}, +, \cdot)$ and $(I_{18x}, +, \cdot)$

◆ **19** Let $(A, +, \cdot)$ and $(B, +, \cdot)$ be ideals of a ring $(S, +, \cdot)$. Prove that $(A + B, +, \cdot)$ is an ideal of $(S, +, \cdot)$. *Answer*

◆ **20** In R_2, as defined in exercise 14, page 198, let $R_2^* = \left\{\frac{2k}{n} \mid k, n \in I, n \neq 0, \text{ and 2 is not a factor of } n\right\}$. Show that $(R_2^*, +, \cdot)$ is an ideal of $(R_2, +, \cdot)$.

◆ **21** By analogy with R_2^* defined in exercise 20, define R_3^*. Prove or disprove that $(R_3^*, +, \cdot)$ is an ideal of $(R_3, +, \cdot)$.

◆ **22** Use exercise 20 to define R_6^*. Prove or disprove that $(R_6^*, +, \cdot)$ is an ideal of $(R_6, +, \cdot)$.

Homomorphisms [*optional*]

30/3

Mathematical systems may appear to be quite different with respect to their sets of elements and their operations, but yet may be very much alike structurally. An example of this similarity is the additive group of integers modulo 4 and the multiplicative group $(\{1, -1, i, -i\}, \cdot)$. The group of integers modulo 4 has as its operation modular addition, and the group whose set of elements is $\{1, -1, i, -i\}$ has as its operation multiplication of complex numbers. The sets involved and the operations are quite different; yet we were able to establish that there exists a one-to-one function from $(I/4, \oplus_4)$ onto the group $(\{1, -1, i, -i\}, \cdot)$ such that the group operations are preserved (see section 22/2). Remember that such a mapping is called an isomorphism.

We first studied isomorphisms in connection with groups in Chapter 2. Then, in section 26/3, we applied the notion of isomorphism to rings, showing how it is possible to embed a ring T in a containing ring S by means of an isomorphism (see exercises 5 through 10, pages 187-188). When two rings are isomorphic, we understand that the isomorphism preserves *both* operations of the two rings.

In this section we will consider functions that preserve operations but that need not be one-to-one functions. In other words, we will permit more than one element of the domain to be mapped onto an element of the range. (In Chapter 1 we referred to such mappings as many-to-one mappings.) Before this kind of function is defined formally, let us discuss an example.

Example The mathematical system $(I, +, \cdot)$ is a ring, as is the system $(I/3, \oplus_3, \odot_3)$. The ring of integers has an infinite set of elements, and the ring of integers modulo 3 has exactly three elements. We will define a mapping of the elements of the ring of integers onto elements in the ring of integers modulo 3 in such a way that the operations of the two rings are preserved. To give a rule for such a mapping, let us recall certain characteristics of $I/3$.

In Chapter 1 we saw that $I/3 = \{\bar{0}, \bar{1}, \bar{2}\}$, where

$$\bar{0} = \{\ldots, -3, 0, 3, \ldots\},$$
$$\bar{1} = \{\ldots, -2, 1, 4, \ldots\},$$
$$\bar{2} = \{\ldots, -1, 2, 5, \ldots\}.$$

Hence, I/3 consists of three equivalence classes, each of which is an infinite subset of I.

Every integer is in exactly one of these three infinite sets, as is shown by the following argument. If x is any integer, then, by the division algorithm, we know that $x = 3q + r$, with $0 \leqq r < 3$. Furthermore, the integers q and r in $x = 3q + r$ are unique, and x belongs to the equivalence class determined by the remainder r. Some examples of how an integer can be expressed in this fashion are given below.

$$7 = 3 \cdot 2 + 1; \text{ hence, } 7 \in \bar{1}.$$
$$47 = 3 \cdot 15 + 2; \text{ hence, } 47 \in \bar{2}.$$
$$0 = 3 \cdot 0 + 0; \text{ hence, } 0 \in \bar{0}.$$
$$-2 = 3 \cdot (-1) + 1; \text{ hence, } -2 \in \bar{1}.$$
$$-13 = 3 \cdot (-5) + 2; \text{ hence, } -13 \in \bar{2}.$$

We will use the division algorithm to define a function whose domain is the set of integers and whose range is the set of integers modulo 3. If x is an integer, then let f be the function given by

$$(x)\text{f} = \bar{r},$$
$$\text{with } x = 3q + r,\ 0 \leqq r < 3.$$

Observe that the function f is such that, if $n \in \bar{r}$, then $(n)\text{f} = \bar{r}$. Why is this relation single-valued? Since it is a single-valued relation, we are justified in calling f a function. We will determine if f preserves the operations of the rings.

As the examples given above show, function f is not one-to-one, but is many-to-one. For instance, $(7)\text{f} = \bar{1}$ and $(-2)\text{f} = \bar{1}$; similarly, $(47)\text{f} = \bar{2}$ and $(-13)\text{f} = \bar{2}$.

In each of the following examples, the function f does preserve the operations of addition in the two rings.

$(-6 + 10)\text{f} = (4)\text{f} = \bar{1}$, and $(-6)\text{f} \oplus_3 (10)\text{f} = \bar{0} \oplus_3 \bar{1} = \bar{1}$.
$(4 + (-32))\text{f} = (-28)\text{f} = \bar{2}$, and $(4)\text{f} \oplus_3 (-32)\text{f} = \bar{1} \oplus_3 \bar{1} = \bar{2}$.
$(0 + 7)\text{f} = (7)\text{f} = \bar{1}$, and $(0)\text{f} \oplus_3 (7)\text{f} = \bar{0} \oplus_3 \bar{1} = \bar{1}$.

If you consider other such examples, you will probably be convinced that function f always preserves the operations of addition. The property of preserving addition can be verified for arbitrary elements x and y of the ring of integers as follows.

If $x = 3q_1 + r_1$ and $y = 3q_2 + r_2$, with $0 \leqq r_1 < 3$ and $0 \leqq r_2 < 3$, then

$$x + y = 3(q_1 + q_2) + r_1 + r_2.$$

By the division algorithm, we can express the integer $r_1 + r_2$ as $r_1 + r_2 = 3q_3 + r_3$, with $0 \leqq r_3 < 3$. Hence,

$$x + y = 3(q_1 + q_2 + q_3) + r_3.$$

Therefore, by the definition of function f,

$$(x + y)\mathrm{f} = \bar{r}_3.$$

We must now show that $(x)\mathrm{f} \oplus_3 (y)\mathrm{f} = \bar{r}_3$. Now $(x)\mathrm{f} = \bar{r}_1$ (Why?), and $(y)\mathrm{f} = \bar{r}_2$ (Why?). Hence,

$$(x)\mathrm{f} \oplus_3 (y)\mathrm{f} = \bar{r}_1 \oplus_3 \bar{r}_2.$$

The definition of addition of integers modulo 3 and the fact that $r_1 + r_2 = 3q_3 + r_3$ imply that $\bar{r}_1 \oplus_3 \bar{r}_2 = \bar{r}_3$. Thus,

$$(x + y)\mathrm{f} = \bar{r}_3 = (x)\mathrm{f} \oplus_3 (y)\mathrm{f}.$$

Now that we have verified that function f preserves addition, let us consider the operations of multiplication for the two rings. In each of the following examples, function f preserves the operations of multiplication.

$(2 \cdot 3)\mathrm{f} = (6)\mathrm{f} = \bar{0}$, and $(2)\mathrm{f} \odot_3 (3)\mathrm{f} = \bar{2} \odot_3 \bar{0} = \bar{0}$.
$(-1 \cdot 7)\mathrm{f} = (-7)\mathrm{f} = \bar{2}$, and $(-1)\mathrm{f} \odot_3 (7)\mathrm{f} = \bar{2} \odot_3 \bar{1} = \bar{2}$.
$(-2 \cdot (-5))\mathrm{f} = (10)\mathrm{f} = \bar{1}$, and $(-2)\mathrm{f} \odot_3 (-5)\mathrm{f} = \bar{1} \odot_3 \bar{1} = \bar{1}$.

From these examples, it would appear that function f preserves the operations of multiplication. The property of preserving multiplication can also be verified for arbitrary elements x and y of the ring of integers.

If $x = 3q_1 + r_1$ and $y = 3q_2 + r_2$, with $0 \leqq r_1 < 3$ and $0 \leqq r_2 < 3$, then

$$x \cdot y = (3q_1 + r_1) \cdot (3q_2 + r_2) = 3(3q_1q_2 + q_1r_2 + q_2r_1) + r_1r_2.$$

By the division algorithm, we can express the integer r_1r_2 as

$$r_1r_2 = 3q_3 + r_3, \text{ with } 0 \leqq r_3 < 3.$$

Hence,

$$x \cdot y = 3(3q_1q_2 + q_1r_2 + q_2r_1 + q_3) + r_3.$$

So, by the definition of f, we have

$$(x \cdot y)\mathrm{f} = \bar{r}_3.$$

We must now show that $(x)\mathrm{f} \odot_3 (y)\mathrm{f} = \bar{r}_3$. Since $(x)\mathrm{f} = \bar{r}_1$ and $(y)\mathrm{f} = \bar{r}_2$, we have

$$(x)\mathrm{f} \odot_3 (y)\mathrm{f} = \bar{r}_1 \odot_3 \bar{r}_2.$$

But the definition of multiplication of integers modulo 3 and the fact that $r_1 \cdot r_2 = 3q_3 + r_3$ imply that $\bar{r}_1 \odot_3 \bar{r}_2 = \bar{r}_3$. Therefore,

$$(x \cdot y)\mathrm{f} = \bar{r}_3 = (x)\mathrm{f} \odot_3 (y)\mathrm{f}.$$

A many-to-one function, such as f, that preserves the operations of the two systems is called a *homomorphism*. A formal definition of a homomorphism is given below.

Definition 52/3 Let $(\mathrm{T}, +, \cdot)$ and $(\mathrm{S}, \oplus, \odot)$ be rings and let f be a function from T onto S. Then f is a *homomorphism* from T onto S if and only if, for each $t_1, t_2 \in \mathrm{T}$,
1) $(t_1 + t_2)\mathrm{f} = (t_1)\mathrm{f} \oplus (t_2)\mathrm{f}$ and
2) $(t_1 \cdot t_2)\mathrm{f} = (t_1)\mathrm{f} \odot (t_2)\mathrm{f}$.

Notice that function f may be either many-to-one or one-to-one. Hence, the set of all isomorphic functions is a subset of the set of all homomorphic functions from one system to another.

Observe that, in the example discussed above, the additive identity of $(\mathrm{I}, +, \cdot)$ is mapped onto the additive identity of $(\mathrm{I}/3, \oplus_3, \odot_3)$. We have previously established, for isomorphisms of groups, that the additive identity corresponds to the additive identity. The property also holds for homomorphisms of rings, as the following theorem establishes.

Theorem 52/3 If $(\mathrm{T}, +, \cdot)$ and $(\mathrm{S}, \oplus, \odot)$ are rings with additive identities 0_T and 0_S, respectively, and if f is a homomorphism from T onto S, then $(0_\mathrm{T})\mathrm{f} = 0_\mathrm{S}$.

Proof Let $t \in \mathrm{T}$, $(t)\mathrm{f} = s$, and $(0_\mathrm{T})\mathrm{f} = s_1$. We will show that $s \oplus s_1 = s$. Because the group $(\mathrm{S}, \oplus)$ is commutative and has a unique additive identity, this will establish that $s_1 = 0_\mathrm{S}$. The computation below shows that $s \oplus s_1 = s$.

$$\begin{aligned} s &= (t)\mathrm{f} \\ &= (t + 0_\mathrm{T})\mathrm{f} \\ &= (t)\mathrm{f} \oplus (0_\mathrm{T})\mathrm{f} \\ &= s \oplus s_1. \end{aligned}$$

The proof of the theorem is complete.

Let us again consider the homomorphism of $(\mathrm{I}, +, \cdot)$ onto $(\mathrm{I}/3, \oplus_3, \odot_3)$. Listed next are some elements in the ring of integers, their additive inverses, and their images under function f. Notice that f maps additive inverses onto additive inverses.

$(7)f = \bar{1}$ and $(-7)f = \bar{2}$. $(5)f = \bar{2}$ and $(-5)f = \bar{1}$.
$(3)f = \bar{0}$ and $(-3)f = \bar{0}$. $(14)f = \bar{2}$ and $(-14)f = \bar{1}$.
$(-11)f = \bar{1}$ and $(11)f = \bar{2}$. $(6)f = \bar{0}$ and $(-6)f = \bar{0}$.

These examples indicate that additive inverses map onto additive inverses under a homomorphism. This is a property of homomorphisms, as the following theorem asserts.

Theorem 53/3 Let $(T, +, \cdot)$ and $(S, \oplus, \odot)$ be rings and let f be a homomorphism from T onto S. If $t \in T$ and if $-t$ denotes the additive inverse of t, then the image of the additive inverse is the additive inverse of the image. That is, $(-t)f = -\big((t)f\big)$.

Proof Let 0_S and 0_T be the additive identities of $(S, \oplus, \odot)$ and $(T, +, \cdot)$, respectively. Then

$$\begin{aligned} 0_S &= (0_T)f \\ &= \big(t + (-t)\big)f \\ &= (t)f \oplus (-t)f. \end{aligned}$$

Hence,

$$(-t)f = -\big((t)f\big).$$

The concepts of a homomorphism and of an ideal are closely related; and, although it is not possible to go very deeply into the subject, we can give one interesting result at this time. The following theorem establishes that if f is a homomorphism from a first ring onto a second ring, then the set of elements that map onto the additive identity of the second ring is an ideal of the first ring.

Theorem 54/3 Let $(T, +, \cdot)$ and $(S, \oplus, \odot)$ be rings; let f be a homomorphism from T onto S; and let K be $\{t \mid t \in T \text{ and } (t)f = 0_S\}$, where 0_S is the additive identity of the ring S. Then the system $(K, +, \cdot)$ is an ideal of $(T, +, \cdot)$.

Proof Recall that the definition of an ideal (Definition 51/3) requires that if $(K, +, \cdot)$ is an ideal of ring T, then K is closed under subtraction and multiplication of elements in K by elements in the ring T. The following computation shows that the closure properties, which are the three conditions of Definition 51/3, are satisfied for K and, hence, K is an ideal of $(T, +, \cdot)$. Let $k, k_1 \in K$ and $t \in T$. Then we have the following equalities:

1) $(k - k_1)f = \big(k + (-k_1)\big)f = (k)f \oplus (-k_1)f = 0_S \oplus 0_S = 0_S$.
2) $(kt)f = (k)f \odot (t)f = 0_S \odot (t)f = 0_S$.
3) $(tk)f = (t)f \odot (k)f = (t)f \odot 0_S = 0_S$.

Since 0_S is the image of the difference of two elements of K and also the image of the products kt and tk, K is closed under these operations. Hence, (K, +, •) is an ideal of (T, +, •).

Exercises

1 Give the reasons for the steps in the proof of Theorem 52/3.

2 Give the reasons for the steps in the proof of Theorem 53/3.

3 Give the reasons for the steps in the proof of Theorem 54/3.

4 Consider the ring (I, +, •). Determine which of the following functions are homomorphisms from I onto a subring of I. If a function is a homomorphism, describe the ideal that is mapped onto the additive identity of the subring.

a $(x)f = x^2 + 5$. *Answer*

b $(x)f = x$.

c $(x)f = 3x$.

d $(x)f = -2$. *Answer*

e $(x)f = |x|$.

f $(x)f = 2x + 1$.

g $(x)f = -4x$.

h $(x)f = 2x$.

5 Let f be a homomorphism from the ring (T, +, •) onto the ring (S, ⊕, ⊙). Prove the following.

a If T is a commutative ring, then S is also a commutative ring. *Answer*

b If T is a ring with identity 1_T, then S is a ring with identity $(1_T)f$.

c If $a, b \in T$, then $(a - b)f = (a)f - (b)f$.

d If $a \in T$ has multiplicative inverse $a^{-1} \in T$, then $(a)f \in S$ has multiplicative inverse $(a^{-1})f \in S$. *Answer*

6 Consider the rings $(I/4, \oplus_4, \odot_4)$ and $(I/2, \oplus_2, \odot_2)$. Let f be the function from I/4 onto I/2 such that $(\bar{0})f = (\bar{2})f = \bar{0}$ and $(\bar{1})f = (\bar{3})f = \bar{1}$. Show that f is a homomorphism.

7 In exercise 6, consider the function g such that $(\bar{0})g = (\bar{1})g = \bar{0}$ and $(\bar{2})g = (\bar{3})g = \bar{1}$. Show that g is *not* a homomorphism from I/4 onto I/2.

8 Find all homomorphisms from I/4 onto I/2. *Answer*

9 Let f be the function from $(I(\sqrt{2}), +, \cdot)$ onto (I, +, •) given by $(a + b\sqrt{2})f = a$. Is f a homomorphism? If it is, what ideal is mapped onto the additive identity of (I, +, •)? *Answer*

10 Let f be the function from $(E_I, +, \cdot)$ onto $(I_{4x}, +, \cdot)$ given by $(x)f = 2x$ for each $x \in E_I$. Is f a homomorphism? If it is, what ideal is mapped onto 0?

11 Let f be the function from $(G(i), +, \cdot)$ onto (I, +, •) given by $(a + bi)f = a$. Is f a homomorphism? If so, what ideal is mapped onto 0?

◆ 12 Let f be the function from $(E_{2 \times 2}, +, \cdot)$ onto $(E_I, +, \cdot)$ given by $(A)f = a_{11}$, where $A \in E_{2 \times 2}$ and a_{11} is the entry in the first row and first column of A. Is f a homomorphism? If it is, what ideal is mapped onto 0?

13 Let f be the function from $(G(i), +, \cdot)$ onto itself given by $(a + bi)f = a - bi$. Is f a homomorphism? If so, what ideal is mapped onto 0?

14 Consider the rings $(T, +, \cdot)$ and $(S, \oplus, \odot)$. Let f be a function from $T \times S$ onto T such that $f = \{((t, s), t) \mid t \in T \text{ and } s \in S\}$. Prove that f is a homomorphism. What ideal of the ring $T \times S$ is mapped onto 0?

◆ 15 Let f be the function from $(R, +, \cdot)$ onto $(I, +, \cdot)$ given by $\left(\frac{a}{b}\right)f = a + b$ for each $\frac{a}{b} \in R$, where a and b are relatively prime. Is f a homomorphism? If so, what ideal is mapped onto 0?

◆ 16 Consider the groups $(I, +)$ and $(G, \cdot) = (\{1, -1, i, -i\}, \cdot)$. Show that $(n)f = i^n$ for each $n \in I$ is a homomorphism from $(I, +)$ onto $(G, \cdot)$.

Polynomial rings

31/3

In this section we will discuss a new example of a commutative ring with identity. This particular kind of ring, which is called a *polynomial ring* (or a ring of polynomials), is important both historically and because some of the properties of the ring are useful in solving equations.

We begin our study of polynomial rings with a definition of a polynomial. Note that this definition is a rather specialized one that is given in the context of a ring. This is done because we will be concerned with polynomials as elements of a ring rather than as expressions to be factored or as functions whose values are to be determined.

Definition 53/3 If $(S, +, \cdot)$ is a commutative ring with identity and $S[x]$ denotes the set of all expressions of the form

$$a_0x^0 + a_1x^1 + a_2x^2 + \ldots + a_nx^n$$

where $a_0, a_1, a_2, \ldots, a_n \in S$, and n is a nonnegative integer, then the elements of $S[x]$ are *polynomials* in x.

The elements $a_0, a_1, a_2, \ldots, a_n$ of S are *coefficients*. The *degree* of the polynomial is the nonnegative integer n. Polynomials of degree 0 are *constants*. We will adopt the notation a_0 for a_0x^0, a_1x for a_1x^1, and x^k for $1 \cdot x^k$. The expressions of the form a_ix^i are called *terms* of the polynomial. The degree of the ith term is $i - 1$ for $i = 1, 2, 3, \ldots, n$. Two polynomials in x are *equal* if they have the same degree and if corresponding coefficients are equal.

In elementary algebra the study of polynomials is usually restricted to those with coefficients in the ring of rational numbers. These polynomials are often called polynomials over the rational numbers. Examples of such polynomials are given below.

Examples 1 $5 + 6x - \frac{1}{2}x^2 + 4x^3$

2 $-4 + 0x - 0x^2 + \frac{3}{2}x^3 - x^4$

3 7

4 $x^2 + x - 3x^5$

Examples 1 and 2, which are written so that the exponents of x increase from the first term at the left to the last term at the right, are in *ascending order.* In example 2, if the terms with zero coefficients are omitted, the polynomial can be written as $-4 + \frac{3}{2}x^3 - x^4$. Example 3 is a *constant polynomial.* Example 4 illustrates that a polynomial need not be written in ascending order. Observe that the degrees of the polynomials in the examples above are 3, 4, 0, and 5, respectively, and that the number of terms in the examples is 4, 5, 1, and 6, respectively.

To form a ring from the set of polynomials S[x], first we must define operations of addition and multiplication for S[x]. Following the definitions of operations, we will show that S[x], under these operations, is a ring. Then some properties of the ring will be determined.

Definition 54/3 Let S[x] be the set of all polynomials with coefficients in (S, +, •), a commutative ring with identity. If

$$f(x) = a_0 + a_1x + a_2x^2 + \ldots + a_nx^n$$

and

$$g(x) = b_0 + b_1x + b_2x^2 + \ldots + b_mx^m$$

are polynomials in the set S[x], where $m \geqq n$, then the *sum* of f(x) and g(x) is as follows:

$$f(x) + g(x) = (a_0 + b_0) + (a_1 + b_1)x + (a_2 + b_2)x^2 + \ldots + (a_n + b_n)x^n + b_{n+1}x^{n+1} + \ldots + b_mx^m.$$

The *product* of the polynomials f(x) and g(x) is as follows:

$$f(x) \cdot g(x) = (a_0b_0) + (a_1b_0 + a_0b_1)x + (a_2b_0 + a_1b_1 + a_0b_2)x^2 + \ldots + (a_ib_0 + a_{i-1}b_1 + \ldots + a_0b_i)x^i + \ldots + (a_nb_0 + \ldots + a_0b_n)x^n + \ldots + (a_nb_m)x^{n+m}.$$

The definitions of the sum and the product of two polynomials appear somewhat more complicated than they actually are. To find the sum of two polynomials, you simply add the coefficients of corresponding terms, that is, of terms of the same degree. To see how the definition of sum is applied, study the examples below that illustrate sums of polynomials whose coefficients are in the ring of rational numbers.

Examples 1 $(6 + 3x + 5x^2) + \big(-3 + x^2 + (-2x^3)\big) = 3 + 3x + 6x^2 + (-2x^3).$

2 $(x^2 + x^5) + \big(3x + (-\frac{1}{4}x^3) + x^4\big) = 3x + x^2 + (-\frac{1}{4}x^3) + x^4 + x^5.$

3 $(3 + 7x^3) + (-3 + x^2) = x^2 + 7x^3.$

The definition of the product of two polynomials is a bit more complicated than the definition of the sum. What multiplication of polynomials really amounts to is repeated use of the distributive property so that each term of the first polynomial is multiplied by each term of the second polynomial. Then the coefficients of the terms of the same degree among the resulting products are added together.

4 $\big(2 + x + (-2x^2)\big)(-3 + x) = -6 + (-1x) + 7x^2 + (-2x^3).$

5 $\big(4x + (-3x^3)\big)\left(7 + \frac{x^2}{2}\right) = 28x + (-19x^3) + \frac{-3x^5}{2}.$

6 $\big(2 + (-4x)\big)(2 + 4x) = 4 + (-16x^2).$

The examples should make clear how to obtain the coefficient of the ith term in the product, but the following generalization may be helpful. The coefficient of the ith term of the product of two polynomials is the sum of all the coefficients among the partial products whose subscripts have as a sum the degree of the term. Thus, the coefficient c_i of the $(i + 1)$st term c_ix^i in the product is

$$a_ib_0 + a_{i-1}b_1 + \ldots + a_{i-j}b_j + \ldots + a_0b_i.$$

In the foregoing examples all the coefficients of the polynomials are in the ring of rational numbers. Notice that the sum or product of two polynomials with rational coefficients is again a polynomial with rational coefficients. However, the definition of addition and multiplication of polynomials is a general one so that the coefficients may be in any ring. As the next step in the development of polynomial rings, we will consider sums and products of polynomials with coefficients in the ring of integers modulo 3. In examples 7 through 10, the coefficients of the sums and products of the polynomials are determined by using the definitions of sums and products in I/3. Remember that $\bar{2}$, for example, represents the equivalence class of integers congruent to 2 modulo 3. To simplify the notation, we have omitted the symbol for modular multiplication, $\odot_3$, between the coefficients and the powers of x; and we have used an ordinary plus sign rather than $\oplus_3$ between the terms of the polynomials.

7 $(\bar{2} + \bar{1}x + \bar{2}x^2) \oplus_3 (\bar{2}x + \bar{1}x^3) = (\bar{2} + \bar{0}x + \bar{2}x^2 + \bar{1}x^3).$

8 $(\bar{2} + \bar{2}x^2 + \bar{1}x^3) \oplus_3 (\bar{2} + \bar{1}x + \bar{1}x^2) = (\bar{1} + \bar{1}x + \bar{0}x^2 + \bar{1}x^3).$

9 $(\bar{1} + \bar{1}x + \bar{2}x^2) \odot_3 (\bar{2} + \bar{1}x) = (\bar{2} + \bar{0}x + \bar{2}x^2 + \bar{2}x^3).$

10 $(\bar{2}x + \bar{2}x^3) \odot_3 (\bar{1} + \bar{2}x + \bar{1}x^2) = (\bar{2}x + \bar{1}x^2 + \bar{1}x^3 + \bar{1}x^4 + \bar{2}x^5).$

From these examples, we see that the coefficients of the sums and products are elements of $(I/3, \oplus_3, \odot_3)$. The preceding discussion suggests that the set of all polynomials over a commutative ring with identity is itself a commutative ring with identity. This is indeed the case, as the following theorem states.

Theorem 55/3 If $(S, +, \cdot)$ is a commutative ring with identity and $S[x]$ is the set of all polynomials in x with coefficients in the ring S, then $(S[x], +, \cdot)$ is a commutative ring with identity.

No proof is given for this theorem because the notation becomes somewhat complicated. However, the following properties of $(S[x], +, \cdot)$ should be apparent. If 1 is the multiplicative identity of the ring S, then $1x^0 = 1$ is the multiplicative identity of the ring $S[x]$. The additive identity of $S[x]$ is the polynomial $0x^0 = 0$, where 0 is the additive identity of S. Also, if a polynomial has coefficients $a_0, a_1, a_2, \ldots, a_n$, then its additive inverse has coefficients $-a_0, -a_1, -a_2, \ldots, -a_n$.

The symbol x has been used throughout this discussion as an *indeterminate*, and the operations as defined in Definition 54/3 show how to treat this symbol so that the resulting system is a ring. However, x also frequently represents a *variable* for any member of the ring S, and thus, it may be replaced by a particular element of S in a particular polynomial to yield an element of the ring S. (Keep in mind that this is different from using the elements of S as replacements for $a_0, a_1, a_2, \ldots, a_n$ to yield elements of $S[x]$.) If x is thought of as a variable, however, one important problem is to choose replacements for $x \in S$ that yield the additive identity, or the zero element, of the ring S. This process is called finding the *zeros of the polynomial* or *solving* the polynomial. There are formulas in terms of radicals of the coefficients for solving polynomials that can be applied to polynomials of degrees 2, 3, and 4, with rational coefficients, but it has been proven that no general formulas exist for polynomials of degree greater than four. However, we are not concerned with deriving or applying formulas here. Instead we want to describe a function from S[x] into S and to investigate the properties of such a function.

Definition 55/3 If (S, +, ·) is a commutative ring with identity and S[x] is the set of polynomials with coefficients in S, then, for each $c \in$ S, f_c is the function given by

$$p(x) \xrightarrow{f_c} p(c) \quad \text{or}$$
$$(p(x))f_c = p(c)$$

for each p(x) $\in$ S[x].

The definition asserts that f_c is a function, but before verifying that this is the case, we will give some examples to illustrate this definition. For the following examples the domain of each function f_c is I[x], the set of all polynomials over the ring of integers, and the range is I.

Examples 1 If $p(x) = 3 + (-2x) + 5x^3$, then

$$(p(x))f_1 = p(1) = 3 + (-2) + 5 = 6 \text{ and}$$
$$(p(x))f_3 = p(3) = 3 + (-6) + 135 = 132.$$

2 If $r(x) = -4 + 3x^2 + x^4$, then

$$(r(x))f_0 = r(0) = -4 + 0 + 0 = -4 \text{ and}$$
$$(r(x))f_{-1} = r(-1) = -4 + 3 + 1 = 0.$$

3 If $s(x) = 16 + (-x^6)$, then

$$(s(x))f_2 = s(2) = 16 + (-64) = -48,$$
$$(s(x))f_1 = s(1) = 16 + (-1) = 15, \text{ and}$$
$$(s(x))f_3 = s(3) = 16 + (-729) = -713.$$

The preceding examples show how to substitute an element of the ring (I, +, ·) for the variable x in a polynomial of I[x] to obtain an element of the ring (I, +, ·). We will now investigate the properties of the arbitrary function f_c of Definition 55/3 and, in the process, verify that the mapping actually *is* a function.

Observe first that, for each p(x) $\in$ S[x], there is a corresponding element p(c) $\in$ S; hence, the relation f_c is *from* S[x]. That f_c is a function is confirmed by observing that if p(x) = q(x), then

$$(p(x))f_c = (q(x))f_c.$$

So far we know that f_c is a function from S[x] into S. Is the function onto? Let $a \in$ S and try to find a polynomial p(x) in

S[x] such that $(\mathrm{p}(x))\mathrm{f}_c = a$. A little thought should convince you that the constant polynomial $\mathrm{p}(x) = a$ is such that $(\mathrm{p}(x))\mathrm{f}_c = a$. Therefore, the function is *onto*.

However, the function f_c need not be one-to-one. We will now give an example to show why this is so. Consider the ring of polynomials I[x] whose coefficients are in the ring of integers (I, +, •). Two elements of this ring are

$$\mathrm{p}(x) = x - 3 \text{ and}$$
$$\mathrm{q}(x) = x^2 + x - 7.$$

If $c = 2$, then

$$(\mathrm{p}(x))\mathrm{f}_c = (\mathrm{p}(x))\mathrm{f}_2 = \mathrm{p}(2) = 2 - 3 = -1 \text{ and}$$
$$(\mathrm{q}(x))\mathrm{f}_c = (\mathrm{q}(x))\mathrm{f}_2 = \mathrm{q}(2) = 2^2 + 2 - 7 = -1.$$

Thus, we see that there are at least two polynomials, $x - 3$ and $x^2 + x - 7$, whose images are -1 under the function f_2. See if you can find other polynomials in I[x] that are mapped by f_2 onto -1. Recall that functions for which more than one domain element has the same image are called many-to-one functions.

In connection with groups and rings, we have considered a special kind of one-to-one function called an isomorphism that preserves the operations of the given mathematical system. Obviously, the polynomial function f_c is not always an isomorphism since we have just given an example of a polynomial function that is not one-to-one. However, this function does preserve the operations of the two rings. The following theorem establishes this claim.

Theorem 56/3 If (S, +, •) is a commutative ring with identity and f_c is the function from the ring S[x] onto the ring S given by $\mathrm{p}(x) \xrightarrow{\mathrm{f}_c} \mathrm{p}(c)$ for a given $c \in$ S, then f_c satisfies

$$\mathrm{p}(x) + \mathrm{q}(x) \xrightarrow{\mathrm{f}_c} \mathrm{p}(c) + \mathrm{q}(c) \text{ and}$$
$$\mathrm{p}(x) \cdot \mathrm{q}(x) \xrightarrow{\mathrm{f}_c} \mathrm{p}(c) \cdot \mathrm{q}(c).$$

Proof Let $\mathrm{p}(x)$ and $\mathrm{q}(x)$ be elements in S[x] that can be expressed as follows, with $m \geqq n$ and with each $a_i, b_i \in$ S:

$$\mathrm{p}(x) = a_0 + a_1x + a_2x^2 + \ldots + a_nx^n,$$
$$\mathrm{q}(x) = b_0 + b_1x + b_2x^2 + \ldots + b_mx^m.$$

To establish that f_c preserves addition, we must show that if

$$\mathrm{p}(x) \xrightarrow{\mathrm{f}_c} \mathrm{p}(c)$$

and

$$q(x) \xrightarrow{f_c} q(c),$$

then

$$p(x) + q(x) \xrightarrow{f_c} p(c) + q(c).$$

In different notation, if f_c preserves addition, then

$$\big(p(x)\big)f_c = p(c) \text{ and } \big(q(x)\big)f_c = q(c)$$

imply that

$$\big(p(x) + q(x)\big)f_c = p(c) + q(c).$$

This result is easily established. First, consider $\big(p(x) + q(x)\big)f_c$. By Definitions 54/3 and 55/3,

$$\begin{aligned}\big(p(x) + q(x)\big)f_c &= [(a_0 + b_0) + (a_1 + b_1)x + \ldots (a_n + b_n)x^n + \ldots + b_mx^m]f_c \\ &= (a_0 + b_0) + (a_1 + b_1)c + \ldots (a_n + b_n)c^n + \ldots + b_mc^m.\end{aligned}$$

Now consider $p(x)f_c + q(x)f_c$. By Definition 52/3,

$$\begin{aligned}\big(p(x)\big)f_c &= p(c) = a_0 + a_1c + a_2c^2 + \ldots + a_nc^n, \\ \big(q(x)\big)f_c &= q(c) = b_0 + b_1c + b_2c^2 + \ldots + b_mc^m.\end{aligned}$$

But by the associative and commutative properties of addition and the distributive property of ring S,

$$p(c) + q(c) = (a_0 + b_0) + (a_1 + b_1)c + \ldots + (a_n + b_n)c^n + \ldots + b_mc^m.$$

Hence, $\big(p(x) + q(x)\big)f_c = p(c) + q(c)$, and f_c preserves addition in $(S[x], +, \cdot)$ and $(S, +, \cdot)$.

The proof that the function f_c preserves multiplication is left as an exercise at the end of the section.

In the previous section we saw that if f is a homomorphism from a ring onto a ring, then the set of elements in the domain that map onto the additive identity of the range forms an ideal. The set of polynomials in $(S[x], +, \cdot)$ that map onto 0_S [the additive identity of $(S, +, \cdot)$] by the homomorphism f_c consists of all polynomials $p(x)$ such that $\big(p(x)\big)f_c = 0_S$. Therefore, the set of polynomials that have c as a root forms an ideal of the ring of polynomials.

Exercises

1 Determine first the sum and then the product of each pair of polynomials given below.

a $3x^2 - 5x^4$, $6 + 4x^2$

b 14, $x - 2x^3 + 3x^4$

c $x - 2$, $x + 2$

d $\frac{1}{4}$, $4 + 16x^2 + 24x^3 - 16x^4$

e $6x$, $5x$

2 Complete the proof of Theorem 56/3 by proving that function f_c defined by $(p(x))f_c = p(c)$, which maps the ring $(S[x], +, \cdot)$ onto the ring $(S, +, \cdot)$, preserves multiplication. Follow the pattern of the proof that $(p(x) + q(x))f_c = p(c) + q(c)$.

Consider the ring $(I/8, \oplus_8, \odot_8)$. If we form the ring of all polynomials in x with coefficients in $I/8$, we have $(I/8[x], \oplus_8, \odot_8)$. Let $f(x)$, $g(x)$, and $h(x) \in I/8[x]$, where

$$f(x) = \bar{3} + \bar{5}x + \bar{1}x^2,$$
$$g(x) = \bar{4} + \bar{2}x + \bar{3}x^3,$$
$$h(x) = \bar{7} + \bar{6}x^3.$$

Use these functions in connection with exercises 3 through 6.

3 Determine the following members of $(I/8[x], \oplus_8, \odot_8)$.

a $f(x) \oplus_8 g(x)$ *Answer*
b $f(x) \oplus_8 h(x)$
c $f(x) \odot_8 g(x)$ *Answer*
d $f(x) \odot_8 h(x)$
e $g(x) \odot_8 h(x)$
f $f(x) \oplus_8 g(x) \oplus_8 h(x)$
g $f(x) \odot_8 g(x) \odot_8 h(x)$

4 Let f_c be a function from $I/8[x]$ onto $I/8$. Determine the following elements of $I/8$.

a $(f(x))f_{\bar{0}}$ *Answer*
b $(f(x))f_{\bar{5}}$
c $(g(x))f_{\bar{3}}$ *Answer*
d $(g(x))f_{\bar{6}}$
e $(h(x))f_{\bar{1}}$
f $(h(x))f_{\bar{4}}$

5 What is the additive identity of $(I/8[x], \oplus_8, \odot_8)$? What is the multiplicative identity of this ring?

6 Determine the additive inverse for the following.

a $f(x)$ *Answer* b $g(x)$ c $h(x)$

◆ 7 Can we form the ring of polynomials in x with coefficients in $I_{2\times 2}$, that is, $(I_{2\times 2}[x], +, \cdot)$? What difficulty is encountered?

Often polynomial rings are defined over a ring with an identity that is not commutative. This is the approach that we will use in exercises 8 through 13. Let $f_R(x)$, $g_R(x)$, $h_R(x)$, and $f_L(x) \in I_{2\times 2}[x]$ be defined as follows:

$$f_R(x) = \begin{pmatrix} 1 & 1 \\ 0 & 1 \end{pmatrix} + \begin{pmatrix} 2 & 0 \\ 2 & 0 \end{pmatrix}x + \begin{pmatrix} 0 & 1 \\ -1 & 0 \end{pmatrix}x^2.$$

$$g_R(x) = \begin{pmatrix} 2 & 0 \\ 1 & -2 \end{pmatrix} + \begin{pmatrix} 1 & 0 \\ 0 & 1 \end{pmatrix}x + \begin{pmatrix} 1 & 3 \\ -3 & 0 \end{pmatrix}x^3.$$

$$h_R(x) = \begin{pmatrix} 1 & 2 \\ -2 & 1 \end{pmatrix} + \begin{pmatrix} 2 & 4 \\ 0 & 0 \end{pmatrix}x^3.$$

$$f_L(x) = \begin{pmatrix} 1 & 1 \\ 0 & 1 \end{pmatrix} + x\begin{pmatrix} 2 & 0 \\ 2 & 0 \end{pmatrix} + x^2\begin{pmatrix} 0 & 1 \\ -1 & 0 \end{pmatrix}.$$

◆ **8** Determine the following members of $(I_{2\times 2}[x], +, \cdot)$.

a $f_R(x) + g_R(x)$ **d** $f_R(x) \cdot g_R(x)$

b $f_R(x) + h_R(x)$ *Answer* **e** $f_R(x) \cdot h_R(x)$

c $g_R(x) + h_R(x)$ **f** $g_R(x) \cdot f_R(x)$

◆ **9** Let f_c be a function from $(I_{2\times 2}[x], +, \cdot)$ onto $(I_{2\times 2}, +, \cdot)$. Compute the following elements of $I_{2\times 2}$.

a $(f_R(x))f_c$, where $c = \begin{pmatrix} 1 & 0 \\ 1 & 1 \end{pmatrix}$ *Answer*

b $(g_R(x))f_c$, where $c = \begin{pmatrix} 1 & 0 \\ 0 & -1 \end{pmatrix}$

c $(h_R(x))f_c$, where $c = \begin{pmatrix} 0 & 1 \\ 1 & 0 \end{pmatrix}$

d $(f_L(x))f_c$, where $c = \begin{pmatrix} 1 & 0 \\ 1 & 1 \end{pmatrix}$

◆ **10** Compare $f_R(x)$ and $f_L(x)$ and define $g_L(x)$. What is $(g_L(x))f_c$, where $c = \begin{pmatrix} 1 & 0 \\ 0 & -1 \end{pmatrix}$? Is $(g_L(x))f_c$, where $c = \begin{pmatrix} 1 & 0 \\ 0 & -1 \end{pmatrix}$ the same as $(g_R(x))f_c$, where $c = \begin{pmatrix} 1 & 0 \\ 0 & -1 \end{pmatrix}$?

◆ **11** Define $h_L(x)$. Is $(h_L(x))f_c$, where $c = \begin{pmatrix} 0 & 1 \\ 1 & 0 \end{pmatrix}$ the same as $(h_R(x))f_c$, where $c = \begin{pmatrix} 0 & 1 \\ 1 & 0 \end{pmatrix}$?

◆ **12** What is the additive identity of $(I_{2\times 2}[x], +, \cdot)$? What is the multiplicative identity?

◆ **13** Determine the additive inverses for the following elements of $I_{2\times 2}[x]$.

a $f_R(x)$ **b** $g_R(x)$ **c** $h_R(x)$ **d** $f_L(x)$

Consider the ring $(G(i), +, \cdot)$. Form the ring of polynomials in x with coefficients in $G(i)$, that is, $(G(i)[x], +, \cdot)$. Let $f(x)$, $g(x)$, and $h(x) \in G(i)[x]$ be defined as follows:

$$f(x) = (2 + 0i) + (1 + 2i)x + (0 - 1i)x^2.$$
$$g(x) = (-3 + 2i) + (4 - 3i)x^2 + (2 + 1i)x^3.$$
$$h(x) = (0 + 5i) + (-1 - 2i)x^2.$$

Use these polynomials in connection with exercises 14 through 17.

14 Determine the following members of $(G(i)[x], +, \cdot)$.

a $f(x) + g(x)$ **d** $f(x) \cdot g(x)$

b $f(x) + h(x)$ **e** $f(x) \cdot h(x)$

c $g(x) + h(x)$ **f** $g(x) \cdot h(x)$

15 Let f_c be a function from $(G(i)[x], +, \cdot)$ onto $(G(i), +, \cdot)$. Compute the following elements of $G(i)$.

a $(f(x))f_c$, where $c = 1 + 1i$

b $(g(x))f_c$, where $c = 0 + 2i$

c $(h(x))f_c$, where $c = 3 - 2i$

16 What is the additive identity of $(G(i)[x], +, \cdot)$? What is the multiplicative identity?

17 Find additive inverses for the following elements of $G(i)[x]$.

a $f(x)$ b $g(x)$ c $h(x)$

18 Consider the ring of polynomials $(I[x], +, \cdot)$ where $p(x) = a_0 + a_1x + a_2x^2 + \ldots + a_nx^n$ is a typical element. Which of the following subsets of $I[x]$ under $+$ and $\cdot$ are subrings of $(I[x], +, \cdot)$?

a $\{p(x) \mid a_0 = 0\}$ *Answer*

b $\{p(x) \mid a_1 = 0\}$

c $\{p(x) \mid a_2 = 0\}$

d $\{p(x) \mid a_0 = a_1 = 0\}$

e $\{p(x) \mid a_0 = 0 \text{ and } a_1 + a_2 = 0\}$

19 Find all subrings of the ring $(I/6[x], \oplus_6, \odot_6)$. *Answer*

20 Find all subrings of the ring of polynomials $(I/12[x], \oplus_{12}, \odot_{12})$.

21 Find all subrings of the ring of polynomials $(I/20[x], \oplus_{20}, \odot_{20})$.

◆ 22 Let $(S, +, \cdot)$ be a commutative ring with identity. Prove that if $(T, +, \cdot)$ is a subring of $(S, +, \cdot)$, then $(T[x], +, \cdot)$ is a subring of $(S[x], +, \cdot)$. *Answer*

◆ 23 Let $(S, +, \cdot)$ be a commutative ring with identity. Prove that if $(T, +, \cdot)$ is an ideal of $(S, +, \cdot)$, then $(T[x], +, \cdot)$ is an ideal of $(S[x], +, \cdot)$.

24 Which of the subrings in exercise 18 are ideals?

25 Consider the subset of $R[x]$ given by $(x^2) = \{kx^2 \mid k \in R\}$. Is $((x^2), +, \cdot)$ an ideal of $(R[x], +, \cdot)$?

26 By analogy with exercise 25, define subset $(x - 1)$ of $R[x]$. Is $((x - 1), +, \cdot)$ an ideal of $(R[x], +, \cdot)$?

27 By analogy with exercise 25, define subset $(x^2 - 1)$ of $R[x]$. Is $((x^2 - 1), +, \cdot)$ an ideal of $(R[x], +, \cdot)$?

28 What is the form of $(x^2) \cap (x - 1)$? Of $(x^2) \cap (x^2 - 1)$? Of $(x - 1) \cap (x^2 - 1)$?

29 What is the form of $(x^2) \cup (x - 1)$? Of $(x^2) \cup (x^2 - 1)$? Of $(x - 1) \cup (x^2 - 1)$?

Integral domains 32/3

So far in this chapter, we have discussed rings, commutative rings, rings with identity, and commutative rings with identity. As the title of this chapter indicates, we will also consider another kind of mathematical system here—a structure that is called an *integral domain*. An integral domain has all the properties of a commutative ring with identity and one more property. To illustrate this new property, we will use the system of real numbers. For real numbers, the property may be expressed as follows: If x and y are real numbers and if the product of x and y is zero, then x is zero or y is zero. Symbolically, if $x, y \in \mathfrak{R}$, then $x \cdot y = 0$ implies that $x = 0$ or $y = 0$.

Certainly, you are already familiar with one important application of this property of real numbers—in the solution of quadratic equations.

Examples 1 For example, if we are given the quadratic equation

$$x^2 - x - 2 = 0,$$

then another way of expressing the same equation is

$$(x + 1)(x - 2) = 0.$$

Since $x + 1$ and $x - 2$ are real numbers, we can apply the property stated above to this particular example to obtain

$$x + 1 = 0 \text{ or } x - 2 = 0.$$

The assumption that $x^2 - x - 2 = 0$ has solutions in $\mathfrak{R}$ leads to the conclusion that $x = -1$ or $x = 2$. When we replace x by -1 or 2 in $x^2 - x - 2 = 0$, we see that each of the two possible solutions is in fact a solution. That is,

$$(-1)^2 - (-1) - 2 = 0, \text{ and}$$
$$2^2 - 2 - 2 = 0.$$

This example illustrates that in determining the solution set of a quadratic equation with coefficients in the set of real numbers, we often use the property that if $x \cdot y = 0$, then $x = 0$ or $y = 0$. We are justified in using this property in connection with this example because it is a property of the real-number system.

However, we have considered some systems in this book that do *not* have this property. Two examples of such systems are the ring of integers modulo 6, $(I/6, \oplus_6, \odot_6)$, and the ring of even 2×2 matrices, $(E_{2 \times 2}, +, \cdot)$. In examples 2 and 3 below, we have chosen elements x and y in these systems for which the product $x \cdot y$ is equal to the additive identity, but neither of the factors is the additive identity.

2 $\bar{2} \odot_6 \bar{3} = \bar{0}$, but $\bar{2} \neq \bar{0}$ and $\bar{3} \neq \bar{0}$.

3 $\begin{pmatrix} 2 & 0 \\ 2 & 0 \end{pmatrix} \cdot \begin{pmatrix} 0 & 0 \\ 0 & 2 \end{pmatrix} = \begin{pmatrix} 0 & 0 \\ 0 & 0 \end{pmatrix}$, but $\begin{pmatrix} 2 & 0 \\ 2 & 0 \end{pmatrix} \neq \begin{pmatrix} 0 & 0 \\ 0 & 0 \end{pmatrix}$ and

$$\begin{pmatrix} 0 & 0 \\ 0 & 2 \end{pmatrix} \neq \begin{pmatrix} 0 & 0 \\ 0 & 0 \end{pmatrix}.$$

If a system contains elements x and y such that $x \cdot y = 0$, but $x \neq 0$ and $y \neq 0$, then the system is said to contain elements that are *divisors of zero*. If, however, for all elements x and y of a system, $x \cdot y = 0$ implies that $x = 0$ or $y = 0$, then the system has no divisors of zero. From examples 1, 2, and 3 we see that the real-number system has no divisors of zero, but $(I/6, \oplus_6, \odot_6)$ and $(E_{2 \times 2}, +, \cdot)$ do have divisors of zero. The property that we have been discussing is the property that distinguishes an integral domain from a commutative ring with identity, as stated in the following definition.

Definition 56/3 If $(S, +, \cdot)$ is a commutative ring with identity, then $(S, +, \cdot)$ is an *integral domain* if and only if S contains no divisors of zero. Symbolically, $(S, +, \cdot)$ is an integral domain if and only if for each $x, y \in S$,

11 $x \cdot y = 0$ implies that $x = 0$ or $y = 0$.

Thus, an integral domain is a mathematical system with the ten properties of a commutative ring with identity and the eleventh property of having no divisors of zero. The name integral domain indicates that there might be some connection between the integers and integral domains. Such a connection may be found in the fact that the integers under addition and multiplication satisfy the eleven properties of an integral domain.

One of the central goals of this book has been to prove, whenever possible, theorems that characterize and classify mathematical systems. We will now prove a theorem about the integers modulo n that will make it possible for us to decide which replacements of n ensure that the ring I/n is an integral domain. In section 26/3 we showed that, for each n, the integers modulo n form a commutative ring with identity. We have also shown that the ring of integers modulo 6 has divisors of zero and, hence, is not an example of an integral domain. Thus, it is apparent that, at least for one replacement of n, I/n is not an integral domain.

Given next are some examples of rings of integers modulo n in which it is possible to obtain $\bar{0}$ as a product without either of the factors being $\bar{0}$. Also listed are some examples of rings of integers modulo n in which it is not possible to obtain $\bar{0}$ as a product unless at least one of the factors is $\bar{0}$.

	System	Example of divisors of zero
Examples	I/2	None
	I/3	None
	I/4	$\bar{2} \odot_4 \bar{2} = \bar{0}$.
	I/5	None
	I/6	$\bar{2} \odot_6 \bar{3} = \bar{0}$.
	I/7	None
	I/8	$\bar{2} \odot_8 \bar{4} = \bar{0}$.
	I/9	$\bar{3} \odot_9 \bar{3} = \bar{0}$.
	I/10	$\bar{5} \odot_{10} \bar{2} = \bar{0}$.
	I/11	None
	I/12	$\bar{4} \odot_{12} \bar{3} = \bar{0}$.
	I/13	None
	I/14	$\bar{7} \odot_{14} \bar{2} = \bar{0}$.
	I/15	$\bar{5} \odot_{15} \bar{3} = \bar{0}$.
	I/17	None

Notice that each system with divisors of zero (I/4, I/6, I/8, I/9, I/10, I/12, I/14, I/15) has a composite number as its modulus. However, each system with no divisors of zero (I/2, I/3, I/5, I/7, I/11, I/13, I/17) has a prime number as its modulus. These examples seem to indicate that the integers modulo n form an integral domain if and only if n is prime. This is indeed the case, as the following theorem establishes.

Theorem 57/3 If $n \in \mathrm{I}$, $n > 1$, then the commutative ring with identity, $(\mathrm{I}/n, \oplus_n, \odot_n)$, is an integral domain if and only if n is prime.

Proof To prove the theorem, it is necessary to establish the conditions under which the ring I/n satisfies the property that if the product of two elements is $\bar{0}$, then one or both of the elements are $\bar{0}$. The theorem has two parts, and we will verify each of these parts.

First, if n is an integer greater than 1 such that I/n is an integral domain, then it is necessary to establish that n is a prime integer. This is best proved by the method of contradiction. We begin by assuming that I/n is an integral domain and that there exist positive integers a and b, with $1 < a < n$ and $1 < b < n$, such that $a \cdot b = n$. In other words, we assume that I/n is an integral domain for some composite integer n. We will show that this assumption leads to a contradiction of property 11 of an integral domain.

Since $a \in \bar{a}$ and $b \in \bar{b}$, the equations $a \cdot b = n$ and $\bar{a} \odot_n \bar{b} = \bar{n}$ are equivalent. So, because $\bar{n} = \bar{0}$, we have

$$\begin{aligned} \bar{a} \odot_n \bar{b} &= \bar{n} \\ &= \bar{0}. \end{aligned}$$

Hence, $\bar{a}$ and $\bar{b}$ are divisors of $\bar{0}$. This contradicts the hypothesis that I/n is an integral domain. The assumption that n is composite leads to a contradiction, so n is prime. Therefore, we have shown that, if the integers modulo n form an integral domain, then n is prime.

We have already verified that (I/n, $\oplus_n$, $\odot_n$) satisfies the properties of a commutative ring with identity. Therefore, to establish the second part of the theorem, it is necessary to show that if n is prime, then there are no zero divisors in the ring (I/n, $\oplus_n$, $\odot_n$).

We will use an indirect proof for this part of the theorem also. That is, we will assume that there exist integers x and y in I, with $1 < x < n$ and $1 < y < n$, such that $\bar{x} \odot_n \bar{y} = \bar{0}$. But, since $\bar{n} = \bar{0}$, this implies that $\bar{x} \odot_n \bar{y} = \bar{n}$. Further, since x and y are less than n, this means that $x \cdot y = n$. If $x \cdot y = n$, then n has integral divisors greater than 1 and less than n, which contradicts the hypothesis that n is prime. Thus, if n is prime, the system (I/n, $\oplus_n$, $\odot_n$) has no zero divisors and is an integral domain.

We have used the property of not having zero divisors to distinguish an integral domain from a commutative ring with identity. Another distinguishing property of an integral domain is the *cancellation property* for multiplication. An alternative definition of an integral domain in terms of this property is given in Definition 57/3, followed by a theorem that demonstrates that the property of having no zero divisors and the cancellation property of multiplication are equivalent.

Definition 57/3 If (S, +, •) is a commutative ring with identity, then (S, +, •) is an integral domain if and only if the multiplicative cancellation property holds. Symbolically, if x, y, $a \in$ S, with $a \neq 0$, then (S, +, •) is an integral domain if and only if

11a $xa = ya$ implies that $x = y$.

Since we have already defined an integral domain in terms of having no zero divisors, we must show that Definition 57/3 is equivalent to Definition 56/3. Notice that we have labeled the multiplicative cancellation property as property 11a to distinguish it from property 11 given in Definition 56/3 and to indicate that property 11a can also be thought of as the eleventh property of an integral domain. The following theorem establishes that 11 and 11a are equivalent properties.

Theorem 58/3 If (S, +, •) is a commutative ring with identity, then (S, +, •) has no zero divisors if and only if (S, +, •) has the cancellation property for multiplication.

Proof To prove the first part of this theorem, we assume that (S, +, •) satisfies the property that, if $u, v \in S$ and $u \cdot v = 0$, then $u = 0$ or $v = 0$. We must show that it follows from this that, if $xa = ya$ with $a \neq 0$, then $x = y$. The steps below establish the proof. You should supply reasons for the steps.

$$xa = ya.$$
$$xa + (-ya) = 0.$$
$$xa + (-y)a = 0.$$
$$\big(x + (-y)\big)a = 0.$$
$$x + (-y) = 0.$$
$$x = y.$$

For the second part of the proof, we assume that (S, +, •) satisfies the property that $xa = ya$ implies $x = y$, where $x, y, a \in S$ and $a \neq 0$. We must show that it follows from this that $x \cdot y = 0$ implies that $x = 0$ or $y = 0$. The steps below establish that if y is assumed to be different from 0, it follows that x must be 0 under the given hypothesis.

$$x \cdot y = 0,\ y \neq 0.$$
$$x \cdot y = 0 \cdot y.$$
$$x = 0.$$

You should give a similar argument to show that if $x \cdot y = 0$ with $x \neq 0$, then $y = 0$.

From Theorem 58/3, it follows that the cancellation property can be used to distinguish integral domains. As we remarked earlier, some books use this property rather than the property of having no zero divisors to define an integral domain.

Exercises

1 Supply reasons for the steps in the proof of Theorem 58/3.

2 Let (S, +, •) be an integral domain. Prove that, if $x \in S$ and $x \cdot x = x$, then $x = 0$ or $x = 1$. *Answer*

3 Determine whether the following rings are also integral domains.

a (R, +, •) *Answer*

b ($\mathfrak{R}$, +, •)

c ($\{6x \mid x \in I\}$, +, •)

d ($\mathbb{S}$, +, •), where $\mathbb{S}$ is the collection of all subsets of a set S, and for each $A, B \in \mathbb{S}$,

$$A + B = \{x \mid x \in A \cup B \text{ and } x \notin A \cap B\},$$
$$A \cdot B = \{x \mid x \in A \cap B\}$$

◆ **e** $(\mathcal{I}, +, \cdot)$, where $\mathcal{I}$ is the set of all functions with domain the set of integers and range in the set of integers, and for each f, g $\in \mathcal{I}$,

$$(x)(\mathrm{f} + \mathrm{g}) = (x)\mathrm{f} + (x)\mathrm{g},$$
$$(x)(\mathrm{f} \cdot \mathrm{g}) = (x)\mathrm{f} \cdot (x)\mathrm{g}$$

[Hint: Consider the product of the two functions $(x)\mathrm{f} = \max\{0, x\}$ and $(x)\mathrm{g} = \max\{0, -x\}$, which are elements of $\mathcal{I}$.]

◆ **f** $(\mathcal{I}, +, \circ)$, where $\mathcal{I}$ is the set of all functions with domain the set of integers and range in the set of integers, and, for each f, g $\in \mathcal{I}$,

$$(x)(\mathrm{f} + \mathrm{g}) = (x)\mathrm{f} + (x)\mathrm{g},$$
$$(x)(\mathrm{f} \circ \mathrm{g}) = \big((x)\mathrm{f}\big)\mathrm{g}$$ *Answer*

4 Determine whether the following polynomial rings are integral domains.

a $(\mathrm{I}/8[x], \oplus_8, \odot_8)$

b $(\mathrm{I}_{2 \times 2}[x], +, \cdot)$ *Answer*

c $\big(\mathrm{G}(i)[x], +, \cdot\big)$

d $(\mathrm{I}/7[x], \oplus_7, \odot_7)$

e $(\mathrm{R}[x], +, \cdot)$

5 Determine whether the following subrings are integral domains.

a $(\{a + 0i \mid a \in \mathrm{I} \text{ and } i^2 = -1\}, +, \cdot)$

b $(\{\mathrm{A} \mid \mathrm{A} \in \mathrm{I}_{2 \times 2} \text{ and } a_{21} = 0\}, +, \cdot)$

c $(\mathrm{R}_2, +, \cdot)$ where $\mathrm{R}_2 = \left\{\frac{m}{n} \mid m, n \in \mathrm{I}, n \neq 0,\ m \text{ and } n \text{ are relatively prime, and 2 is not a factor of } n\right\}$ *Answer*

d $(\mathrm{R}_6, +, \cdot)$ where $\mathrm{R}_6 = \left\{\frac{m}{n} \mid m, n \in \mathrm{I},\ n \neq 0,\ m \text{ and } n \text{ are relatively prime, and 6 is not a factor of } n\right\}$ *Answer*

e $(\{\mathrm{A} \mid \mathrm{A} \in \mathrm{M}_{2 \times 2}, a_{12} = a_{21} = 0\}, +, \cdot)$

f $\left(\left\{\frac{a}{2^n} \mid a, n \in \mathrm{I}\right\}, +, \cdot\right)$

g $\left(\left\{\frac{a}{2^m \cdot 3^n} \mid a, m, n \in \mathrm{I}\right\}, +, \cdot\right)$

h $\left(\left\{\frac{a}{2^m \cdot 6^n} \mid a, m, n \in \mathrm{I}\right\}, +, \cdot\right)$

i $(\{a + b\sqrt[4]{5} \mid a, b \in \mathrm{I}\}, +, \cdot)$

j $(\{a + b\sqrt[4]{9} \mid a, b \in \mathrm{I}\}, +, \cdot)$ *Answer*

◆ **6** Show that in an integral domain the commutative property of addition may be established from the additive-identity and the distributive properties. Could this be established in a commutative ring with identity? A commutative ring? A ring? [Hint: Expand $(a + b) \cdot (1 + 1)$ in two ways.]

◆ 7 Prove that if $(D, +, \cdot)$ is an integral domain, then $(D[x], +, \cdot)$ is an integral domain.

8 By analogy with the definitions of a subgroup and of a subring, define a subdomain of the integral domain $(D, +, \cdot)$.

◆ 9 Let $(D, +, \cdot)$ be an integral domain and S be a subset of D. Prove that $(S, +, \cdot)$ is a subdomain of $(D, +, \cdot)$ if $(S, +, \cdot)$ contains the identities of $(D, +, \cdot)$, S is closed under addition, and $a \in S$ implies $-a \in S$.

Chapter review

1 Show that if a ring $(S, +, \cdot)$ has a multiplicative identity e, then e is unique.

2 Let $(G, +)$ be a commutative group. Define $a \cdot b = 0$ for each $a, b \in G$, where 0 is the additive identity of $(G, +)$. Prove that $(G, +, \cdot)$ is a ring. Is $(G, +, \cdot)$ commutative? Does it have a multiplicative identity?

3 Which of the following sets form rings under addition and multiplication defined in the usual manner? If a system is not a ring, explain why.

a Complex numbers

b Positive rational numbers

c Integral multiples of 6

d $\{i, \ -1, \ -i, \ 1\}$

e $\{0, \ 1, \ -1\}$

4 Let $I_{2 \times 2}$ be the set of 2 by 2 matrices with integers as entries. Let the operations be matrix addition and multiplication. Is $(I_{2 \times 2}, +, \cdot)$ a ring? Does it have zero divisors? Is it commutative? Does it have an identity? Does every element have a multiplicative inverse? If the answer to any of the above is no, explain why; if yes, prove the property.

5 Prove the following properties of an arbitrary ring $(S, +, \cdot)$.

a $a\big(b + (-c)\big) = ab + (-ac)$ for all $a, b, c \in S$.

b $-(a + b) = -a + (-b)$ for all $a, b \in S$.

c $-(-a) = a$ for all $a \in S$.

d $a + (-b) + \big(b + (-c)\big) = a + (-c)$ for all $a, b, c \in S$.

6 Let $S = \{a + b\sqrt{3} \mid a, b \in I\}$. Show that there exist elements $s_1, s_2 \in S$, $s_1 \neq 0$, such that for no $x \in S$ is it true that $s_1 x = s_2$.

7 Determine if the set of matrices of each of the following forms is a subring under matrix addition and multiplication of the ring $(I_{2 \times 2}, +, \cdot)$.

a $\begin{pmatrix} 0 & a \\ 0 & 0 \end{pmatrix}$ d $\begin{pmatrix} 0 & 0 \\ a & b \end{pmatrix}$

b $\begin{pmatrix} 0 & 0 \\ a & 0 \end{pmatrix}$ e $\begin{pmatrix} a & b \\ c & 0 \end{pmatrix}$

c $\begin{pmatrix} a & 0 \\ b & 0 \end{pmatrix}$ f $\begin{pmatrix} a & b \\ 0 & 0 \end{pmatrix}$

8 In exercise 7 above, determine which of the subrings formed have the following properties.
  a Commutativity of multiplication
  b A multiplicative identity
  c Zero divisors

9 Prove that if (S, +, •) is a ring satisfying $x^2 = x$ for all $x \in S$, then (S, +, •) is a commutative ring.

10 Prove that if (S, +, •) is a ring, then
$$(a + b)^2 = a^2 + ab + ba + b^2.$$

11 Suppose that the system (S, +, •) is known to satisfy all ring properties except commutativity of addition. Suppose further that (S, +, •) has a multiplicative identity. Then show that (S, +, •) is a ring with identity.

12 Give an example showing that ($M_{2 \times 2}$, +, •) is not an integral domain.

* 13 Show that every ideal of (I, +, •) is of the form (I_{nx}, +, •) for each $x \in I$ and each $n \in C$.

* 14 Establish a homomorphism from (I/8, $\oplus_8$, $\odot_8$) onto (I/4, $\oplus_4$, $\odot_4$).

* 15 Define a function f from (I, +, •) onto (I/5, $\oplus_5$, $\odot_5$) that is a homomorphism.

* 16 What subset of I is mapped onto $\bar{0}$ in I/5 under the homomorphism given in exercise 15? Prove that this subset is an ideal of (I, +, •).

Cumulative review

1 Let $A = \{(x, y) \mid x, y \in \Re \times \Re \text{ and } x + y > 3\}$ and let $B = \{(x, y) \mid x, y \in \Re \times \Re \text{ and } x - y > 3\}$. Give a standard description of each of the following sets.
  a $A \cap B$ b $A \cup B$ c $\tilde{A}$

2 Let A = {a, b, c, d}, B = {1, 2, 3, 4}, and C = {A, B}.
  a How many subsets does A have?
  b How many subsets does B have?
  c How many subsets does C have?
  d How many subsets does $A \cup B$ have?

3 Determine a function f from $(I/6, \oplus_6)$ onto $(I/3, \oplus_3)$ that preserves the operations of the two groups.

4 Let a function f on $\mathfrak{R} \times \mathfrak{R} \times \mathfrak{R}$ be defined by $(x, y, z)f = x^2 + yz$. Is f a binary operation?

5 Find all commutative subgroups of the group of motions of the square.

6 Prove that every subgroup of a commutative group is commutative.

7 Give examples of each of the following.

a The union of two groups that is a group

b The union of two groups that is not a group

8 Find all the generators of the group $(I/36, \oplus_{36})$.

* 9 Find all the groups with four elements that are distinct with respect to isomorphism. There are two.

10 Prove that $I/2_{2 \times 2}$ is a ring under matrix addition and multiplication. Determine the number of elements in this ring.

* 11 Suppose that addition in $(I/2 \times I/2 \times I/2 \times I/2, +, \cdot)$ is defined as

$$(\bar{a}, \bar{b}, \bar{c}, \bar{d}) + (\bar{e}, \bar{f}, \bar{g}, \bar{h}) = (\bar{a} \oplus_2 \bar{e}, \bar{b} \oplus_2 \bar{f}, \bar{c} \oplus_2 \bar{g}, \bar{d} \oplus_2 \bar{h})$$

and that multiplication is defined as

$$(\bar{a}, \bar{b}, \bar{c}, \bar{d}) \cdot (\bar{e}, \bar{f}, \bar{g}, \bar{h}) =$$
$$(\bar{a} \odot_2 \bar{e} \oplus_2 \bar{b} \odot_2 \bar{g}, \bar{a} \odot_2 \bar{f} \oplus_2 \bar{b} \odot_2 \bar{h}, \bar{c} \odot_2 \bar{e} \oplus_2 \bar{d} \odot_2 \bar{g}, \bar{c} \odot_2 \bar{f} \oplus_2 \bar{d} \odot_2 \bar{h}),$$

for each $(\bar{a}, \bar{b}, \bar{c}, \bar{d}), (\bar{e}, \bar{f}, \bar{g}, \bar{h}) \in I/2 \times I/2 \times I/2 \times I/2$. Is this system a ring?

* 12 Are the rings described in exercises 10 and 11 isomorphic?

13 Prove that if $(S, +, \cdot)$ is a ring and if $a, b, c \in S$, then $-a((-b) + (-c)) = ab + ac$.

14 In the ring $(I/6, \oplus_6, \odot_6)$, find the subrings that are integral domains.

* 15 Let f be a function from $I/8$ onto $I/4$ such that $(\bar{0})f = (\bar{4})f = \bar{0}$, $(\bar{1})f = (\bar{5})f = \bar{1}$, $(\bar{2})f = (\bar{6})f = \bar{2}$, and $(\bar{3})f = (\bar{7})f = \bar{3}$. Show that f is a homomorphism. Use f to describe an ideal of $(I/8, \oplus_8, \odot_8)$.

16 In the ring of polynomials with coefficients from $M_{2 \times 2}$, find the additive inverse of the element

$$\begin{pmatrix} 1 & 0 \\ 0 & 2 \end{pmatrix} + \begin{pmatrix} 2 & 1 \\ 1 & 3 \end{pmatrix} x + \begin{pmatrix} 1 & 3 \\ 2 & 1 \end{pmatrix} x^2.$$

Suppose that x is replaced by $\begin{pmatrix} 0 & 1 \\ 1 & 0 \end{pmatrix}$. Determine the element of $M_{2 \times 2}$ that is equal to the given polynomial.

Chapter **4**

Fields

33 *The properties of a field*

34 *The characteristic of a field*

35 *Subfields*

36 *Simple field extensions*

Introduction

Some of the algebraic systems that have been discussed so far are semi-groups, groups, commutative groups, rings, commutative rings with identity, and integral domains. This chapter deals with the final mathematical system to be considered in this book—the field.

The mathematical system called a field is not a new concept and has been studied by mathematicians for many years; yet it can properly be considered a part of modern mathematics since much research is still being done in field theory. In this chapter, we will confine ourselves to introducing some of the elementary properties of a field and establishing some theorems concerning the structure of such a system.

The properties of a field

33/4

In developing new mathematical systems from familiar ones, we have usually added one or more properties to the system already developed. For example, the concept of a group was developed from the semi-group by requiring the identity and inverse properties; the idea of a ring was developed from the group by requiring the closure and associative properties for a second operation and also the distributive property; and so on. We will develop the field from the integral domain by requiring another property—the multiplicative-inverse property. To illustrate this property, we will decide whether or not conditions of the form $ay = 1$, where 1 denotes the multiplicative identity of the system, have solutions in various examples of integral domains.

Examples 1 As you know, one example of an integral domain is the system of integers, (I, +, •). You also know that it is not always possible to solve conditions of the form $ay = b$, where a and b are integers and y is an integer to be determined. In other words, there exist integers a and b for which $ay = b$ has no integral solution. A particular instance is the condition $3y = 5$ since there is no integer y such that $3y = 5$.

We are particularly interested in determining if a given system has solutions for conditions of the form $ay = 1$, where a and y are arbitrary elements of the system. Let us now see whether $ay = 1$ can be solved in the system of integers. There certainly are integers a such that $ay = 1$ has *no* solution in I; for example, if $a = 2$, then the condition $2y = 1$ has no solution for y in I.

You should have no trouble in naming other integers a such that $ay = 1$ has no solution in I. On the other hand, there are particular integers a such that $ay = 1$ does have a solution for y in the set of integers. For example, if $a = 1$, then $1y = 1$ has a solution; namely, the integer 1. As a second example, note that if $a = -1$, then $-1y = 1$ has a solution in the set of integers; namely, -1. Are there any other integers a such that $ay = 1$ has a solution in the set of integers?

In summary, we see that, for some integers a, the condition $ay = 1$ has a solution in the integers, while, for other integers a, no such solution exists.

2 Next we will consider solutions of conditions of the form $ay = 1$ in the mathematical system of Gaussian integers, $\big(G(i), +, \cdot\big)$, which is also an example of an integral domain. Remember that every element in the set of Gaussian integers is of the form $a + bi$, where $a, b \in I$ and $i^2 = -1$. Remember also that the operations of addition and multiplication in the system of Gaussian integers are defined as follows:

$$(a + bi) + (c + di) = (a + c) + (b + d)i.$$
$$(a + bi) \cdot (c + di) = (ac - bd) + (ad + bc)i.$$

We will now consider solutions of conditions of the form $uy = 1 + 0i = 1$, where $u, y \in G(i)$; that is, where u and y are to be replaced by numbers of the form $a + bi$. Are there any Gaussian integers u such that $uy = 1$ has a solution for y in G(i)? From example 1, we might suspect that if u is replaced by $1 + 0i = 1$, then the resulting condition will have a solution in G(i). Replacement of u by 1 in the condition $uy = 1$ gives the condition $1y = 1$ which does have a solution in the system; namely, $y = 1 + 0i = 1$. Similarly, the replacement $-1 + 0i = -1$ for u yields the condition $-1y = 1$, which has the solution $y = -1 + 0i = -1$ in the system.

One reason why these two particular replacements for u seemed natural to try immediately is that I $\subset$ G(i), and example 1 shows that these replacements yield solutions of $uy = 1$ in I. Unlike the integers, however, there are other replacements for u in the system of Gaussian integers that yield a solution for y in the system. Specifically, if u is replaced by $0 + 1i = i$, then $iy = 1$ has the solution $y = 0 - 1i = -i$; and if u is replaced by $0 - 1i = -i$, then $-iy = 1$ has the solution $y = 0 + 1i = i$. You can convince yourself by experimentation that, if any Gaussian integers other than 1, -1, i, and $-i$ are used as replacements for u in the condition $uy = 1$, then there is no solution for y in G(i). This follows from the fact that no integers other than 1 and -1 have multiplicative inverses.

In examples 1 and 2 the condition $uy = 1$ has a solution only for a finite set of elements u in the given integral domain. Consider the following example in which there are infinitely many elements u such that $uy = 1$ has a solution for y in the system.

3 This example concerns the set of all polynomials of the form $a_0x^0 + a_1x^1 + a_2x^2 + \ldots + a_{n-1}x^{n-1} + a_nx^n$ with the coefficients a_i (where $i = 0, 1, 2, \ldots, n$) in the set of rational numbers. We have already seen that this set under addition and multiplication forms an integral domain (exercise 4e, section 32/3, page 223), denoted by (R[x], +, $\cdot$). The multiplicative identity of this integral domain is the polynomial $1x^0 = 1$. Now let us consider conditions of the form $uy = 1$ and, for a given element u in R[x], determine whether or not there are solutions for y in R[x].

By analogy with the previous two examples, it is natural to expect that both $1y = 1$ and $-1y = 1$ will have solutions in the set of polynomials with rational coefficients. In the first of these conditions, $1y = 1$, the polynomial u has been replaced by $1x^0 = 1$ and, similarly, for the second, u has been replaced by $-1x^0 = -1$. Remember that constant polynomials are but special cases of polynomials, and that, in particular, the polynomials 1 and -1 belong to R[x]. It is true that both $1y = 1$ and $-1y = 1$ have solutions in R[x], and you should be able to tell what the polynomial y must be in each case. But there are other replacements for u in $uy = 1$ so that the resulting condition has a solution for y in R[x]. For example, the condition $\frac{2}{3}y = 1$ has the solution $\frac{3}{2}$. In fact, for each nonzero rational number $\frac{a}{b}$, the condition $\frac{a}{b}y = 1$ has the solution $\frac{b}{a}$. Because there are infinitely many constant polynomials u of the form $\frac{a}{b}x^0 = \frac{a}{b}$, with $b \neq 0$, in R[x], there are infinitely many conditions $\frac{a}{b}y = 1$ that have solution $\frac{b}{a}$ in R[x].

But notice that there are also infinitely many replacements for u in $uy = 1$ so that there is no solution for y in R[x]. For example, the infinite set of polynomials

$$\{x,\ 2x,\ 3x,\ 4x,\ \ldots,\ kx,\ \ldots\} = \{kx \mid k \in \mathrm{C}\}$$

is such that, for each replacement of u by an element kx of the set, the condition

$$(kx)y = 1$$

has no solution for y in R[x]. If such a condition did have a solution in R[x], it would be of the form $\frac{1}{k} \cdot \frac{1}{x}$ or $\frac{1}{k}x^{-1}$, but no polynomial in R[x] has a negative exponent. You should determine other polynomials u such that $uy = 1$ has no solution for y in R[x].

You have probably already realized that, when we find a solution for y in the condition $uy = 1$ for a given u, we are simply determining a *multiplicative inverse* of u. The three examples were chosen to illustrate that various situations are possible with reference to the existence of multiplicative inverses in integral domains. In all three of these examples, only some of the elements have multiplicative inverses. However, in the remainder of this chapter we will consider only those integral domains with the property that *every nonzero* element has a multiplicative inverse. We must consider only nonzero elements of the set because we have already observed that the element that is the additive identity of a system (usually called zero) does not have a multiplicative inverse. This follows from the property that $0 \cdot y = 0$ for each y of an integral domain.

We will now state the definition of the kind of mathematical system that is to be studied in the remainder of this chapter.

Definition 58/4 Let (S, $+$, $\cdot$) be an integral domain whose multiplicative identity is denoted by 1 and whose additive identity is denoted by 0. Then

(S, +, •) is a *field* if and only if, for each $a \in S$ with $a \neq 0$, there exists an element $a^{-1} \in S$ such that

Multiplicative inverse 12 $a^{-1} \cdot a = a \cdot a^{-1} = 1.$

The element a^{-1} is the *inverse* of a; the element a is the *inverse* of a^{-1}.

This definition requires that a set under two binary operations satisfy twelve properties—the eleven properties of an integral domain and the multiplicative-inverse property—in order to be classified as a field. This list of properties is one that is generally accepted. Requiring all twelve properties, however, is redundant, in the sense that one of the twelve properties is dependent upon the other eleven. Since it is possible to define a field with a list of only eleven properties and since some other texts offer this list, we now will show that the property that the system has no zero divisors (property 11 of Definition 56/3) can be proved to follow from the other eleven field properties.

Theorem 59/4 If (S, +, •) is a commutative ring with identity that satisfies the multiplicative-inverse property, then (S, +, •) is a field.

Proof To prove the theorem, it is sufficient to establish that a commutative ring with identity that also satisfies the multiplicative-inverse property has no zero divisors. Assume that there exist elements $a, b \in S$ such that $ab = 0$. We must show that $ab = 0$ implies $a = 0$ or $b = 0$. Suppose that $b \neq 0$. Then we have

$$\begin{aligned} ab &= 0, \\ (ab)b^{-1} &= 0b^{-1}, \\ a(bb^{-1}) &= 0, \\ a(1) &= 0, \\ a &= 0. \end{aligned}$$

You should justify these steps. We have just shown that $ab = 0$ and $b \neq 0$ together imply $a = 0$. This is equivalent to showing that $ab = 0$ implies $a = 0$ or $b = 0$. Therefore, the proof of the theorem is complete.

It is important to see that, although the existence of a multiplicative-inverse property in a system implies that the system has no divisors of 0, the converse does *not* hold. That is, it is possible for a system to be an integral domain without being a field. The integral domain (I, +, •) is an example of such a system. Theorem 59/4 establishes that there are eleven basic properties for a field. These eleven field properties are given in the following chart.

Properties of a field $(S, +, \cdot)$

Closure for $+$	1	For each $a, b \in S$, $a + b \in S$.
Associativity for $+$	2	For each $a, b, c \in S$, $(a + b) + c = a + (b + c)$.
Identity for $+$	3	There exists an element in S, denoted by 0, such that for each $a \in S$, $0 + a = a + 0 = a$.
Inverse for $+$	4	For each $a \in S$, there exists an inverse in S, denoted by $-a$, such that $-a + a = a + (-a) = 0$.
Commutativity for $+$	5	For each $a, b \in S$, $a + b = b + a$.
Closure for $\cdot$	6	For each $a, b \in S$, $ab \in S$.
Associativity for $\cdot$	7	For each $a, b, c \in S$, $(ab)c = a(bc)$.
Distributive property	8	For each $a, b, c \in S$, 1) $a(b + c) = ab + ac$, and 2) $(a + b)c = ac + bc$.
Identity for $\cdot$	9	There exists an element in S, denoted by e, with $e \neq 0$ such that for each $a \in S$, $ea = ae = a$.
Commutativity for $\cdot$	10	For each $a, b \in S$, $ab = ba$.
Inverse for $\cdot$	11	For each $a \in S$, $a \neq 0$, there exists an inverse in S, denoted by a^{-1} such that $a^{-1}a = aa^{-1} = e$.

Since the topic of redundant requirements for a system has been introduced, it can be remarked that the dependence or independence of the axioms of a system is of prime importance to some branches of mathematics, notably mathematical logic and the study of foundations. Notice that the multiplicative-inverse property requires that an inverse element be both a right and a left multiplicative inverse for each nonzero element of the system. However, since commutativity had already been required for multiplication, there is a redundancy in the multiplicative-inverse property insofar as it would have been sufficient to require the existence of either a left multiplicative inverse or a right multiplicative inverse for each nonzero element. If the existence of either a left or a right multiplicative inverse for each nonzero element is postulated, then it can be shown that not only does this element serve as both a left and a right multiplicative inverse, but also that the inverse is unique. Furthermore, once commutativity is required for addition and for multiplication, only a left or a right identity element need be postulated for each operation, only a left or right inverse element need be stated for addition, and only one form of the distributive property need be given. However, because we developed these properties before the commutative properties, it was necessary to require both right and left identities and right and left additive inverses and also two forms of the distributive property.

Much of mathematics, and indeed much of your previous and current studies in mathematics, deals directly or indirectly with number systems. Three very important number systems that are examples of fields are the complex numbers, the real numbers, and the rational numbers. These systems, along with some of their subsystems, have been used repeatedly for examples of all of the kinds of structures studied here. However, there are also other examples of fields that are important. We will consider some of them in this chapter. The remainder of this section is devoted to showing that there are infinitely many fields of a certain type.

We have seen that there exist examples of integral domains with an infinite set of elements, such as the system of integers and the system of Gaussian integers, and that there exist examples of finite integral domains, such as each system $(I/n, \oplus_n, \odot_n)$ where n is prime. The following theorem establishes that every *finite* integral domain is also a field.

Theorem 60/4 If (S, +, •) is a finite integral domain, then (S, +, •) is a field.

Proof By hypothesis, the mathematical system (S, +, •) satisfies properties 1 through 10 of an integral domain. Therefore, to show that (S, +, •) is a field it is sufficient to show that the system satisfies the multiplicative-inverse property. In other words, we must establish that, for each nonzero element a of the integral domain (S, +, •), there exists an element a^{-1} in the integral domain that is the multiplicative inverse of a, that is, $a^{-1} \cdot a = e$.

Denote by $a_1, a_2, a_3, \ldots, a_n$ the distinct nonzero elements in the integral domain and denote by a any arbitrary nonzero element. Thus, $a \in \{a_1, a_2, \ldots, a_n\}$. Consider the following n products.

$$a_1a, a_2a, a_3a, \ldots, a_na.$$

Why is each of these n products an element of set S? How do you know that each of these products is nonzero?

As a first step in the proof we will show that each of the n products is distinct. That is, the products a_ia and a_ja with $i \neq j$ are such that $a_ia \neq a_ja$. For, if it were the case that $a_ia = a_ja$ for some i and j, with $i \neq j$, then, by the cancellation property of multiplication in an integral domain, it would follow that $a_i = a_j$.

But, since $i \neq j$, this is a contradiction. Therefore, the n products listed above are all distinct.

To summarize, and to extend the argument further, we are considering n products, each of which is a distinct nonzero element contained in the finite integral domain $(S, +, \cdot)$. Therefore, the list is just the n nonzero elements of S (perhaps listed in some order other than $a_1, a_2, \ldots, a_n$). But $(S, +, \cdot)$ is an integral domain and, hence, contains a multiplicative identity. Therefore, one of the n products $a_1a, a_2a, \ldots, a_na$ is the multiplicative-identity element (denoted by e). So, there exists an element a_k in S such that $a_ka = e$. This shows that the element a_k is the multiplicative inverse of the element a; that is, $a_k = a^{-1}$. Since a was chosen as any arbitrary nonzero element of the integral domain, we have shown that each nonzero element has a multiplicative inverse in the system. This completes the proof of the theorem.

We know that the set of integers modulo n is finite, and we know by Theorem 57/3 that $(I/n, \oplus_n, \odot_n)$ is an integral domain if and only if n is prime. Therefore, we have the following corollary to Theorem 60/4.

Corollary 60/4 The system $(I/n, \oplus_n, \odot_n)$ forms a field if and only if n is prime.

Since $(I/n, \oplus_n, \odot_n)$ forms a finite field when n is prime and since the set of prime integers is infinite, it follows that there are infinitely many finite fields.

Exercises

1 Prove that the condition $uy = 1$ has a solution in $G(i)$ only when $u = 1, -1, i, -i$. [Hint: Let $a + bi = u$ and $c + di = y$ where $a, b, c, d \in I$. Show that, if y satisfies $uy = 1$, then $c = \dfrac{a}{a^2 + b^2}$ and $d = \dfrac{-b}{a^2 + b^2}$. From this, show that u must be equal to $1 + 0i$, $-1 + 0i$, $0 + 1i$, or $0 - 1i$.]

2 Consider the set of all polynomials with rational coefficients, $R[x]$. Indicate how you could form an infinite set of polynomials in $R[x]$, different from the set given in the text on page 230, in which no member has a multiplicative inverse.

3 Explain why each of the following systems is not a field.

a $(\{\bar{0}, \bar{2}, \bar{4}, \bar{6}, \bar{8}, \overline{10}\}, \oplus_{12}, \odot_{12})$

b $(I/8_{2 \times 2}, +, \cdot)$ *Answer*

c $(I/10, \oplus_{10}, \odot_{10})$

d $(R_2, +, \cdot)$, where $R_2 = \left\{\dfrac{m}{n} \mid m, n \in I, n \neq 0, m \text{ and } n \text{ are relatively prime and 2 is not a factor of } n\right\}$ *Answer* e $(\{a + b\sqrt[4]{5} \mid a, b \in \mathrm{R}\}, +, \cdot)$ *Answer*

f $(\{\bar{a} + \bar{b}\sqrt{2} \mid \bar{a}, \bar{b} \in \mathrm{I}/3\}, +, \cdot)$, where addition and multiplication are defined as follows:

$$(\bar{a} + \bar{b}\sqrt{2}) + (\bar{c} + \bar{d}\sqrt{2}) = (\bar{a} \oplus_3 \bar{c}) + (\bar{b} \oplus_3 \bar{d})\sqrt{2}.$$
$$(\bar{a} + \bar{b}\sqrt{2}) \cdot (\bar{c} + \bar{d}\sqrt{2}) = (\bar{a} \odot_3 \bar{c}) + (\bar{b} \odot_3 \bar{d})\sqrt{2}.$$ *Answer*

g $(\mathrm{R}_6, +, \cdot)$, where $\mathrm{R}_6 = \left\{\frac{m}{n} \mid m, n \in \mathrm{I}, n \neq 0, m \text{ and } n \text{ are relatively prime and 6 is not a factor of } n\right\}$

4 Determine which of the following systems are fields.

a $(\{x \mid x \in \mathrm{I} \text{ and } x > 0\}, +, \cdot)$

b $(\{a + b\sqrt{3} \mid a, b \in \mathrm{I}\}, +, \cdot)$

c $(\{a + b\sqrt{3} \mid a, b \in \mathrm{R}\}, +, \cdot)$

d $(\{a + b\sqrt[3]{2} \mid a, b \in \mathrm{R}\}, +, \cdot)$ *Answer*

e $(\{x \mid x \in \mathrm{I}\}, +, \cdot)$

f $(\mathrm{G}(i), +, \cdot)$

g $(\mathrm{E_I}, +, \cdot)$

h $(\{a + b\sqrt[3]{2} + c\sqrt[3]{4} \mid a, b, c \in \mathrm{R}\}, +, \cdot)$

i $(\{\bar{0}, \bar{1}, \bar{5}, \bar{7}, \overline{11},\}, \oplus_{12}, \odot_{12})$

j $(\{x \mid x \in \mathrm{R} \text{ and } x \notin \mathrm{I}\}, +, \cdot)$

k $(\{x \mid x \in \mathfrak{R} \text{ and } x \notin \mathrm{R}\}, +, \cdot)$

l $(\{a + b\sqrt[4]{9} \mid a, b \in \mathrm{R}\}, +, \cdot)$ *Answer*

m $(\{a + b\sqrt{3} + c\sqrt{5} + d\sqrt{15} \mid a, b, c, d \in \mathrm{I}\}, +, \cdot)$

5 Consider the set of all elements of the form $\frac{a}{b}$ where a is an integer and b is a nonnegative integral power of 2; that is, $\left\{\frac{a}{b} \mid a \in \mathrm{I},\ b = 2^n, n \in \mathrm{I}, \text{ and } n \geqq 0\right\}$. Show that each of the following statements is true.

a This set under addition and multiplication forms an integral domain.

b There are infinitely many elements in this set that have multiplicative inverses.

c There are infinitely many elements that do *not* have multiplicative inverses.

6 Repeat exercise 5 for $\left\{\frac{a}{b} \mid a \in \mathrm{I}, b = 2^m \cdot 3^n, m, n \geqq 0, \text{ and } m, n \in \mathrm{I}\right\}$.

7 Let $(\mathrm{F}, +, \cdot)$ be a field. Prove that, if $a \in \mathrm{F}$ and $a^{-1} \cdot a = 1$, then $a \cdot a^{-1} = 1$. That is, prove that a left multiplicative inverse of a field element is also a right multiplicative inverse of that field element.

8 Let $(F, +, \cdot)$ be a field. Prove that if $a \in F$ and $a^{-1} \cdot a = a \cdot a^{-1} = 1$ and $x \cdot a = a \cdot x = 1$, then $x = a^{-1}$. That is, prove that the multiplicative inverse of a field element is unique. *Answer*

◆ **9** Is $(\{a + b\sqrt[3]{3} \mid a, b \in R\}, +, \cdot)$ an integral domain? Construct an infinite set of elements in this system, all of which have multiplicative inverses. Construct an infinite set of elements in this system that do not have multiplicative inverses.

◆ **10** Repeat exercise 9 for the system

$$(\{a + b\sqrt[3]{3} + c\sqrt[3]{9} \mid a, b, c \in R\}, +, \cdot).$$

◆ **11** In $(I/12, \oplus_{12}, \odot_{12})$, consider the subset $S = \{\bar{0}, \bar{6}\}$. Form the cosets of S, $S \oplus_{12} \bar{x} = \{\bar{c} \mid \bar{c} = s \oplus_{12} \bar{x}$ and $\bar{s} \in S\}$. For this set of cosets, define two binary operations ☆ and ∘ as follows:

$$(S \oplus_{12} \bar{x}) ☆ (S \oplus_{12} \bar{y}) = S \oplus_{12} (\bar{x} \oplus_{12} \bar{y}) \text{ and}$$
$$(S \oplus_{12} \bar{x}) \circ (S \oplus_{12} \bar{y}) = S \oplus_{12} (\bar{x} \odot_{12} \bar{y}).$$

Does this set of cosets under ☆ and ∘ form an integral domain? A field? *Answer*

◆ **12** Repeat exercise 11 for $S = \{\bar{0}, \bar{3}, \bar{6}, \bar{9}\}$.

The characteristic of a field

34/4

We have often mentioned that among the most important theorems of algebra are those that enable us to classify algebraic systems. In this section, we will investigate a property of certain systems called the *characteristic*, and this property will lead to another classification theorem. We will begin by considering some examples that illustrate the various kinds of characteristics that a system may have.

Examples 1 Consider the integral domain $(I, +, \cdot)$. If a is any nonzero element of I, then, for any number of addends of a,

$$a + a + \ldots + a \neq 0.$$

As a particular case, note that, for any number of addends,

$$7 + 7 + \ldots + 7 \neq 0.$$

Similarly, for any number of addends,

$$(-3) + (-3) + \ldots + (-3) \neq 0.$$

2 In contrast to the first example, consider the commutative ring with identity $(I/6, \oplus_6, \odot_6)$. Notice that in this system

$$\bar{1} \oplus_6 \bar{1} \oplus_6 \bar{1} \oplus_6 \bar{1} \oplus_6 \bar{1} \oplus_6 \bar{1} = \bar{0}.$$

Furthermore, in the same mathematical system, the sum $\bar{2} \oplus_6 \bar{2} \oplus_6 \bar{2}$ is $\bar{0}$, the sum $\bar{3} \oplus_6 \bar{3}$ is $\bar{0}$, the sum $\bar{4} \oplus_6 \bar{4} \oplus_6 \bar{4}$ is $\bar{0}$, and the sum $\bar{5} \oplus_6 \bar{5} \oplus_6 \bar{5} \oplus_6 \bar{5} \oplus_6 \bar{5} \oplus_6 \bar{5}$ is $\bar{0}$. These examples show that, in the integers modulo 6, we need add any nonzero element to itself at most 6 times to obtain the additive identity.

If it is possible to obtain the additive identity of a system by adding a nonzero element to itself a finite number of times, then we say that the *additive order* of the element is the *least* number of addends needed to obtain the identity (see Definition 39/2). For instance, in the integers modulo 6, the additive order of $\bar{1}$ is 6, the additive order of $\bar{2}$ is 3;* the additive order of $\bar{3}$ is 2; the additive order of $\bar{4}$ is 3; and the additive order of $\bar{5}$ is 6. If it is *not* possible to obtain the additive identity by adding an element to itself a finite number of times, then the additive order of the element is defined to be 0.

3 As a third example, consider the system of integers modulo 7, $(I/7, \oplus_7, \odot_7)$. In this field, every nonzero element has additive order 7. That is, if $\bar{1}$ is used as an addend 7 times, the sum is $\bar{0}$; if $\bar{2}$ is used as an addend 7 times, the sum is $\bar{0}$; and so on. Thus, the additive order of each nonzero element of $I/7$ is the same.

These three examples illustrate the following possibilities for the additive order of the elements of a given system:

1) The additive order of each nonzero element is 0 (example 1).
2) The additive order of each nonzero element is a positive integer, but not all elements have the same order (example 2).
3) The additive order of each nonzero element is the same positive integer (example 3).

Notice that in examples 1 and 3, each nonzero element has the same additive order, either 0 or a positive integer. In example 2, which deals with a system that has divisors of zero, the elements have different additive orders. In the remainder of this section,

* Notice that the additive order of $\bar{2}$ is 3 because $\bar{2} \oplus_6 \bar{2} \oplus_6 \bar{2} = \bar{0}$. It is also true that $\bar{2} \oplus_6 \bar{2} \oplus_6 \bar{2} \oplus_6 \bar{2} \oplus_6 \bar{2} \oplus_6 \bar{2} = \bar{0}$, but 3 is the least number of addends of $\bar{2}$ needed to obtain the identity.

we will consider only those mathematical systems that satisfy all the properties of an integral domain.

To define the concept of additive order in connection with a field, we can make use of a notion that was introduced in earlier discussions. In Chapter 2 we defined the product of a nonnegative integer and an element of a group (see Definitions 35/2 and 36/2). Then, in Chapter 3, we gave an analogous definition of the product of a nonnegative integer and an element of a ring (see Definition 49/3). Since every field is also a ring, we can discuss the product of an integer and a field element without giving a new definition. Therefore, we can discuss products of the form $n \cdot a$, where n is a nonnegative integer and a is any element of a field. Since the product $n \cdot a$ represents n addends of the field element a, we know that if $n \cdot a = 0$, and if n is the least such integer, then n is the additive order of a. We can now prove that every nonzero element of a field has the same additive order.

Theorem 61/4 If $(S, +, \cdot)$ is a field, then the additive order of all nonzero elements is the same.

To avoid confusion in the following proof, we will use $\cdot$ to represent the second operation of the field and $\times$ to denote "multiplication" of an element of S by a positive integer.

Proof Suppose that a is a nonzero element of S and that the additive order of a is n; that is, suppose that $n \times a = 0$. We must show that, if b is any nonzero element of S, then $n \times b$ also is equal to 0. By Theorem 38/2 we have

$$\begin{aligned} n \times (a \cdot b) &= (n \times a) \cdot b \\ &= 0 \cdot b \\ &= 0. \end{aligned}$$

Also,

$$\begin{aligned} n \times (a \cdot b) &= n \times (b \cdot a) \\ &= (n \times b) \cdot a. \end{aligned}$$

Therefore, $(n \times b) \cdot a = 0$. But, because $a \neq 0$ and $(S, +, \cdot)$ is a field, it follows that

$$n \times b = 0.$$

Supply the reason for each step in the computation given above.

We have established that, for any nonzero elements a and b, if n is the least positive integer such that $n \times a = 0$, then $n \times b = 0$. But is it possible that there exists a positive integer m such that $m < n$ and $m \times b = 0$? In other words, is it possible that the additive order of b is some integer less than n? The proof that this is not possible is given as an exercise at the end of the section. It follows that n is the additive order of b.

The remaining case is easy. If there exists no positive integer n such that, for each nonzero element a of S, $n \times a = 0$, then each nonzero element of S has the same additive order, 0.

We have just shown that in a field the additive order of all the nonzero elements is the same. We can now define the characteristic of a field.

Definition 59/4. If (S, +, •) is a field and if there exists a positive integer k such that $k \cdot a = 0$ for each nonzero element a of S, then the least such integer n is the *characteristic* of the field. If no such positive integer n exists, then the characteristic of the field is 0.

Notice that the characteristic of a field (S, +, •) is in fact equal to the additive order of each nonzero element of the field. Although the definition is stated for fields, it applies also to integral domains. We have previously given an example of a commutative ring with identity in which the additive order is not the same for all elements (the integers modulo 6); thus, it is not possible to talk about the characteristic of a ring that is not an integral domain. The following theorem establishes that the characteristic of every finite field is prime.

Theorem 62/4 If (S, +, •) is a field with a positive integral characteristic n, then n is a prime integer.

In the proof of this theorem, the symbol • will again represent multiplication in the system (S, +, •) and the symbol $\times$ will again represent the operation between integers and field elements.

Proof Since n is a positive integer, n is either prime or composite. We will use the method of contrapositive proof to show that n is prime. By this method, we assume that n is composite and, therefore, that there exist positive integers r and s such that

$$1 < r < n,\ 1 < s < n, \text{ and } n = rs.$$

We must show that this assumption leads to a contradiction.

If a is any nonzero element of S, then

$$0 = n \times a = (rs) \times a.$$

But by Theorem 38/2 it follows that

$$(rs) \times a = r \times (s \times a) = 0.$$

Since $a \neq 0$ and s is an integer greater than 1 and less than n, $s \times a$ is a nonzero element of S. If $s \times a$ *were* equal to 0, it would not be true that n is the additive order of a. But the statements $r \times (s \times a) = 0$ and $s \times a \neq 0$ imply that the additive order of $s \times a$ and, hence, the characteristic of S, is r or some integer less than r. Since $r < n$, this contradicts the hypothesis that n is the characteristic of S. The assumption that n is composite has led to a contradiction; hence, the characteristic n must be a prime number.

Now we will use the idea of the characteristic of a field along with Theorem 62/4 to prove a theorem for classifying fields. Remember that in section 21/2 we defined a generator of a cyclic group (Definition 37/2) as an element $a \in G$ such that each element of G is an integral multiple of a. Here we are interested in the group generated by a particular element of the field, so a specific definition is given below for the set in which we are interested.

Definition 60/4 If $(S, +, \cdot)$ is a field with multiplicative identity e, then $\{n \times e \mid n \in I\}$ is the set generated by e.

The set $\{n \times e \mid n \in I\}$ under the operation $+$ of the field is a subgroup of $(S, +)$. This statement can be verified by showing that $\{n \times e \mid n \in I\}$ is a nonempty subset of S that satisfies the closure and inverse properties for addition (see Theorem 28/2).

We are now able to classify completely the subgroup generated by the multiplicative identity of a field. Since a field has two operations and a group has only one, we will use the term *additive subgroup* to refer to a group such as $(T, +)$ where T is a nonempty subset of S and $(S, +, \cdot)$ is a field.

Theorem 63/4 If $(S, +, \cdot)$ is a field with multiplicative identity e, then the additive subgroup generated by e is classified as follows:

1) If the characteristic of $(S, +, \cdot)$ is p, where p is a prime number, then the additive subgroup $(\{n \times e \mid n \in I\}, +)$ is isomorphic to the group of integers modulo p under addition.
2) If the characteristic of $(S, +, \cdot)$ is 0, then the additive subgroup $(\{n \times e \mid n \in I\}, +)$ is isomorphic to the group of integers under addition.

Proof To prove part 1 of the theorem, we must first prove that the additive subgroup generated by e has exactly p elements. We begin by establishing that the following p elements are distinct:

$$p \times e, 1 \times e, 2 \times e, \ldots, (p-1) \times e.$$

If these elements were not distinct, then there would exist two elements in the set $m \times e$ and $n \times e$, with $1 < m \leqq p$, $1 \leqq n < p$, and $m > n$, such that $m \times e = n \times e$. But the equality

$$m \times e = n \times e$$

implies that

$$(m \times e) - (n \times e) = 0$$

or, equivalently, that

$$(m - n) \times e = 0.$$

But, since $0 < (m - n) < p$, this would mean that $m - n$, or some positive integer less than $m - n$, and not p, would be the characteristic of (S, +, •). This contradicts the assumption in part 1 that p is the characteristic of (S, +, •); so we conclude that there are at least p different elements in the set $\{n \times e \mid n \in \mathrm{I}\}$.

But it is also true that there are no more than p distinct elements in $\{n \times e \mid n \in \mathrm{I}\}$. To see why this is so, suppose that k is an arbitrary integer. We will show that $k \times e$ is contained among the p elements. By the division algorithm, we have

$$k = qp + r \text{ where } 0 \leqq r < p.$$

Therefore,

$$\begin{aligned} k \times e &= (qp + r) \times e \\ &= \big((qp) \times e\big) + (r \times e) \\ &= \big(q \times (p \times e)\big) + (r \times e) \\ &= (q \times 0) + (r \times e) \\ &= 0 + (r \times e) \\ &= r \times e. \end{aligned}$$

Notice that $p \times e = 0$ because p is the characteristic of (S, +, •). Give reasons for the other steps above.

Since $r < p$, the element $r \times e = k \times e$ already appears in the list $p \times e,\ 1 \times e,\ 2 \times e, \ldots, (p - 1) \times e$. Therefore, no more than p distinct elements are contained in the set $\{n \times e \mid n \in \mathrm{I}\}$. It follows that

$$\{n \times e \mid n \in \mathrm{I}\} = \{p \times e, 1 \times e, 2 \times e, \ldots, (p - 1) \times e\}.$$

Now that the set $\{n \times e \mid n \in \mathrm{I}\}$ has been determined, the elements themselves suggest how to define an isomorphic function from the set $\{n \times e \mid n \in \mathrm{I}\}$ onto the integers modulo p. The integers modulo p consist of the equivalence classes $\bar{0}, \bar{1}, \bar{2}, \ldots, \overline{p - 1}$. For each $i \times e$ in $\{n \times e \mid n \in \mathrm{I}\}$, the formula

$$(i \times e)\mathrm{f} = \bar{i}, \text{ where } 0 \leqq i \leqq p - 1,$$

defines a one-to-one function whose domain is $\{n \times e \mid n \in \mathrm{I}\}$ and whose range is I/p. The function also preserves the addition operations of the groups. The verification of these statements is left as an exercise.

The proof of part 2 of the theorem, which closely parallels the proof of part 1, is also left as an exercise.

Exercises

1 Determine if possible the additive order of each nonzero element contained in the following rings.

a $(I/7, \oplus_7, \odot_7)$

b $(I/8, \oplus_8, \odot_8)$ *Answer*

c $(I/10, \oplus_{10}, \odot_{10})$

d $(I/13, \oplus_{13}, \odot_{13})$

e $(I/12, \oplus_{12}, \odot_{12})$

f $(I, +, \cdot)$

g $(\{a + b\sqrt{2} \mid a, b \in I\}, +, \cdot)$ *Answer*

h $(\{a + b\sqrt{2} \mid a, b \in R\}, +, \cdot)$

If $\bar{a}, \bar{b}, \bar{c}, \bar{d} \in I/n$, then we define $+$ and $\cdot$ as follows:

$$(\bar{a} + \bar{b}\sqrt{2}) + (\bar{c} + \bar{d}\sqrt{2}) = (\bar{a} \oplus_n \bar{c}) + (\bar{b} \oplus_n \bar{d})\sqrt{2}.$$
$$(\bar{a} + \bar{b}\sqrt{2}) \cdot (\bar{c} + \bar{d}\sqrt{2}) = (\bar{a} \odot_n \bar{c}) + (\bar{b} \odot_n \bar{d})\sqrt{2}.$$

2 Determine which of the following systems are integral domains and which are fields.

a $(\{\bar{a} + \bar{b}\sqrt{2} \mid \bar{a}, \bar{b} \in I/3\}, +, \cdot)$ *Answer*

b $(\{\bar{a} + \bar{b}\sqrt{2} \mid \bar{a}, \bar{b} \in I/6\}, +, \cdot)$

c $(\{\bar{a} + \bar{b}\sqrt{2} \mid \bar{a}, \bar{b} \in I/5\}, +, \cdot)$

d $(\{\bar{a} + \bar{b}\sqrt{2} \mid \bar{a}, \bar{b} \in I/4\}, +, \cdot)$

3 In exercise 2a, find the additive orders of $\bar{2} + \bar{1}\sqrt{2}$, $\bar{0} + \bar{2}\sqrt{2}$, and $\bar{1} + \bar{0}\sqrt{2}$. *Answer*

4 In exercise 2b, find the additive orders of $\bar{4} + \bar{3}\sqrt{2}$, $\bar{1} + \bar{2}\sqrt{2}$, and $\bar{2} + \bar{0}\sqrt{2}$.

5 In exercise 2c, find the additive orders of $\bar{0} + \bar{4}\sqrt{2}$, $\bar{3} + \bar{3}\sqrt{2}$, and $\bar{2} + \bar{0}\sqrt{2}$.

6 In exercise 2d, find the additive orders of $\bar{2} + \bar{3}\sqrt{2}$, $\bar{3} + \bar{1}\sqrt{2}$, and $\bar{3} + \bar{0}\sqrt{2}$.

◆ 7 Let F be a field with 4 elements. Explain why the characteristic of F must be a prime. How do you know that if the characteristic of F is p, then $p = 2$ or $p = 3$? Prove by the contrapositive method of proof that $p = 2$. [Hint: Show that the assumption that $p = 3$ leads to a contradiction in the construction of the addition table for F.]

Consider the system $(Q_n, +, \cdot)$, where

$$Q_n = \left\{\frac{\bar{a}}{\bar{b}} \mid \bar{a}, \bar{b} \in I/n \text{ and } \bar{b} \neq \bar{0}\right\}$$

and where, for each $\frac{\bar{a}}{\bar{b}}, \frac{\bar{c}}{\bar{d}} \in Q_n$, addition, multiplication, and equality are defined as follows:

$$\frac{\bar{a}}{\bar{b}} + \frac{\bar{c}}{\bar{d}} = \frac{(\bar{a} \odot_n \bar{d}) \oplus_n (\bar{b} \odot_n \bar{c})}{\bar{b} \odot_n \bar{d}};$$

$$\frac{\bar{a}}{\bar{b}} \cdot \frac{\bar{c}}{\bar{d}} = \frac{\bar{a} \odot_n \bar{c}}{\bar{b} \odot_n \bar{d}};$$

$$\frac{\bar{a}}{\bar{b}} = \frac{\bar{c}}{\bar{d}} \text{ if and only if } \bar{a} \odot_n \bar{d} = \bar{b} \odot_n \bar{c}.$$

◆ **8** Tell how many distinct elements are contained in each of the following systems. Then determine if the system is a ring, an integral domain, or a field.

a $(Q_3, +, \cdot)$ *Answer* **b** $(Q_4, +, \cdot)$ **c** $(Q_5, +, \cdot)$

9 Find the characteristic of each of the following fields.

a $(I/5, \oplus_5, \odot_5)$ *Answer*

b $(R, +, \cdot)$

c $(\{a + b\sqrt{2} \mid a, b \in R\}, +, \cdot)$

d $(\mathfrak{R}, +, \cdot)$

e $(I/11, \oplus_{11}, \odot_{11})$

f $(\{\bar{a} + \bar{a}\sqrt{3} \mid \bar{a} \in I/3\}, +, \cdot)$, where

$$(\bar{a} + \bar{a}\sqrt{3}) + (\bar{b} + \bar{b}\sqrt{3}) = (\bar{a} \oplus_3 \bar{b}) + (\bar{a} \oplus_3 \bar{b})\sqrt{3}, \text{ and}$$
$$(\bar{a} + \bar{a}\sqrt{3}) \cdot (\bar{b} + \bar{b}\sqrt{3}) = (\bar{a} \odot_3 \bar{b}) + (\bar{a} \odot_3 \bar{b})\sqrt{3}$$

g $(\{\bar{a}\sqrt{5} \mid \bar{a} \in I/7\}, +, \cdot)$, where

$$(\bar{a}\sqrt{5}) + (\bar{b}\sqrt{5}) = (\bar{a} \oplus_7 \bar{b})\sqrt{5}, \text{ and}$$
$$(\bar{a}\sqrt{5}) \cdot (\bar{b}\sqrt{5}) = (\bar{a} \odot_7 \bar{b})\sqrt{5}$$ *Answer*

◆ **10** In Theorem 61/4 of this section, show that no positive integer m exists such that $m < n$ and $m \times b = 0$. *Answer*

11 Let $(S, +, \cdot)$ be a field with multiplicative identity e. Prove that $(\{n \times e \mid n \in I\}, +)$ is a subgroup of $(S, +)$.

12 In the first part of Theorem 63/4, show that the mapping f indicated by

$$\begin{array}{cccccc} p \times e & 1 \times e & 2 \times e & 3 \times e & \ldots & (p-1) \times e \\ \updownarrow & \updownarrow & \updownarrow & \updownarrow & & \updownarrow \\ \bar{0} & \bar{1} & \bar{2} & \bar{3} & \ldots & \overline{p-1} \end{array}$$

is an isomorphism from

$$\{p \times e,\ 1 \times e,\ 2 \times e,\ \ldots,\ (p-1) \times e\} \text{ onto } \{\bar{0},\ \bar{1},\ \bar{2},\ \ldots,\ \overline{p-1}\}.$$

◆ **13** In Theorem 63/4, part 2, show that the mapping $(n \times e)\mathrm{f} = n$ for each $n \in I$ is an isomorphism from $\{n \times e \mid n \in I\}$ onto I.

◆ **14** Let $(A, +, \cdot)$ be a ring such that if $x \in A$, then $x \cdot x = x$. Show that the characteristic of A is 2.

15 In an integral domain $(S, +, \cdot)$, we define $(a + b)^2 = (a + b)(a + b)$ and $(a + b)^3 = (a + b)(a + b)(a + b)$ for each $a, b \in S$. Prove that if the characteristic of $(S, +, \cdot)$ is 2, $(a + b)^2 = a^2 + b^2$.

16 For exercise 15, prove that if the characteristic of $(S, +, \cdot)$ is 3, then $(a + b)^3 = a^3 + b^3$.

Subfields 35/4

In this section we will discuss *subfields* and a special class of subfields, called *prime subfields.* From your studies of the subgroups of a group and the subrings of a ring, you can probably anticipate the definition of a subfield. Many of the examples of fields that we have considered are subfields of some other fields. For example, the field of rational numbers is a subfield of the field of real numbers. A precise definition of a subfield is given below.

Definition 61/4 If $(S, +, \cdot)$ is a field and $T \subseteq S$, then the mathematical system $(T, +, \cdot)$ is a *subfield* of $(S, +, \cdot)$ if and only if $(T, +, \cdot)$ is a field.

Although a subfield consists of a set and two operations, we will sometimes refer simply to set T as a subfield, without mentioning the operations.

Definition 61/4 cannot be used to determine whether or not a subset of a field is a subfield without verifying all the properties of a field. However, the following theorem provides an easier way to determine if a subset of a field is a subfield.

Theorem 64/4 If $(S, +, \cdot)$ is a field and T is a nonempty subset of S, then $(T, +, \cdot)$ is a subfield of $(S, +, \cdot)$ if and only if the following conditions hold:

1) For each $a, b \in T$, $a - b \in T$.
2) For each $a, b \in T$, with $b \neq 0$, $ab^{-1} \in T$.

The first condition stated in the theorem is the *closure property of subtraction* (or of *addition of inverses*). We will refer to the second condition stated in the theorem as the *closure property of multiplication by inverses.* Thus, the theorem can be expressed as follows: T is a subfield if and only if T is closed under addition of inverses and multiplication by inverses.

Proof Let us assume first that the system $(T, +, \cdot)$ is a subfield and show that the two conditions of the theorem are satisfied.

1) $a, b \in T$.	Hypothesis
$-b \in T$.	Additive-inverse property
$a + (-b) = (a - b) \in T$.	Closure property of addition
2) $a, b \in T, b \neq 0$.	Hypothesis
$b^{-1} \in T$.	Multiplicative-inverse property
$a \cdot b^{-1} \in T$.	Closure property of multiplication

These two arguments establish that if (T, $+$, $\cdot$) is a subfield, then T is closed under addition of inverses and multiplication by inverses.

Next, we must verify that if a subset of a field satisfies the conditions of closure under addition of inverses and multiplication by inverses, then it is indeed a subfield. We can accomplish this by showing that each of the eleven field properties given in the chart on page 232 is satisfied. In the proof of Theorem 49/3, we saw that closure under subtraction implies that the five properties of a commutative group under addition are satisfied for (T, $+$). Properties 7, 8, and 10 hold for (T, $+$, $\cdot$) because T is a subset of S. You should recall what these properties are and give the reasons that support this statement.

It remains now for us to verify the closure property of multiplication, the multiplicative-identity property, and the multiplicative-inverse property; that is, the field properties 6, 9, and 11, respectively. We shall verify these properties in the following order: the multiplicative-identity property, the multiplicative-inverse property, and the closure property for multiplication.

You should study the proofs to see why it is convenient to verify the properties in this order.

We will show first that the multiplicative identity e of S is contained in T. If $a \in T$, $a \neq 0$, then $a \cdot a^{-1} \in T$ by condition 2 of the hypothesis. Since $a \cdot a^{-1} = e$, it follows that $e \in T$. Because e is the multiplicative identity of S, it is the multiplicative identity of T. Why? Hence, property 9 is established.

We will show next that, if $b \in T$, $b \neq 0$, then b^{-1}, the multiplicative inverse of b, also is contained in T. Since we have just seen that $e \in T$, it follows from condition 2 of the hypothesis that $e \cdot b^{-1} \in T$. But, because e is the multiplicative identity, $e \cdot b^{-1} = b^{-1}$; hence, $b^{-1} \in T$.

Finally, we will show that closure under multiplication by inverses (condition 2 of the hypothesis) implies closure of multiplication (property 6). To this end, let $a, b \in T$. The argument of the previous paragraph shows that if $b \neq 0$, then $b^{-1} \in T$, so $a \cdot (b^{-1})^{-1} = a \cdot b \in T$ by condition 2. On the other hand, if $b = 0$, then $a \cdot b = a \cdot 0 = 0$. Since $0 \in T$, it follows that T is closed under multiplication. The proof of the theorem is complete.

You might try to establish the closure, identity, and inverse properties of multiplication in that order to see what difficulties are encountered.

It should be noted that every field has at least one subfield, namely, the field containing all the elements of the given field.

In other words, every field is a *trivial subfield* of itself. A field may, of course, have proper subfields. It is these subfields with which we will be concerned in the remainder of this section.

In section 20/2 we showed that the intersection of two subgroups is a subgroup. We can use a similar method to show that the intersection of two subfields is again a subfield. Generally, we can show that the intersection of any number of subfields is a subfield. The method of proof is essentially the same as that already used for the intersection of subgroups. Although we will not give the proof in the text, we will now state the theorem.

Theorem 65/4 If (S, +, •) is a field and if K is a collection of subfields of (S, +, •), then the intersection of all the subfields in set K is a subfield of (S, +, •).

The subfield that is the intersection of all subfields of S is called the *smallest subfield* of S. Thus, if (S, +, •) is a field and (T, +, •) is the subfield obtained by the intersection of all subfields of (S, +, •), then there is no subfield of (S, +, •) that is a proper subfield of (T, +, •). The subfield that is the intersection of all subfields of a field is of particular importance and is defined below.

Definition 62/4 If (S, +, •) is a field and if (P, +, •) is the subfield that is the intersection of all subfields of (S, +, •), then (P, +, •) is called the *prime subfield of* (S, +, •).

At first glance, Definition 62/4 might seem not only to describe the prime subfield, but also to give a method of determining it. Although this is true, there are some difficulties in selecting those elements that are common to all subfields. These difficulties can be better appreciated after reading the next section, where we establish that the field of real numbers has infinitely many subfields. Instead of forming the intersection of all subfields of a field to determine a prime subfield, we can use the idea of the characteristic of a field for this purpose. The properties of the prime subfields of finite and infinite fields are described in the next two theorems.

Theorem 66/4 If (S, +, •) is a field and has characteristic p, where p is a prime integer, then the prime subfield P of the field S is

$$(\{n \times e \mid 1 \leqq n \leqq p\}, +, \cdot).$$

This prime subfield is isomorphic to the field of integers modulo p.

Proof By the definition of a prime subfield, it is clear that P must contain the multiplicative identity e. Furthermore, since any subfield is closed under addition and subtraction, the prime subfield P must contain all integral multiples of the multiplicative identity e. Thus, we know that $\{n \times e \mid 1 \leqq n \leqq p\} \subseteq P$.

In the proof of Theorem 63/4, we established that, for a field with characteristic p, the elements of $\{n \times e \mid 1 \leqq n \leqq p\} = \{p \times e,\ 1 \times e,\ 2 \times e,\ \ldots,\ (p-1) \times e\}$ are distinct and that every integral multiple of e is a member of this set. Also, we know that this set is the additive subgroup generated by e. We now assert that the set $\{p \times e,\ 1 \times e,\ 2 \times e,\ \ldots,\ (p-1) \times e\}$ is a field under addition and multiplication and is, in fact, the prime subfield P. Eleven properties must be verified to show that

$$(\{p \times e,\ 1 \times e,\ 2 \times e,\ \ldots,\ (p-1) \times e\}, +, \cdot)$$

is a field. We have verified properties 1 through 5 in proving, in Theorem 63/4, that under addition this set forms a subgroup of $(S, +, \cdot)$. It should be easy for you to show why properties 7 (associative for multiplication), 8 (distributive), 9 (multiplicative identity), and 10 (commutative for multiplication) are satisfied. You are asked to establish these properties in exercise 4 at the end of the section.

We will now verify property 6 (closure for multiplication). Let $m \times e$ and $n \times e$ be arbitrary elements of P such that $1 \leqq m \leqq p$ and $1 \leqq n \leqq p$. By the division algorithm, we can express the product $m \cdot n$ as $q \cdot p + r$, with $0 \leqq r < p$. So,

$$(m \times e) \cdot (n \times e) = (m \cdot n) \times (e \cdot e) = (m \cdot n) \times e = (q \cdot p + r) \times e,$$

where $0 \leqq r < p$. Now,

$$\begin{aligned}(q \cdot p + r) \times e &= \big((q \cdot p) \times e\big) + (r \times e)\\ &= (q \times 0) + (r \times e)\\ &= 0 + (r \times e)\\ &= r \times e.\end{aligned}$$

Thus, $(m \times e) \cdot (n \times e) = r \times e$. Since $0 \leqq r < p$, the element $r \times e$ is in set P, and the closure property of multiplication is verified.

It remains to show that property 11, the multiplicative-inverse property, is satisfied. That is, we must show that there exists an element $n \times e$ in P which is the multiplicative inverse of $m \times e$, where $m \times e$ is any nonzero element of P. Since $p \times e = 0$, we know that $m < p$. Because p is prime and $m < p$, it follows that m and p are relatively prime. Therefore, by a property of integers, there exist integers a and b such that

$$am + bp = 1.$$

Now if a is an element of $\{1,\ 2,\ \ldots,\ p-1\}$, we choose a as the desired n so that $n \times e$ is the multiplicative inverse of $m \times e$. If a is not in this set, then it is congruent modulo p to an element n of the set. That is,

$$a \equiv n \bmod p.$$

If $a \equiv n \bmod p$, we know that $a - n = kp$, or $n = a - kp$. Thus, we select n from the set $\{1, 2, \ldots, p - 1\}$ so that it satisfies one of the following conditions:

1) $nm = 1 - bp$;
2) $n = a - kp$, with $am + bp = 1$.

We can verify that, in either case, $n \times e$ is the multiplicative inverse of $m \times e$. Let us consider first the case in which $nm = 1 - bp$.

$$\begin{aligned}(n \times e) \cdot (m \times e) &= (n \cdot m) \times e \\ &= (1 - bp) \times e \\ &= (1 \times e) - (bp \times e) \\ &= e - \big(b \times (p \times e)\big) \\ &= e - (b \times 0) \\ &= e.\end{aligned}$$

For the second case,

$$\begin{aligned}(n \times e) \cdot (m \times e) &= (n \cdot m) \times e \\ &= \big((a - kp) \cdot m\big) \times e \\ &= (am - kpm) \times e \\ &= \big((1 - bp) - kpm\big) \times e \\ &= (1 \times e) - \big(b \times (p \times e)\big) - \big(km \times (p \times e)\big) \\ &= e - (b \times 0) - (km \times 0) \\ &= e.\end{aligned}$$

Thus, it is always possible to select an integer n so that $n \times e$ is in P and so that $n \times e$ is the multiplicative inverse of the given nonzero element $m \times e$.

Before we continue with the proof, let us review the argument so far. We started with a field (S, +, •) with prime characteristic p and showed that $\{n \times e \mid 1 \leqq n \leqq p\}$, which we know to be a subset (proper or improper) of set P, forms a field under addition and multiplication. But since the prime subfield P is the smallest subfield of S, it follows that subfield $P \subseteq (\{n \times e \mid 1 \leqq n \leqq p\}, +, \cdot)$. Therefore, since each of these subfields contains the other, $P = (\{n \times e \mid 1 \leqq n \leqq p\}, +, \cdot)$.

The final step in the proof of Theorem 66/4 consists of showing that P is isomorphic to the field I/p. In brief, the correspondence

$$m \times e \leftrightarrow \bar{m}, \text{ where } 1 \leqq m \leqq p$$

is a function from P onto I/p that is one-to-one and that preserves both operations. In an exercise at the end of this section, you are asked to establish each of these properties.

Theorem 66/4 describes the structure of the prime subfield P of a field if the characteristic of the field is a prime number by establishing that $P \cong I/p$. However, in section 34/4 we showed that there exist fields whose characteristic is 0. We will now prove a theorem that describes the structure of the prime subfield of a field whose characteristic is 0.

Theorem 67/4 If $(S, +, \cdot)$ is a field whose characteristic is 0, then the prime subfield P is isomorphic to the field of rational numbers.

Proof We will give only the important steps in the proof, leaving many of the details for you to verify because the arguments can be patterned after those just presented for Theorem 66/4.

First of all, the smallest subfield P must contain the multiplicative identity e and all integral multiples of e. So it follows that

$$\{\ldots, -2 \times e, -1 \times e, 0 \times e, 1 \times e, 2 \times e, \ldots\} \subseteq P.$$

We have shown that the additive subgroup generated by e is isomorphic to the integers (Theorem 63/4). We now need to determine the smallest subfield that contains this set. For each nonzero element $m \times e$ that is in P, there must also be a multiplicative inverse in P (Why?), which we will denote by $\frac{1}{m} \times e$. Since P is closed under multiplication, it contains elements of the form $(n \times e) \cdot \left(\frac{1}{m} \times e\right)$. If we use the notation $\frac{n}{m} \times e$ for such products, then we can establish that the system

$$\left(\left\{\frac{n}{m} \times e \mid n, m \in I \text{ and } m \neq 0\right\}, +, \cdot\right)$$

is a field. Since P must contain all such products, and yet must be the smallest field, it follows that P is precisely the set

$$\left\{\frac{n}{m} \times e \mid n \in I \text{ and } m \in I \text{ and } m \neq 0\right\}.$$

The verification that the correspondence $\frac{n}{m} \leftrightarrow \frac{n}{m} \times e$ is an isomorphism between the field of rational numbers R and field P is left as an exercise.

Exercises

1 Let F be a field, and let $(S, +, \cdot)$ and $(T, +, \cdot)$ be subfields of F. Prove that $(S \cap T, +, \cdot)$ is a subfield of F. *Answer*

2 Prove Theorem 65/4.

3 Let $(F, +, \cdot)$ be a field, and let $(S, +, \cdot)$ be the subfield obtained by the intersection of all subfields of F. Prove that there could not exist a subfield $(T, +, \cdot)$ of F such that $(T, +, \cdot) \subset (S, +, \cdot)$. *Answer*

4 Verify the associative, identity, and commutative properties for multiplication and also the distributive property in Theorem 66/4.

5 Prove that the correspondence given in Theorem 66/4 between $(P, +, \cdot)$ and $(I/p, \oplus_p, \odot_p)$ is an isomorphism.

6 Prove that the correspondence between the field of rational numbers and the prime subfield P with characteristic 0 is an isomorphism (Theorem 67/4). *Answer*

◆ 7 For exercise 7 of section 34/4, construct the addition and multiplication table for F. Thus, show that the elements of F which do not belong to the prime subfield satisfy the relation $x \cdot x = x + 1$, or $x \cdot x - x - 1 = 0$.

◆ 8 Find all the subfields of the field of exercise 7.

9 Assume that $\{a + bi \mid a, b \in \mathfrak{R} \text{ and } i^2 = -1\}$ is a field under addition and multiplication. Which of the following sets of complex numbers are subfields of the complex numbers?

a $\{x \mid x \in I \text{ and } x \geqq 0\}$
b $\{x \mid x \in I\}$ *Answer*
c $\{a + b\sqrt{2} \mid a, b \in R\}$
d $\{a + b\sqrt{3} \mid a, b \in \mathfrak{R}\}$ *Answer*
e $\{a + b\sqrt{5} \mid a, b \in I\}$
f $\{x \mid x \in R \text{ and } x \notin I\}$
g $\{x \mid x \in \mathfrak{R} \text{ and } x \notin R\}$
h $\{a + bi \mid a, b \in I \text{ and } i^2 = -1\}$
i $\{a + bi \mid a, b \in R \text{ and } i^2 = -1\}$
j $\{a + bi \mid a, b \in \mathfrak{R} \text{ and } i^2 = -1\}$
k $\{a + b\sqrt{3}i \mid a, b \in R \text{ and } i^2 = -1\}$
l $\{a + b\sqrt[3]{2}i \mid a, b \in \mathfrak{R} \text{ and } i^2 = -1\}$ *Answer*

10 Does the set of all polynomials with rational coefficients under addition and multiplication form a field? An integral domain?

11 Find the prime subfield of each of the following fields.

◆ a $(R, +, \cdot)$
b $(\mathfrak{R}, +, \cdot)$
c $(\{a + bi \mid a, b \in R \text{ and } i^2 = -1\}, +, \cdot)$
d The field given in exercise 9f, section 34/4
e The field given in exercise 9g, section 34/4

Simple field extensions 36/4

In the previous section we first defined the prime subfield of a field as the intersection of all subfields of the given field and then proved theorems that gave us practical methods for determining the prime subfield. Specifically, we proved that the prime subfield of a field is isomorphic to the field of integers modulo p when the characteristic of the field is the prime number p and is isomorphic to the field of rational numbers when the characteristic of the field is 0. Let us now apply these results to the field of real numbers.

First of all, observe that the prime subfield of the real numbers must contain the number 1. But the additive order of 1 is zero; hence, the characteristic of the field of real numbers is zero. (Can you give another argument to show that the characteristic of the field of real numbers is zero?) Therefore, Theorem 67/4 assures that the prime subfield of the field of real numbers is isomorphic to the field of rational numbers; in fact, the prime subfield *is* the field of rational numbers because $R \subset \mathfrak{R}$.

In this section we will be concerned with determining some of the fields that are "between" the field of real numbers and its prime subfield. That is, our concern will be with determining some of the fields S such that $R \subset S \subset \mathfrak{R}$. The sentence "$R \subset S \subset \mathfrak{R}$" is a brief way of expressing the two relations, R is included in S and S is included in $\mathfrak{R}$. Such fields S are called *intermediate fields* because they are "between" a field and its prime subfield.

We will now discuss an example of an intermediate field of $(\mathfrak{R}, +, \cdot)$ in some detail.

Example 1 We have previously shown that the following subset of the real numbers,

$$R(\sqrt{2}) = \{a + b\sqrt{2} \mid a, b \in R\},$$

under addition and multiplication is a commutative ring with identity. Therefore, to establish that $R(\sqrt{2})$ is a field we need only to show that, for each nonzero element of the set, there exists a multiplicative inverse that is also contained in the set. First, it may be helpful to consider a specific element of $R(\sqrt{2})$ to give us some idea of what form the multiplicative inverse might have. One element of $R(\sqrt{2})$ is $3 + 4\sqrt{2}$. We know that the multiplicative inverse of $3 + 4\sqrt{2}$ can be represented as $\dfrac{1}{3 + 4\sqrt{2}}$. This inverse, however, is not easily recognizable as a member of the set $R(\sqrt{2})$. Consequently, it is necessary to determine rational numbers a, b such that

$$a + b\sqrt{2} = \frac{1}{3 + 4\sqrt{2}}.$$

We can accomplish this by the familiar process known as *rationalizing the denominator*. Using this process, we have

$$\frac{1}{3 + 4\sqrt{2}} = \frac{1}{3 + 4\sqrt{2}} \cdot \frac{3 - 4\sqrt{2}}{3 - 4\sqrt{2}} = \frac{3 - 4\sqrt{2}}{9 - 32} = \frac{-3}{23} + \frac{4\sqrt{2}}{23}.$$

Thus, if $a = \frac{-3}{23}$ and $b = \frac{4}{23}$, then the multiplicative inverse of $3 + 4\sqrt{2}$ is contained in the set $R(\sqrt{2})$. Although this is a special case, we can use the same procedure to determine the multiplicative inverse of an arbitrary nonzero element $a + b\sqrt{2}$ in the set $R(\sqrt{2})$. Hence, we have

$$\frac{1}{a + b\sqrt{2}} = \frac{1}{a + b\sqrt{2}} \cdot \frac{a - b\sqrt{2}}{a - b\sqrt{2}} = \frac{a}{a^2 - 2b^2} - \frac{b}{a^2 - 2b^2}(\sqrt{2}),$$

which is the multiplicative inverse of $a + b\sqrt{2}$. Now

$$\frac{a}{a^2 - 2b^2} - \frac{b}{a^2 - 2b^2}\sqrt{2}$$

is in $R(\sqrt{2})$ only if, for each $a, b \in R$, $a^2 - 2b^2 \neq 0$. You are asked to show, in exercise 1 at the end of the section, this is the case unless $a - b\sqrt{2} = 0$. Thus, every nonzero element of $R(\sqrt{2})$ has a multiplicative inverse and, hence, $(R(\sqrt{2}), +, \cdot)$ is a field.

Now that we have established that $(R(\sqrt{2}), +, \cdot)$ is a field, we must show that

$$R \subset R(\sqrt{2}) \subset \mathfrak{R}.$$

Since it may not be clear why R is a proper subfield of $R(\sqrt{2})$ and why $R(\sqrt{2})$ is a proper subfield of $\mathfrak{R}$, some discussion will be devoted to establishing each of these.

First, why is $R \subset R(\sqrt{2})$? To answer this, we must demonstrate that every element of R is contained in $R(\sqrt{2})$ and also that there is at least one element of $R(\sqrt{2})$ that is not in R. Let r be any element of R and note that if $a = r$ and $b = 0$, then $r = r + 0\sqrt{2} = a + b\sqrt{2}$. Therefore, if $r \in R$, then $r \in R(\sqrt{2})$. Next, note that if $a = 0$ and $b = 1$, then $a + b\sqrt{2} = 0 + 1 \cdot \sqrt{2} = \sqrt{2}$. Thus, $\sqrt{2} \in R(\sqrt{2})$, but, because $\sqrt{2}$ is irrational, $\sqrt{2} \notin R$. Hence, $R \subset R(\sqrt{2})$.

Second, is the field $R(\sqrt{2})$ a proper subfield of $\mathfrak{R}$? Every element $a + b\sqrt{2} \in R(\sqrt{2})$ is a real number; hence, $R(\sqrt{2}) \subseteq \mathfrak{R}$. But does $\mathfrak{R}$ contain at least one element not in $R(\sqrt{2})$? One such real number is $\sqrt{3}$. To verify this statement, we must show that there do not exist rational numbers a and b such that

$a + b\sqrt{2} = \sqrt{3}$. If we assume that there are such numbers a and b, we have

$$\begin{aligned} a + b\sqrt{2} &= \sqrt{3}, \\ b\sqrt{2} &= \sqrt{3} - a, \\ 2b^2 &= 3 + a^2 - 2a\sqrt{3}, \\ 2b^2 - 3 - a^2 &= -2a\sqrt{3}. \end{aligned}$$

But $2b^2 - 3 - a^2$ is a rational number (Why?), while $-2a\sqrt{3}$ is zero or irrational. If we assume that $-2a\sqrt{3}$ is irrational, then we have a contradiction. Suppose, however, that $-2a\sqrt{3} = 0$. Then a must be 0. Replacing a by 0 in $2b^2 - 3 - a^2 = -2a\sqrt{3}$ yields

$$\begin{aligned} 2b^2 - 3 - 0 &= 0, \\ 2b^2 &= 3, \\ b^2 &= \tfrac{3}{2}, \\ b &= \pm\sqrt{\tfrac{3}{2}}, \\ b &= \frac{\pm\sqrt{6}}{2}. \end{aligned}$$

However, b cannot be equal to $\frac{\pm\sqrt{6}}{2}$ since, by hypothesis, b is rational, and $\frac{\pm\sqrt{6}}{2}$ is irrational. Thus, we have a contradiction when we assume that $-2a\sqrt{3} = 0$. You should supply the reasons for each of the steps in the argument.

Because $\sqrt{3} \in \mathfrak{R}$, but $\sqrt{3} \notin R(\sqrt{2})$, it follows that $R(\sqrt{2}) \subset \mathfrak{R}$. Hence, we have established that $R \subset R(\sqrt{2}) \subset \mathfrak{R}$. We conclude, therefore, that $R(\sqrt{2})$ is an intermediate field of $\mathfrak{R}$.

Earlier, we said that in this section we would be concerned with intermediate fields that are "between" the field of real numbers and its prime subfield, the field of rational numbers. We will also restrict the discussion to *simple extensions* of fields. A definition of what is meant by a simple extension is given next.

Definition 63/4 If $(S, +, \cdot)$ is a field, $(T, +, \cdot)$ is a subfield of $(S, +, \cdot)$, and $c \in S$, then the smallest subfield of S that contains both T and c, denoted by $(T(c), +, \cdot)$ is the *simple extension* of the field T by the element c.

Observe that there is at least one subfield that contains both T and c, namely, S. But there may be more than one such subfield of S. The intersection of all subfields containing both T and c is a subfield and is the smallest subfield containing both T and c.

The notation of Definition 63/4 generalizes in a natural way the notation used in example 1. Thus, if $S = \mathfrak{R}$, $T = R$, and $c = \sqrt{2}$, then $R(\sqrt{2}) = (\{a + b\sqrt{2} \mid a, b \in R\}, +, \cdot)$ is in fact the simple extension of the field of rational numbers by $\sqrt{2}$.

The rest of this discussion will be restricted to the field of real numbers as the field S and the field of rational numbers as the subfield T in Definition 63/4. Let us now see what kinds of simple extensions can be obtained by making various choices for the real number c.

Suppose that c is a rational number. Then the field $R(c)$ is just the field of rational numbers because the field of rational numbers contains the set of all rational numbers, including c. Therefore, R is the smallest field that contains both R and c, and by Definition 63/4, R is the simple extension of the field of rational numbers by the rational number c.

Because a simple extension of the field of rational numbers by a rational number c results in the field of rational numbers, we say that, in such cases, no *proper* extension occurs. Consequently, such extensions are of no interest. For this reason, we will be concerned with simple extensions of the field of rational numbers by irrational numbers. For purposes of classifying such extensions, real numbers are partitioned into two subsets, the *algebraic* numbers and *nonalgebraic* (or *transcendental*) numbers. The distinction between these two kinds of numbers is given in the following definition.

Definition 64/4 If $(S, +, \cdot)$ is a field, $(T, +, \cdot)$ is a subfield of S, and $c \in S$, then c is *algebraic* over T if and only if there exists a polynomial

$$p(x) = a_0 + a_1x^1 + a_2x^2 + \ldots + a_nx^n,$$

with $a_0, a_1, a_2, \ldots, a_n \in T$ such that

$$p(c) = a_0 + a_1c^1 + a_2c^2 + \ldots + a_nc^n = 0.$$

If no such polynomial exists, the element c is called *nonalgebraic* (or *transcendental*) over T.

In terms of the field of real numbers, an irrational number is algebraic if it is a root of a polynomial function with rational coefficients. An irrational number is transcendental if it is *not* a root of such a function. Thus, the element $\sqrt{2}$ is algebraic over the subfield of rational numbers because $\sqrt{2}$ is a root of

$$2 + 0x - x^2 = 0.$$

Give polynomials to show that $\sqrt{3}$, $\sqrt{7}$, $\sqrt{p}$ (where p is a counting number that is not a perfect square) are each algebraic over the subfield of rational numbers. Since

$$r - x = 0$$

has a root r for any rational number r, it follows that every rational number is algebraic. There *are* real numbers that are nonalgebraic, or transcendental, over the field of rational numbers, and, while the proof of the existence of such numbers is beyond the level of this discussion, we remark that the familiar number π and the number e are examples of transcendental real numbers.

We will now consider another specific example of a simple, proper extension of the rational numbers by an algebraic number [remember that the first example was the field $R(\sqrt{2})$].

Example 2 The real number $\sqrt{3}$ is an irrational real number; it is also algebraic over the rational numbers because it is a root of the polynomial $x^2 - 3 = 0$. We now wish to determine the field $R(\sqrt{3})$. The following theorem shows that the field $R(\sqrt{3})$ consists of precisely those elements of the form $a + b\sqrt{3}$, where a and b are rational numbers.

Theorem 68/4 The simple, proper extension $(R(\sqrt{3}), +, \cdot)$ of $(R, +, \cdot)$ by $\sqrt{3}$ is the subfield $(\{a + b\sqrt{3} \mid a, b \in R\}, +, \cdot)$.

Proof The simple extension of the rational numbers R by the irrational number $\sqrt{3}$ is the smallest subfield that contains both R and $\sqrt{3}$, which is the intersection of all subfields that contain both R and $\sqrt{3}$. The theorem asserts that the system $(\{a + b\sqrt{3} \mid a, b \in R\}, +, \cdot)$ is a subfield, contains every element of R and also contains $\sqrt{3}$, and is the least such field. The arguments that follow will verify each of these statements.

With reference to the statement that $\{a + b\sqrt{3} \mid a, b \in R\}$ is a field, remember that this set has been discussed on several occasions and that in exercise 4c on page 235, you were asked to decide if this system is a field. In exercise 4 at the end of this section you are asked to prove formally that $(\{a + b\sqrt{3} \mid a, b \in R\}, +, \cdot)$ is a field.

If $r \in R$, then the choice of $a = r$ and $b = 0$ in $a + b\sqrt{3}$ shows that $r \in R(\sqrt{3})$. Similarly, the choice $a = 0$ and $b = 1$ in $a + b\sqrt{3}$ shows that $\sqrt{3}$ belongs to the set $R(\sqrt{3})$. These remarks establish that $\sqrt{3}$ and every element of R belong to $\{a + b\sqrt{3} \mid a, b \in R\}$.

The final step is to show that the field $(\{a + b\sqrt{3} \mid a, b \in R\}, +, \cdot)$ is the smallest subfield that contains both R and $\sqrt{3}$. But if F is a subfield of $(\mathfrak{R}, +, \cdot)$ that contains both R and $\sqrt{3}$, then F must contain a and b, for each $a, b \in R$, and also must contain $\sqrt{3}$. Since F is a field and, hence, is closed under addition and multiplication, it follows that, for each $a, b \in R$, $a + b\sqrt{3} \in F$; thus $R(\sqrt{3}) \subseteq F$. This shows that $(\{a + b\sqrt{3} \mid a, b \in R\}, +, \cdot)$ is the smallest subfield that contains both R and $\sqrt{3}$ because $R(\sqrt{3})$ is included in every subfield F that contains both R and $\sqrt{3}$. The theorem is established.

In the discussion above, we have dealt with two examples of simple algebraic extensions of the field of rational numbers, $R(\sqrt{2}) = (\{a + b\sqrt{2} \mid a, b \in R\}, +, \cdot)$ and $R(\sqrt{3}) = (\{a + b\sqrt{3} \mid a, b \in R\}, +, \cdot)$. Although the examples we have chosen are relatively easy, the generalization of this idea is not very difficult. Theorem 69/4, which is given without proof, expresses this generalization.

Theorem 69/4 If $(S, +, \cdot)$ is a field and if $(T, +, \cdot)$ is a subfield of S with $c \in S$ such that c is algebraic over T, then the simple field extension $T(c)$ consists of all polynomial expressions of the form

$$a_0 + a_1c^1 + a_2c^2 + \ldots + a_nc^n,$$

with $a_0, a_1, a_2, \ldots, a_n \in T$.

It remains to discuss the case where the element c is transcendental over the field T. Such extensions are called *transcendental extensions*. Theorem 70/4 describes a transcendental extension.

Theorem 70/4 Suppose that $(S, +, \cdot)$ is a field, that $(T, +, \cdot)$ is a subfield of S and that $d \in S$ such that d is transcendental over the field T. Then the simple transcendental extension, denoted by $T(d)$, consists of the field of all rational expressions

$$\frac{a_0 + a_1d^1 + \ldots + a_nd^n}{b_0 + b_1d^1 + \ldots + b_md^m}$$

with $a_0, a_1, \ldots, a_n \in T$ and $b_0, b_1, \ldots, b_m \in T$.

The pair of companion theorems, 69/4 and 70/4, which are given here without proof, completely describe the fields that are obtained by simple algebraic and transcendental extensions. Note that the difference between simple algebraic extensions and simple transcendental extensions lies in the fact that in the first case the set consists of polynomials, while in the second case the set consists of quotients of polynomials.

Exercises

1 In showing that $a + b\sqrt{2}$ has a multiplicative inverse, we made use of the fact that $a^2 - 2b^2 \neq 0$ for $a, b \in R$. Prove this by assuming that $a^2 - 2b^2 = 0$ and deducing a contradiction concerning $\sqrt{2}$.

2 Let $R(\sqrt{5}) = \{a + b\sqrt{5} \mid a, b \in R\}$. Show that $R(\sqrt{5})$ is a field and also that $R \subset R(\sqrt{5}) \subset \Re$.

3 Prove that $\sqrt{3}$ is irrational. Do this by assuming that $\sqrt{3} = \frac{a}{b}$ for integers a, b, where a and b are relatively prime. *Answer*

4 Prove that $R(\sqrt{3}) = \{a + b\sqrt{3} \mid a, b \in R\}$ is a field. How does the field $R(\sqrt{3})$ compare with the field $R(1 + \sqrt{3})$? How do you know that $R(1 + \sqrt{3})$ is a field?

5 Determine whether each of the following real numbers is algebraic over R or transcendental over R and justify your answer.

a $\sqrt{6}$

b $1 + \sqrt{2}$ *Answer*

c $\sqrt[3]{4}$

d $-1 + \sqrt[3]{5}$ [Hint: Consider $x^3 + 3x^2 + 3x - 4 = 0$.]

e $\sqrt[4]{5}$

f $-2 + \sqrt{3}$

g $2 - \sqrt[3]{4}$

h $\sqrt{2} + \sqrt{3}$ [Hint: Consider $x^4 - 10x^2 - 1 = 0$.]

i $-2 + \sqrt[4]{7}$

6 In Theorem 69/4, let $S = \mathfrak{R}$, $T = R$, and $c = \sqrt{5}$. Is c algebraic over T? What is the simple field extension $T(c)$? Show that $T(c) = \{a + b\sqrt{5} \mid a, b \in R\}$.

7 In Theorem 69/4, let $S = \mathfrak{R}$, $T = R$, and $c = \sqrt[3]{3}$. Is c algebraic over T? What is the simple field extension $T(c)$? Show that $T(c) = \{a + b\sqrt[3]{3} + c\sqrt[3]{9} \mid a, b, c \in R\}$.

8 Describe the following simple field extensions of the rational numbers.

a $R(\sqrt{7})$

b $R(\sqrt[3]{2})$

c $R(\sqrt[3]{5})$ *Answer*

d $R(\sqrt[4]{2})$

e $R(\sqrt[5]{2})$

f $R(\sqrt[4]{3})$

9 Determine if the following pairs of simple field extensions of the rational numbers are identical.

a $R(\sqrt{5})$ and $R(1 + \sqrt{5})$ *Answer*

b $R(1 + \sqrt{3})$ and $R(\sqrt[4]{3})$ *Answer*

c $R(\sqrt{2})$ and $R(\sqrt{2} - 2)$

d $R(\sqrt[3]{2})$ and $R(\sqrt[3]{4})$

e $R(\sqrt{5})$ and $R(\sqrt{7})$

f $R(\sqrt[4]{2})$ and $R(\sqrt[4]{8})$

10 Which elements x contained in $R(\sqrt{5})$ are such that $R(x) = R(\sqrt{5})$? *Answer*

11 Which elements x of $R(\sqrt{3})$ are such that $R(x) = R(\sqrt{3})$?

12 Let $a = k^2b$, where $a, b, k \in R^+$. Show that $R(\sqrt{a}) = R(\sqrt{b})$.

13 In $R(\sqrt[3]{2})$, what is the multiplicative inverse of $1 + \sqrt[3]{2} + \sqrt[3]{4}$? *Answer*

14 In $R(\sqrt[3]{5})$, what is the multiplicative inverse of $2 + 3\sqrt[3]{5}$?

15 Consider the simple field extension of the rational numbers, $R(\sqrt{2} + \sqrt{3})$. Describe this field. Then show that $\sqrt{2}$, $\sqrt{3}$, and $\sqrt{6}$ are elements of $R(\sqrt{2} + \sqrt{3})$. Is $R(\sqrt{2}) \subset R(\sqrt{2} + \sqrt{3})$?

16 Consider the simple field extension of the rational numbers, $R(\sqrt[6]{2})$. Describe this field. Then show that $\sqrt{2}$ and $\sqrt[3]{2}$ are elements of $R(\sqrt[6]{2})$. Is $R(\sqrt[3]{2}) \subset R(\sqrt[6]{2})$?

17 Consider the simple field extensions $R(\sqrt{2})$ and $R(\sqrt{3})$. Is $\sqrt{2} \in R(\sqrt{2}) \cup R(\sqrt{3})$? Is $\sqrt{3} \in R(\sqrt{2}) \cup R(\sqrt{3})$? Is $R(\sqrt{2}) \cup R(\sqrt{3})$ a field? *Answer*

18 If we define

$R(\sqrt{2}) \star R(\sqrt{3}) = \{a + b\sqrt{2} + c\sqrt{3} + d\sqrt{6} \mid a, b, c, d \in R\}$,

is $R(\sqrt{2}) \subset R(\sqrt{2}) \star R(\sqrt{3})$? Is $R(\sqrt{3}) \subset R(\sqrt{2}) \star R(\sqrt{3})$? Is $R(\sqrt{6}) \subset R(\sqrt{2}) \star R(\sqrt{3})$? Is $R(\sqrt{2}) \star R(\sqrt{3})$ a field?

◆ 19 Is $\sqrt{3}$ algebraic over the field $R(\sqrt{2})$? Describe the simple field extension of $R(\sqrt{2})$ by $\sqrt{3}$, that is, $\big(R(\sqrt{2})\big)(\sqrt{3})$. How does this compare with $R(\sqrt{2}) \star R(\sqrt{3})$ of exercise 18?

20 Determine an element x of $R(\sqrt[3]{2})$ different from $\sqrt[3]{2}$ such that $R(x) = R(\sqrt[3]{2})$. Is there more than one such x?

21 Determine an element x of $R(\sqrt[3]{3})$ different from $\sqrt[3]{3}$ such that $R(x) = R(\sqrt[3]{3})$. Is there more than one such x?

◆ 22 Assume that $(I/5, \oplus_5, \odot_5)$ is contained in a field F. Let $c \in F$ and $\bar{1}c^2 - \bar{2} = \bar{0}$, where $\bar{1}, \bar{2}, \bar{0} \in I/5$. Is c algebraic over $(I/5, \oplus_5, \odot_5)$? Is $c \in I/5$? What is the simple field extension of $(I/5, \oplus_5, \odot_5)$ by c if $c = \sqrt{\bar{2}}$? *Answer*

Chapter review

1 Determine which of the following are fields and give reasons to support your answers.

a $(\{a + b\sqrt{5} \mid a, b \in R\}, +, \cdot)$

b $(\{\bar{0}, \bar{4}, \bar{8}\}, \oplus_{12}, \odot_{12})$

c $(I/2 \times I/2, +, \cdot)$, where $(\bar{a}, \bar{b}) + (\bar{c}, \bar{d}) = (\bar{a} \oplus_2 \bar{c}, \bar{b} \oplus_2 \bar{d})$ and $(\bar{a}, \bar{b}) \cdot (\bar{c}, \bar{d}) = (\bar{a} \odot_2 \bar{c}, \bar{b} \odot_2 \bar{d})$ for each $(\bar{a}, \bar{b}), (\bar{c}, \bar{d}) \in I/2 \times I/2$

d $(\{a + b\sqrt[4]{8} \mid a, b \in R\}, +, \cdot)$

2 Determine the characteristic of each integral domain in exercise 1 and the prime subfield of each field.

3 For each integer $n = 2, 3, 4, 5$, and 7, find an integral domain with n elements, and determine which of these integral domains are fields.

4 Suppose that G is a set of elements which forms a commutative group under both the operations of addition and multiplication. Show that $(G, +, \cdot)$ is a field if $a(b + c) = ab + ac$ for all $a, b, c \in G$.

5 Find the intersection of the two subfields of $(\mathfrak{R}, +, \cdot)$, $(\{a + b\sqrt{3} \mid a, b \in R\}, +, \cdot)$ and $(\{a + b\sqrt{5} \mid a, b \in R\}, +, \cdot)$.

6 Show that $(R(\pi), +, \cdot)$ is isomorphic to $(R(\sqrt[3]{\pi}), +, \cdot)$.

7 Determine whether or not any of the following pairs of field extensions of the rational numbers are identical.

a $R(\sqrt[3]{5})$ and $R(\sqrt{5})$

b $R(\sqrt[4]{16})$ and $R(\sqrt{16})$

c $R(\sqrt[3]{7} + 5)$ and $R(\sqrt[3]{14} + 3)$.

8 Find the subfields of $R(\sqrt[6]{3})$. What is the prime subfield?

9 In $R(\sqrt[4]{3})$, find the inverse of $1 + \sqrt[4]{3} + \sqrt[4]{9}$.

10 List ten fields that are "between" $(R, +, \cdot)$ and $(\mathfrak{R}, +, \cdot)$.

11 The integers I form an integral domain under the operations of addition and multiplication. What is the smallest field containing I?

Cumulative review

1 Let $A = \{x \mid x \in \mathfrak{R} \text{ and } x > \frac{3}{2}\}$ and let $B = \{x \mid x \in \mathfrak{R} \text{ and } x < \frac{3}{2}\}$.

a Determine $A \times B$, $A \cup B$, and $A \cap B$.

b Is $C \subseteq A \cup B$?

c Is $R \subseteq A \cup B$?

d Is $\mathfrak{R} \subseteq A \cup B \cup \{\frac{3}{2}\}$?

2 Let $R = \{(x, y) \mid x, y \in \mathfrak{R} \text{ and } y = x^3\}$. Describe the domain and the range of R. Tell whether R is many-to-one or one-to-one. Is relation R a function? Is R a binary operation?

3 Suppose that $f = \{(x, y) \mid x, y \in \mathfrak{R} \text{ and } y = x^2\}$ and that $g = \{(x, y) \mid x, y \in \mathfrak{R} \text{ and } y = \sqrt{x}\}$. Is the composition of f and g defined? If not, what change should be made in the domain of f so that $f \circ g$ is defined? Determine the images of 0, 3, and $\sqrt{2}$ under $f \circ g$.

4 Which of the properties of an equivalence relation does the relation "relatively prime to" satisfy in the set of positive integers?

5 Solve the following conditions in $(I/5, \oplus_5)$.

a $\bar{x} \oplus_5 \bar{2} = \bar{1}$.

b $\bar{x} \oplus_5 \bar{4} = \bar{3}$.

c $\bar{x} \oplus_5 \bar{3} = \bar{1}$.

d $\bar{x} \oplus_5 \bar{y} = \bar{4}$ and $\bar{x} \oplus_5 \bar{2}y = \bar{2}$.

6 Determine which of the following are groups.

a $(E_I, +)$

b $(E_I, \cdot)$

c $(O_I, +)$

d $(O_I, \cdot)$

e $(I/6, \oplus_6)$

f $(I/6, \odot_6)$

7 List the elements in the symmetric group G_3. Which elements are inverses of each other? Describe all subgroups of G_3.

8 Tabulate the subsets I_{3x} and I_{7x} of I. Is $(I_{3x}, +)$ a group? Is $(I_{7x}, +)$ a group? Tabulate $I_{3x} \cap I_{7x}$. Is this set a group under addition? Is $(I_{3x} \cup I_{7x}, +)$ a group?

9 Determine all the subgroups of the group of nonzero integers modulo 21 under multiplication. What are the generators of each of these subgroups?

* 10 Find all the generators of the group $G = (I/6 \times I/7, +)$. What are the subgroups of G and what are the generators of each of these subgroups? What is the order of the elements in G?

* 11 Find all the distinct commutative groups of 32 elements.

12 Show that $(I/6 \times I/6 \times I/6, +, \cdot)$ is a ring if addition and multiplication are defined as follows for each $(\bar{a}, \bar{b}, \bar{c})$ and $(\bar{d}, \bar{e}, \bar{f}) \in I/6 \times I/6 \times I/6$:

$$(\bar{a}, \bar{b}, \bar{c}) + (\bar{d}, \bar{e}, \bar{f}) = (\bar{a} \oplus_6 \bar{d}, \bar{b} \oplus_6 \bar{e}, \bar{c} \oplus_6 \bar{f}).$$
$$(\bar{a}, \bar{b}, \bar{c}) \cdot (\bar{d}, \bar{e}, \bar{f}) = (\bar{a} \odot_6 \bar{d}, \bar{b} \odot_6 \bar{e}, \bar{c} \odot_6 \bar{f}).$$

13 Prove that $\{A/A \in M_{2 \times 2}, a_{ij} = 4k, \text{ and } k \in I\}$ is a subring under matrix addition and multiplication of $(M_{2 \times 2}, +, \cdot)$.

* 14 Consider the mapping $(x)f = r$, with $x = 5q + r$, $x, q, r \in I$, and $0 \leqq r < 5$. Show that this mapping is a homomorphism from I onto I/5. Show that the subset of I mapped onto $\bar{0}$ of I/5 forms an ideal of $(I, +, \cdot)$.

15 Decide whether or not the following rings are integral domains.

a $(I/5[x], +, \cdot)$

b $(\{A \mid A \in M_{2 \times 2}, a_{12} = a_{21} = 0, \text{ and } a_{11}, a_{22} \in I\}, +, \cdot)$

c $(I/31, \oplus_{31}, \odot_{31})$

d $\left(\left\{\dfrac{a}{2^m \cdot 3^n} \mid a, m, n \in I\right\}, +, \cdot\right)$

16 Let $(\mathcal{F}, +, \cdot)$ be the set of constant functions from $\mathfrak{R}$ into $\mathfrak{R}$; that is, $(x)f = c$, where c is a constant in $\mathfrak{R}$ for all $x \in \mathfrak{R}$ and all $f \in \mathcal{F}$. Let addition and multiplication be defined respectively as

$$(x)(f + g) = (x)f + (x)g;$$
$$(x)(f \cdot g) = (x)f \cdot (x)g.$$

Show that $(\mathcal{F}, +, \cdot)$ is a field.

17 Find a subring of $(M_{2 \times 2}, +, \cdot)$ that is a field. What is the prime subfield of this field? What is the characteristic of this field?

18 Which of the following simple field extensions of the rational numbers is equal to $R(\sqrt[4]{5})$? Justify your answer.

a $R(\sqrt{5})$ b $R(\sqrt[4]{5} + \sqrt{5})$ c $R(\sqrt[4]{5} + 6)$ d $R(\sqrt[4]{625})$

Answers to selected exercises

Certain of the exercises in the various sections of each chapter are labeled with the word "*Answer.*" Some of the exercises so labeled were chosen because they are representative of a whole group of similar exercises; some were chosen because their answers involve important generalizations; and some were chosen because they are considered particularly difficult. The answers to these exercises are given in this section. The numerals in the margin indicate the pages on which the exercises are located.

13 **2b** $\{x \mid x$ is a month of the year with exactly 30 days$\}$

3e $\{36, 25, 16, 9, 4, 1, 0\}$

3i $\{2, 8, 18, 32, 50, 72, \ldots, 2k^2, \ldots\}$, where $k \in C$

17-18 **1j** True. For example, $\frac{1}{2} \in \mathfrak{R}$, but $\frac{1}{2} \notin I$.

2j True. Since the set of all rectangles is the set of all quadrilaterals with four right angles, the set of all squares is a proper subset of the set of all rectangles.

3e $\{x \mid x \in I$ and $-3 < x < 6\} = \{-2, -1, 0, 1, 2, 3, 4, 5\}$. Hence, this set has 2^8, or 256, subsets.

5 If A is a nonempty finite set with n elements, then A has 2^n subsets. For any element $a \in A$, the number of subsets of A containing a is equal to the number of subsets not containing a; that is, there are 2^{n-1} subsets that contain a and 2^{n-1} subsets that do not contain a. Of the 2^{n-1} subsets that do not contain a, x of these subsets have an even number of members and y of them have an odd number of members. This means that of the 2^{n-1} subsets of A that do contain a, there are y subsets with an even number of members and x subsets with an odd number of members. Thus, there are $x + y$ subsets of A with an even number of members and $y + x$ subsets with an odd number of members. Since $x + y = y + x$, the number of subsets of A with an even number of members is equal to the number of subsets with an odd number of members.

21-22 **1c** $A = \{-1, 0, 1\}$ and $B = \{1, 2, 3, 4\}$. Therefore,

$$A \times B = \{(-1, 1), (-1, 2), (-1, 3), (-1, 4), (0, 1), (0, 2), (0, 3), (0, 4), (1, 1), (1, 2), (1, 3), (1, 4)\}.$$

4 Each element (a, b) of $A \times B$, where $a \in A$ and $b \in B$, can be paired with an element (b, a) of $B \times A$ and, conversely, every element (b, a) of $B \times A$ can be paired with an element (a, b) of $A \times B$. Hence, $A \times B$

and B × A can be put in one-to-one correspondence, which implies that N(A × B) = N(B × A).

26-27 **4** The graph of $\{(x, y) \mid x, y \in \mathfrak{R} \text{ and } |x| + |y| = 8\}$ is the set of all points in the sides of the square with vertices (8, 0), (0, 8), (−8, 0), and (0, −8).

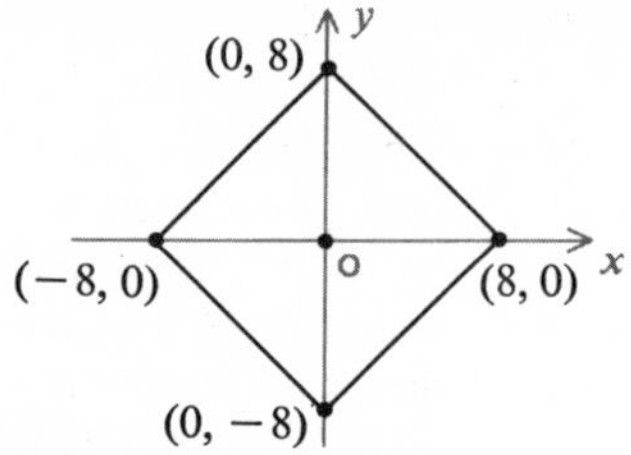

13 The graph of $\{(x, y) \mid x, y \in I \text{ and } (|x| - 3)(|y| - 5) = 0\}$ is the set of points associated with ordered pairs of integers in the lines $x = 3$, $x = -3$, $y = 5$, and $y = -5$.

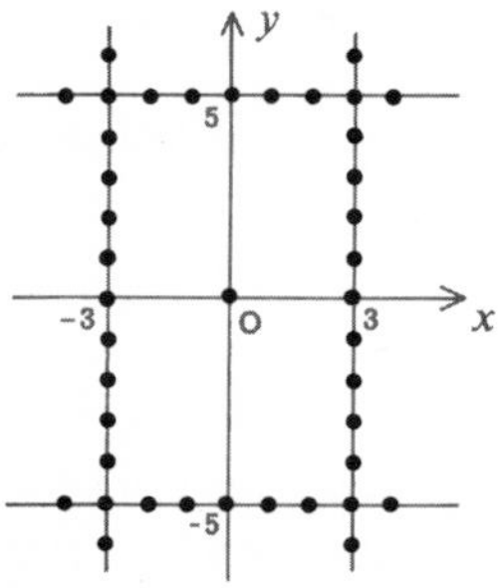

16 $\{(0, -\frac{2}{3}), (3, \frac{1}{6}), (8, \frac{6}{11})\}$

30 **8** (a) The domain is all of set A. (b) The range is $\{5, 17, \frac{53}{6}, -\frac{19}{6}, 6, -6, \frac{28}{5}, -\frac{32}{5}, 2, -10, 1, -11\}$. (c) The relation is from A since all of A is included in the domain. (d) The relation is not onto B since the range is a proper subset of $\mathfrak{R}$. For example, $\sqrt{6}$, −1, π, and so on, are not in the range. (e) Images of 0 are 6 and −6. (f) Images of 4 are 2 and −10.

12 (a) Domain is {0}. (b) Range is {0}. (c) No, $\{0\} \neq W$. (d) No, $\{0\} \neq W$. (e) 0 (f) There is no image of 4.

20 (a) Domain is $\{\ldots, -2k, \ldots, -2, 0\}$, where $k \in I^+$. (b) Range is E_C. (c) No, the domain is a proper subset of A. (d) Yes (e) 2 (f) There is no image of 4.

35-36 **9** Yes, a function. Many-to-one; for example, (0, 0) and (180, 0), or (π, 0), are both contained in the function.

21 Yes, a function. Many-to-one; for example, (1, 1) and ($\frac{5}{4}$, 1) are both contained in the function.

29 Many-to-one; for example, (−6, −6) and (−12, −6) are both contained in the function.

39 **1** (a) Domain is I × I. (b) Range is every element of R of the form $\frac{a}{2}$, where a is an integer. (c) $\frac{8}{2}$ or 4 (d) $\frac{13}{2}$ (e) A binary operation with domain I × I and range included in R

43-44 **11** $A \cap B = \emptyset$. $A \cup B = \{(x, y) \mid [-3 \leqq x < 5 \text{ and } y = |x|] \text{ or } [-3 < x \leqq 5 \text{ and } y = \frac{1}{4}(x + 15)]\}$.

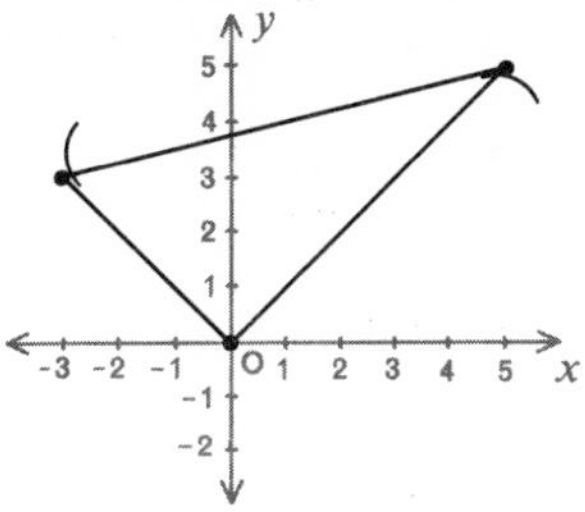

Since $A \cap B = \emptyset$, there are no points in the graph of $A \cap B$. The graph of $A \cup B$ is the set of all points in the three segments determined by (0, 0), (−3, 3), and (5, 5).

17 If we assume that $A = B$, then $A \cap B = A \cap A = A$ and $A \cup B = A \cup A = A$. Hence, $A \cap B = A \cup B$. Now we assume that $A \cup B = A \cap B$ and show that $A = B$. For each $x \in A$, $x \in A \cup B$. Since $A \cup B = A \cap B$ by hypothesis, it follows that $x \in A \cap B$. But this implies that $x \in B$. Thus, $A \subseteq B$. Similarly, $y \in B$ implies that $y \in A \cup B$, that $y \in A \cap B$, and, hence, that $y \in A$. Hence, $B \subseteq A$. Therefore, $A = B$.

49 **3** (a) Domain and range of f are $\mathfrak{R}$. (b) Domain of g is $\{x \mid x \in \mathfrak{R} \text{ and } x \neq \frac{5}{2}\}$. Range of g is $\{y \mid y \in \mathfrak{R} \text{ and } y \neq 0\}$. The domain of g does not contain the range of f since $\frac{5}{2}$ is contained in the range of f but not in the domain of g. (c) Function h does not exist because $\frac{5}{2}$, which is in the range of f, cannot be in the domain of h. (d) Since h does not exist, its domain and range cannot be defined.

9 Let $f = \{(x, y) \mid x, y \in \mathfrak{R}, y = x \text{ if } x \neq 0, \text{ and } y = 1 \text{ if } x = 0\}$ and let $g = \{(x, y) \mid x, y \in \mathfrak{R}, y = x + 1 \text{ if } x < -1, y = 0 \text{ if } -1 \leqq x \leqq 1, \text{ and } y = x - 1 \text{ if } x > 1\}$. As a second example, let $f = \{(x, y) \mid x, y \in \mathfrak{R} \text{ and } y = e^x\}$, and let $g = \{(x, y) \mid x, y \in \mathfrak{R} \text{ and } y = \ln x\}$.

53 **6** This relation satisfies the reflexive and symmetric properties, but not the transitive property. For example, if parcel x weighs 1 lb., parcel y weighs $1\frac{3}{4}$ lb., and parcel z weighs $2\frac{1}{2}$ lb., parcel x does *not* weigh within 1 lb. of parcel z.

58-59 **1i** {1, 3, 9, 27}

1l $\{x \mid x \in I \text{ and } x \equiv 16 \bmod 18\}$

2 By the division algorithm, we can express a and b as follows: $a = q_1n + r_1$ and $b = q_2n + r_2$, with $q_1, q_2, r_1, r_2 \in I$, $0 \leqq r_1 < n$, and $0 \leqq r_2 < n$. Now the fact that $(a, b) \in R_n$, or $a \equiv b \bmod n$, implies that $r_1 = r_2$. So, $a - b = (q_1 - q_2)n + (r_1 - r_2) = (q_1 - q_2)n$. Since q_1, $q_2 \in I$, $q_1 - q_2 = k \in I$. Hence, $a - b = kn$.

3 Let $a = q_1n + r_1$ and let $b = q_2n + r_2$, as in the answer to exercise 2. Then $a - b = (q_1 - q_2)n + (r_1 - r_2)$. But by assumption, $a - b = kn$, with $k \in I$ and $n \in I^+$. This means that $r_1 - r_2$ must be a multiple of n, say, pn, where $p \in I$. Hence, $r_1 = r_2 + pn$.

If we assume that $r_1 \geqq r_2$, we have $pn \geqq 0$. Since n is a positive integer, it follows that $p \geqq 0$. Because $n > r_1$, $n > r_2 + pn$, and, hence, $n(1 - p) > r_2 \geqq 0$. This means that, since $n \in I^+$, $1 - p > 0$; that is, $1 > p$. But $p \geqq 0$, $p \in I$, and $1 > p$ imply that $p = 0$. Thus, $p = 0$ and $r_1 = r_2 + pn$ imply that $r_1 = r_2$. Therefore, $a \equiv b \bmod n$, or $(a, b) \in R_n$.

If we assume that $r_2 \geqq r_1$, then $r_2 = r_1 - pn$ implies that $pn \leqq 0$. Since $n \in I^+$, it follows that $p \leqq 0$. Since n is greater than r_2, $n > r_1 - pn$. Thus, $n(1 + p) > r_1 \geqq 0$. This implies that $1 + p > 0$, or $p > -1$. Now $p > -1$, $x \in I$, and $p \leqq 0$ imply that $p = 0$. Therefore, $r_1 = r_2$, and $(a, b) \in R_n$.

5

+	$\bar{0}$	$\bar{1}$	$\bar{2}$	$\bar{3}$	$\bar{4}$
$\bar{0}$	$\bar{0}$	$\bar{1}$	$\bar{2}$	$\bar{3}$	$\bar{4}$
$\bar{1}$	$\bar{1}$	$\bar{2}$	$\bar{3}$	$\bar{4}$	$\bar{0}$
$\bar{2}$	$\bar{2}$	$\bar{3}$	$\bar{4}$	$\bar{0}$	$\bar{1}$
$\bar{3}$	$\bar{3}$	$\bar{4}$	$\bar{0}$	$\bar{1}$	$\bar{2}$
$\bar{4}$	$\bar{4}$	$\bar{0}$	$\bar{1}$	$\bar{2}$	$\bar{3}$

11

•	$\bar{0}$	$\bar{1}$	$\bar{2}$	$\bar{3}$	$\bar{4}$	$\bar{5}$
$\bar{0}$	$\bar{0}$	$\bar{0}$	$\bar{0}$	$\bar{0}$	$\bar{0}$	$\bar{0}$
$\bar{1}$	$\bar{0}$	$\bar{1}$	$\bar{2}$	$\bar{3}$	$\bar{4}$	$\bar{5}$
$\bar{2}$	$\bar{0}$	$\bar{2}$	$\bar{4}$	$\bar{0}$	$\bar{2}$	$\bar{4}$
$\bar{3}$	$\bar{0}$	$\bar{3}$	$\bar{0}$	$\bar{3}$	$\bar{0}$	$\bar{3}$
$\bar{4}$	$\bar{0}$	$\bar{4}$	$\bar{2}$	$\bar{0}$	$\bar{4}$	$\bar{2}$
$\bar{5}$	$\bar{0}$	$\bar{5}$	$\bar{4}$	$\bar{3}$	$\bar{2}$	$\bar{1}$

68-69 **1b** Yes. If $x, y \in E_C$, then $x = 2m$ and $y = 2n$, where m and n are counting numbers. So, $x \cdot y = 2m \cdot 2n = 4mn = 2(2mn)$.

1k Yes. $(a + b\sqrt[3]{2}) + (c + d\sqrt[3]{2}) = (a + c) + (b + d)\sqrt[3]{2}$. Since the integers are closed under addition, $(a + c) + (b + d)\sqrt[3]{2} \in I(\sqrt[3]{2})$.

1q No. For example, $(0 + \sqrt[3]{2}) \cdot (0 + \sqrt[3]{2}) = 0 + \sqrt[3]{4}$, and $0 + \sqrt[3]{4} \notin I(\sqrt[3]{2})$.

4 Since the range of f is included in the domain of g, $f \circ g$ is defined. By the definition of composition, $(x)f \circ g = \big((x)f\big)g$, which implies that if x is in the domain of $f \circ g$, then x is in A, the domain of f. Thus, the domain of $f \circ g$ is included in A. Since the range of f is a subset of A, if $x \in A$, then $(x)f \in A$. But A is also the domain of g, so $\big((x)f\big)g = (x)f \circ g$ is defined. Hence, if $x \in A$, x is in the domain of $f \circ g$. Thus, A is included in the domain of $f \circ g$. Because the domain of $f \circ g$ is included in A and A is included in the domain of $f \circ g$, the domain of $f \circ g$ is A.

Now suppose that y is in the range of $f \circ g$. This means that there is an $x \epsilon A$ such that $(x)f \circ g = ((x)f)g = y$. But the range of g is a subset of A; hence, $y \epsilon A$. Thus, the range of $f \circ g$ is a subset of A. Therefore, because the domain of $f \circ g$ is A and the range of $f \circ g$ is a subset of A, $f \circ g \epsilon \mathcal{F}$.

6g Operation ☆ is closed in E_I. If $x, y \epsilon E_I$, then $x = 2m$ and $y = 2n$, with $m, n \epsilon I$. So, $x ☆ y = 2m ☆ 2n = \frac{1}{2}(2m)(2n) = 2mn$. $2mn \epsilon E_I$; therefore, $x ☆ y \epsilon E_I$.

76 **1f** This system is associative. Let $a + bi, c + di, e + fi \epsilon G(i)$. By the definition of multiplication,

$$((a + bi) \cdot (c + di)) \cdot (e + fi) = ((ac - bd) + (ad + bc)i) \cdot (e + fi)$$
$$= (ace - bde - adf - bcf) + (acf - bdf + ade + bce)i.$$
$$(a + bi) \cdot ((c + di) \cdot (e + fi)) = (a + bi) \cdot ((ce - df) + (cf + de)i)$$
$$= (ace - adf - bcf - bde) + (acf + ade + bce - bdf)i.$$

3 In exercise 3 of section 12/2, it was established that $\cup$ and $\cap$ are closed binary operations. Therefore, we need only show that these operations are associative to show that $(\mathbb{S}, \cup)$ and $(\mathbb{S}, \cap)$ are semi-groups.

By definition of union, if $x \epsilon A \cup (B \cup C)$, $x \epsilon A$ or $x \epsilon B \cup C$. Thus, $x \epsilon A$ or $x \epsilon B$ or $x \epsilon C$. This implies that $x \epsilon A \cup B$ or $x \epsilon C$. Hence, $x \epsilon (A \cup B) \cup C$, and so $A \cup (B \cup C) \subseteq (A \cup B) \cup C$. By a similar argument, beginning with $x \epsilon (A \cup B) \cup C$, it follows that $(A \cup B) \cup C \subseteq A \cup (B \cup C)$. Therefore, $A \cup (B \cup C) = (A \cup B) \cup C$, and $(\mathbb{S}, \cup)$ is a semi-group.

By definition of intersection, if $x \epsilon A \cap (B \cap C)$, then $x \epsilon A$ and $x \epsilon B \cap C$. Thus, $x \epsilon A$ and $x \epsilon B$ and $x \epsilon C$. This implies that $x \epsilon (A \cap B)$ and $x \epsilon C$. Hence, $x \epsilon (A \cap B) \cap C$, and $A \cap (B \cap C) \subseteq (A \cap B) \cap C$. By a similar argument, beginning with $x \epsilon (A \cap B) \cap C$, it follows that $(A \cap B) \cap C \subseteq A \cap (B \cap C)$. Therefore, $A \cap (B \cap C) = (A \cap B) \cap C$, and $(\mathbb{S}, \cap)$ is a semi-group.

5a Not a semi-group because the operation is not associative. For example, $1 ☆ (2 ☆ 3) = 1 ☆ 7 = 8$ and $(1 ☆ 2) ☆ 3 = 3 ☆ 3 = 12$.

5f A semi-group. Closure of ☆: Let $x, y \epsilon E_C$. Then $x = 2m$ and $y = 2n$, with $m, n \epsilon C$. So $x ☆ y = 2m ☆ 2n = \frac{1}{2}(2m)(2n) = 2(mn)$, which is an element of E_C. Associativity of ☆: $(x ☆ y) ☆ z = (\frac{1}{2}xy) ☆ z = \frac{1}{4}xyz$ and $x ☆ (y ☆ z) = x ☆ (\frac{1}{2}yz) = \frac{1}{4}xyz$.

5i Not a semi-group because the operation is not associative. For example, $(2 ☆ \frac{1}{2}) ☆ 1 = 1 ☆ 1 = 1$ and $2 ☆ (\frac{1}{2} ☆ 1) = 2 ☆ 0 = 0$.

81-82 **1f** The identity is $1 + 0i$, or 1. To verify this, let $a + bi$ be an arbitrary element of $G(i)$. Then

$(1 + 0i) \cdot (a + bi) = a - (0 \cdot b) + (0 + b)i = a + bi$ and
$(a + bi) \cdot (1 + 0i) = a - (b \cdot 0) + (b + 0)i = a + bi$.

6 The fact that $(I/n, \oplus_n)$ has an identity was to be proved in exercise 2. Denote this identity by $\bar{0}$ and assume that an element $\bar{e} \neq \bar{0}$ is contained in I/n such that, for each $\bar{a} \epsilon I/n$, $\bar{e} \oplus_n \bar{a} = \bar{a} \oplus_n \bar{e} = \bar{a}$. In particular, let $\bar{a}$ be replaced by $\bar{0}$. Then $\bar{e} \oplus_n \bar{0} = \bar{0} \oplus_n \bar{e} = \bar{0}$. But $\bar{0}$ is known to be an identity, so $\bar{e} \oplus_n \bar{0} = \bar{0} \oplus_n \bar{e} = \bar{e}$. Hence, $\bar{e} = \bar{0}$, and $\bar{0}$ is the unique identity of $(I/n, \oplus_n)$.

8 Define function h so that, for each $x \in A$, $(x)h = x$. Since the domain and range of h are A, $h \in \mathcal{F}$. By definition of h, $(x)f \circ h = ((x)f)h = (x)f$, and $(x)h \circ f = ((x)h)f = (x)f$. Therefore, $f \circ h = h \circ f = f$.

9b The identity for this system is 2. By definition of operation ☆, $2 ☆ x = \frac{1}{2} \cdot 2 \cdot x = x$ and $x ☆ 2 = \frac{1}{2} \cdot x \cdot 2 = x$.

9f The identity for this system is 0. By definition of operation ☆, $0 ☆ x = [0 + x] = x$ and $x ☆ 0 = [x + 0] = x$.

85-86 **3** Only the elements $1 + 0i$, $-1 + 0i$, $0 + 1i$, $0 - 1i$ have inverses. $1 + 0i$ is its own inverse, $-1 + 0i$ is its own inverse, and $0 + 1i$ and $0 - 1i$ are inverses of each other. This follows from the fact that only 1 and -1 have inverses in the set of integers.

8e $(x)f' = \dfrac{3x - 2}{4}$ since $\dfrac{4(\frac{3x-2}{4}) + 2}{3} = \dfrac{3x}{3} = x$. Function $f' \notin A$ because its range is not included in the set of nonnegative real numbers. For example, $(0)f' = -\frac{1}{2}$.

8k $(x)f' = \sqrt{\dfrac{x^2 - 3}{2}}$ since $\sqrt{\dfrac{2(x^2 - 3)}{2} + 3} = \sqrt{x^2} = x$. Function $f' \notin A$ because, for example, $(1)f' = \sqrt{-1}$, and $\sqrt{-1} \notin A$.

10a This system does not satisfy the inverse property. The identity of the system is 0, and for each $x \in R$ that has an inverse under operation ☆, the inverse is $\dfrac{-x}{1 + x}$. That is,

$$x ☆ \frac{-x}{1 + x} = x - \frac{x}{1 + x} - \frac{x^2}{1 + x} = \frac{x + x^2 - x - x^2}{1 + x} = \frac{0}{1 + x} = 0.$$

However, $-1 \in R$ does not have an inverse because division by zero is undefined.

95-96 **8h** This system is not a group because not every element has an inverse. For example, $2 + 0i = 2$ does not have an inverse.

8n This system is not a group because the closure property is not satisfied. For example, $\sqrt{2} + (-\sqrt{2}) = 0$, and $0 \notin \{x \mid x \in \Re \text{ and } x \notin R\}$.

10 Let (G, ☆) be a group with identity e. Suppose that there exists $f \in G$ such that, for each $a \in G$, $f ☆ a = a ☆ f = a$; that is, suppose that f is an identity element for G. Then, since $e \in G$, $f ☆ e = e ☆ f = e$. But, since e is an identity for G, $f ☆ e = e ☆ f = f$. Hence, $f = e$.

11 Let (G, ☆) be a group, and let $a', b \in G$ be inverses of $a \in G$ and let $e \in G$ be the identity of (G, ☆). Then

$$a' = a' ☆ e = a' ☆ (a ☆ b) = (a' ☆ a) ☆ b = e ☆ b = b.$$

Hence, $a' = b$, and the inverse is unique in (G, ☆).

13 By assumption, $a \circ x = b \circ x$; so $(a \circ x) \circ x' = (b \circ x) \circ x'$, where x' is the inverse of x. By the associative property, $a \circ (x \circ x') = b \circ (x \circ x')$. Since $x \circ x' = e$, we have $a \circ e = b \circ e$, or $a = b$, which was to be proved.

15 First we will show that a'_l, the left inverse of a, is also the right inverse of a. Since G has a left-inverse property and a left-identity property, for each $a \in G$, there exists $a'_l \in G$ such that $a'_l \star a = e_l$. But, since $a'_l \in G$, there exists b_l such that $b_l \star a'_l = e_l$. Since e_l is a left identity,

$$\begin{aligned} a \star a'_l &= a \star (e_l \star a'_l) \\ &= a \star \big((a'_l \star a) \star a'_l\big). \end{aligned}$$

If we multiply each side of $a \star a'_l = a \star \big((a'_l \star a) \star a'_l\big)$ on the left by a'_l, we have

$$\begin{aligned} a'_l &= (a'_l \star a) \star a'_l \\ &= a'_l \star (a \star a'_l), \end{aligned}$$

by the associative property of a semi-group. If we now multiply both sides of $a'_l = a'_l \star (a \star a'_l)$ on the left by b_l, the left inverse of a'_l, we have $e_l = a \star a'_l$. This last equality shows that a'_l is also a right inverse of a with respect to the left identity e_l. Hence, a'_l is an inverse of a.

Now we will show that e_l, the left identity of G, is also a right identity. We use the fact that a'_l is an inverse of a:

$$\begin{aligned} a \star e_l &= a \star (a'_l \star a) \\ &= (a \star a'_l) \star a \\ &= e_l \star a \\ &= a. \end{aligned}$$

Because e_l is also a right identity, e_l is *the* identity. We have shown that semi-group (G, ☆) has both an identity and an inverse property. Hence, (G, ☆) is a group.

17 Since $x \circ a = b$ has solution x in G, it follows that $c \circ a = a$ has solution c in G. If $b \in G$, then $b = a \circ y$ has a solution $y \in G$. Then

$$\begin{aligned} c \circ b &= c \circ (a \circ y) \\ &= (c \circ a) \circ y \\ &= a \circ y \\ &= b. \end{aligned}$$

Since $c \circ a = a$ and $c \circ b = b$, it follows that c is a left identity for each $a, b \in G$. Further, for each $a \in G$, $y \circ a = c$ has a solution y in G. But, since c is the left identity of G, y is the left inverse of a in G.

The semi-group (G, ∘) has been shown to have a left identity and a left inverse. Hence, by exercise 15, (G, ∘) is a group.

24 Let $(x)\mathrm{f} = ax + b$, $(x)\mathrm{g} = cx + d$, and $(x)\mathrm{h} = ex + f$, where a, c, and e are different from 0 and where $\mathrm{f, g, h} \in \mathcal{F}$. First, we establish the closure property by showing that $\mathrm{f} \circ \mathrm{g} \in \mathcal{F}$. By definition of composition of functions,

$$\begin{aligned} (x)\mathrm{f} \circ \mathrm{g} &= \big((x)\mathrm{f}\big)\mathrm{g} \\ &= (ax + b)\mathrm{g} \\ &= c(ax + b) + d \\ &= (ca)x + (cb + d). \end{aligned}$$

By the closure properties of R and $\mathfrak{R}$, ca and $cb + d \in R$; also, since $a \neq 0$ and $c \neq 0$, $ca \neq 0$. Hence,

$$\big((ca)x + cb + d\big) \in \{(x, y) \mid y = ax + b,\ a \neq 0,\ a, b \in R, \text{ and } x \in \mathfrak{R}\}.$$

Thus, $\mathcal{F}$ is closed under composition.

By Theorem 15/2, $(\mathcal{F}, \circ)$ is associative. Hence, $f \circ (g \circ h) = (f \circ g) \circ h$.

The identity element of $(\mathcal{F}, \circ)$ is the function j such that $(x)j = x + 0 = x$. Function $j \in \mathcal{F}$ since it is of the form $ax + b$, with $a = 1$ and $b = 0$. To show that $(x)j$ is the identity, we must show that $j \circ f = f \circ j = f$ for each $f \in \mathcal{F}$. By definition of j, for each $x \in R$, we have

$$(x)j \circ f = ((x)j)f = (x)f \text{ and}$$
$$(x)f \circ j = ((x)f)j = (ax + b)j = ax + b = (x)f.$$

Hence, function j is the identity for $(\mathcal{F}, \circ)$.

Since it is given that $a \neq 0$, every element of $\mathcal{F}$ has an inverse function p of the form $(x)p = \frac{1}{a}x - \frac{b}{a}$. To show that for each $f \in \mathcal{F}$, its inverse p is of this form, we must show that $p \circ f = f \circ p = j$, where j is the identity function described above. For $(x)f = ax + b$, we have

$$(x)p \circ f = ((x)p)f = (\tfrac{1}{a}x - \tfrac{b}{a})f = a(\tfrac{1}{a}x - \tfrac{b}{a}) + b = x - b + b = x = (x)j.$$

Also,

$$(x)f \circ p = ((x)f)p = (ax + b)p = \tfrac{1}{a}(ax + b) - \tfrac{b}{a} = x + \tfrac{b}{a} - \tfrac{b}{a} = x = (x)j.$$

Hence, each $f \in \mathcal{F}$ has an inverse p of the form $(x)p = \frac{1}{a}x - \frac{b}{a}$.

We have established that the system $(\mathcal{F}, \circ)$ satisfies the closure, associative, identity, and inverse properties. Hence, this system is a group.

109-111 **4** G_4 contains $4 \cdot 3 \cdot 2 \cdot 1 = 24$ elements. Permutation groups are given in parts a, c, e, f, g. Each of these sets contains the identity P_1. That each set satisfies the closure and inverse properties can easily be verified by using the composition table in Display 44, and the associative property is satisfied because the operation is associative for any subset of G_4. The other subsets do not form subgroups.

9a The inverse is $\begin{pmatrix} 1 & 2 & 3 & 4 & 5 \\ 5 & 1 & 2 & 3 & 4 \end{pmatrix}$ since the composition of these two permutations is the identity permutation.

10 G_n contains $n \cdot (n - 1) \cdot \ldots \cdot 3 \cdot 2 \cdot 1 = n!$ elements.

14 The full cycle of G_5 is $C = \begin{pmatrix} 1 & 2 & 3 & 4 & 5 \\ 2 & 3 & 4 & 5 & 1 \end{pmatrix}$. $C^1 = \begin{pmatrix} 1 & 2 & 3 & 4 & 5 \\ 2 & 3 & 4 & 5 & 1 \end{pmatrix}$.

$C^2 = \begin{pmatrix} 1 & 2 & 3 & 4 & 5 \\ 3 & 4 & 5 & 1 & 2 \end{pmatrix}$.

$C^3 = \begin{pmatrix} 1 & 2 & 3 & 4 & 5 \\ 4 & 5 & 1 & 2 & 3 \end{pmatrix}$.

$C^4 = \begin{pmatrix} 1 & 2 & 3 & 4 & 5 \\ 5 & 1 & 2 & 3 & 4 \end{pmatrix}$.

$C^5 = \begin{pmatrix} 1 & 2 & 3 & 4 & 5 \\ 1 & 2 & 3 & 4 & 5 \end{pmatrix}$.

$\circ$	C^1	C^2	C^3	C^4	C^5
C^1	C^2	C^3	C^4	C^5	C^1
C^2	C^3	C^4	C^5	C^1	C^2
C^3	C^4	C^5	C^1	C^2	C^3
C^4	C^5	C^1	C^2	C^3	C^4
C^5	C^1	C^2	C^3	C^4	C^5

16 It seems reasonable that the nth power of the full cycle of G_n is the identity permutation.

21 It appears that the set of powers from 1 to n of the full cycle of G_n satisfies the closure and inverse properties under composition of functions. Hence, it seems reasonable to conclude that this system is a permutation group.

116-117 **3** To satisfy the identity property, one of the two elements must be an identity. Let e denote the identity element, let a denote the other element, and let ☆ denote the group operation. Since e is the identity, $e ☆ a = a ☆ e = a$. Also $e ☆ e = e ☆ e$ and $a ☆ a = a ☆ a$. Hence, the group is commutative.

10 It seems reasonable to assume that the group whose elements are the powers from 1 to n of the full cycle of G_n is a commutative group.

11 Since $(G, \circ)$ is a group, for each $a, b \in G$, $a \circ b \in G$. Also, because each element is its own inverse, $b \circ a = (b \circ a)'$. By Theorem 25/2, $(b \circ a)' = a' \circ b'$. So, $b \circ a = a' \circ b'$. But $a' = a$ and $b' = b$; hence, $b \circ a = a \circ b$. Therefore, $(G, \circ)$ is a commutative group.

12 By assumption, $(a \circ b) \circ (a \circ b) = (a \circ a) \circ (b \circ b)$ for each $a, b \in G$. Since $(G, \circ)$ is a group, the associative property holds; so

$$a \circ \big(b \circ (a \circ b)\big) = a \circ \big(a \circ (b \circ b)\big).$$

From this, it follows that

$$b \circ (a \circ b) = a \circ (b \circ b).$$

Again by the associative property, we have

$$(b \circ a) \circ b = (a \circ b) \circ b.$$

Thus, $b \circ a = a \circ b$, and $(G, \circ)$ is a commutative group.

122-124 **2h** S does not form a subgroup since the closure property, for one, is not satisfied. For example, $\bar{2} \oplus_6 \bar{3} \notin S$.

2i S does not form a subgroup since the closure property, for one, is not satisfied. For example, $\bar{3} \oplus_6 \bar{5} \notin S$.

2n $(S, \odot_{11})$ is a subgroup. The closure and inverse properties can easily be verified by reference to the following multiplication table.

$\odot_{11}$	$\bar{1}$	$\bar{3}$	$\bar{4}$	$\bar{5}$	$\bar{9}$
$\bar{1}$	$\bar{1}$	$\bar{3}$	$\bar{4}$	$\bar{5}$	$\bar{9}$
$\bar{3}$	$\bar{3}$	$\bar{9}$	$\bar{1}$	$\bar{4}$	$\bar{5}$
$\bar{4}$	$\bar{4}$	$\bar{1}$	$\bar{5}$	$\bar{9}$	$\bar{3}$
$\bar{5}$	$\bar{5}$	$\bar{4}$	$\bar{9}$	$\bar{3}$	$\bar{1}$
$\bar{9}$	$\bar{9}$	$\bar{5}$	$\bar{3}$	$\bar{1}$	$\bar{4}$

2t S does not form a subgroup since the closure property, for one, is not satisfied.

3 Since $S \subseteq G$, if $a, x \in S$, then $a, x \in G$. Since e is the identity of G, $a ☆ e = a$. By hypothesis, $a ☆ x = a$. Hence, $a ☆ e = a ☆ x$. Thus, $e = x$.

6 Since the set of all ordered pairs of real numbers of the form $(1, b)$ is a subset of the set of all ordered pairs of real numbers (a, b), with $a \neq 0$, we need only establish the closure and inverse properties (by Theorem 28/2) to show that this set forms a subgroup under operation ☆. Let $(1, x)$ and $(1, y)$ be arbitrary elements of the subset under consideration. By definition of operation ☆,

$$(1, x) \star (1, y) = (1, x + y).$$

Since $x + y \in \mathfrak{R}$, $(1, x + y)$ is again an element of this set, and the closure property is satisfied. To establish the inverse property, we must show that, for each element $(1, b)$ of the set, an inverse (c, d) is an element of the set. Since $(1, 0)$ is the identity, we have

$$(1, b) \star (c, d) = (1, 0).$$

By definition of operation ☆,

$$(1, b) \star (c, d) = (c, bc + d).$$

From these two equations, it follows that

$$(c, bc + d) = (1, 0).$$

Hence, $c = 1$ and $bc + d = b + d = 0$. Thus, $d = -b$. That is, $(c, d) = (1, -b)$. Since $-b \in \mathfrak{R}$, $(1, -b)$ is again an element of the set of ordered pairs of real numbers of the form $(1, b)$. By definition of operation ☆, we see that $(1, -b) \star (1, b) = (1, 0) = (1, b) \star (1, -b)$. Therefore, $(1, -b)$ is the inverse of $(1, b)$, and the inverse of each element in this set is again an element of this set. Therefore, the set does form a group under operation ☆.

7a This set does form a subgroup under addition modulo 6. The right cosets are: $S \oplus_6 \bar{0} = \{\bar{0}, \bar{2}, \bar{4}\}$ and $S \oplus_6 \bar{1} = \{\bar{1}, \bar{3}, \bar{5}\}$. Notice that $S \oplus_6 \bar{2} = S \oplus_6 \bar{4} = S \oplus_6 \bar{0}$ and that $S \oplus_6 \bar{3} = S \oplus_6 \bar{5} = S \oplus_6 \bar{1}$.

8c This set forms a subgroup under multiplication modulo 13. The right cosets are:

$S \odot_{13} \bar{1} = \{\bar{1}, \bar{3}, \bar{9}\} = S \odot_{13} \bar{3} = S \odot_{13} \bar{9}$.
$S \odot_{13} \bar{2} = \{\bar{2}, \bar{6}, \bar{5}\} = S \odot_{13} \bar{5} = S \odot_{13} \bar{6}$.
$S \odot_{13} \bar{4} = \{\bar{4}, \overline{12}, \overline{10}\} = S \odot_{13} \overline{10} = S \odot_{13} \overline{12}$.
$S \odot_{13} \bar{7} = \{\bar{7}, \bar{8}, \overline{11}\} = S \odot_{13} \bar{8} = S \odot_{13} \overline{11}$.

9 Suppose that there exists $c \in G$ such that $c \in S \star a$ and $c \in S \star b$. This means that there exists $d \in S$ such that $c = d \star a$ and also $f \in S$ such that $c = f \star b$. But $c = d \star a$ implies that $a = d' \star c$, where d' is the inverse of d. Let x be an arbitrary element of $S \star a$. This means that there exists $g \in S$ such that $g \star a = x$. Hence, $x = g \star a = g \star d' \star c = g \star d' \star f \star b$. Now $g \star d' \star f \in S$. This is so because $g, d \in S$ and because $d' \in S$ since $d \in S$ and $(S, \star)$ is a group. Since $g \star d' \star f \in S$, $(g \star d' \star f) \star b = x \in S \star b$. Since x, which was chosen as an arbitrary element of $S \star a$, has been shown to be an element of $S \star b$, it follows that $S \star a \subseteq S \star b$.

By a similar argument, $c = f \star b$ implies that $b = f' \star c$, where f' is the inverse of f. If y is an arbitrary element of $S \star b$, then there exists $h \in S$ such that $y = h \star b = h \star f' \star c$. But, $c = d \star a$; thus, $y = h \star f' \star d \star a$. By reasoning similar to that used for x above,

$h \star f' \star d \in S$; so $(h \star f' \star d) \star a = y \in S \star a$. Therefore, $S \star b \subseteq S \star a$. By these two arguments $S \star a = S \star b$.

13 Each of the following sets forms a subgroup under operation $\odot_7$: $\{\bar{1}\}$, $\{\bar{1}, \bar{6}\}$, $\{\bar{1}, \bar{2}, \bar{4}\}$, and $\{\bar{1}, \bar{2}, \bar{3}, \bar{4}, \bar{5}, \bar{6}\}$.

17 Let $(S, \star)$ be a subgroup of the commutative group $(G, \star)$. By exercise 15, it is sufficient to show that $x \star s \star x' \in S$ for each $x \in G$ and each $s \in S$. But, since $S \subseteq G$ and since G is commutative, $x \star s \star x' = x \star x' \star s = e \star s$, where e is the identity of both G and S. Now $e \star s = s$, and $s \in S$. Hence, $x \star s \star x' \in S$ and $(S, \star)$ is normal.

21 Let $(G, \star)$ be a group and let C be the center of G. Then, by exercise 20, if $x \in C$, $x \star a = a \star x$ for all $a \in G$. Hence, $(a \star x) \star a' = (x \star a) \star a' = x \star (a \star a') = x$. Therefore, $a \star x \star a' \in C$ for all $x \in C$, and $(C, \star)$ is a normal subgroup of $(G, \star)$.

129-131

2c $S \cap T = \{\bar{0}, \bar{6}\}$.

2d $S \cap T = \{\bar{1}\}$.

4b $(A \cup B, \oplus_{24})$ is not a subgroup since the closure property is not satisfied. For example, $\bar{8} \oplus_{24} \bar{3} = \overline{11}$, and $\overline{11} \notin A \cup B$.

4e $A \cup B = A$; hence, since $(A, \oplus_{24})$ is a subgroup, $(A \cup B, \oplus_{24})$ is a subgroup.

4f $(A \cup B, \oplus_{24})$ is not a subgroup since the closure property is not satisfied. For example, $\bar{6} \oplus_{24} \bar{4} = \overline{10}$, and $\overline{10} \notin A \cup B$.

5b $(C \cup D, \circ)$ is not a subgroup since the closure property is not satisfied.

For example, $\begin{pmatrix} 1 & 2 & 3 & 4 \\ 1 & 4 & 2 & 3 \end{pmatrix} \circ \begin{pmatrix} 1 & 2 & 3 & 4 \\ 1 & 2 & 4 & 3 \end{pmatrix} = \begin{pmatrix} 1 & 2 & 3 & 4 \\ 1 & 3 & 2 & 4 \end{pmatrix}$ is not an element of $C \cup D$.

7 No, since the closure property is not satisfied. For example, $6, 15 \in S \cup T$, but $6 + 15 \notin S \cup T$. Yes, $S \cup T$ is a subgroup. Since every multiple of 30 is also a multiple of 6, $S \cup T = S$.

138-140

1d The elements $\bar{2}$ and $\bar{3}$ are generators.

1h The elements $\bar{3}$ and $\bar{4}$ are generators. $\bar{5}$ and $\bar{9}$ are also generators.

2c This set forms a group under composition. The composition of any two elements in the set is again an element in the set. Composition of functions of this type is associative. The identity is $\begin{pmatrix} 1 & 2 & 3 & 4 \\ 1 & 2 & 3 & 4 \end{pmatrix}$.

The elements $\begin{pmatrix} 1 & 2 & 3 & 4 \\ 4 & 1 & 2 & 3 \end{pmatrix}$ and $\begin{pmatrix} 1 & 2 & 3 & 4 \\ 2 & 3 & 4 & 1 \end{pmatrix}$ are inverses of each other, and the other two elements are their own inverses. A generator of the set is $\begin{pmatrix} 1 & 2 & 3 & 4 \\ 2 & 3 & 4 & 1 \end{pmatrix}$. Notice that this group is generated by the full cycle of G_4.

5b This group is not cyclic because none of the elements generates all the elements of the set. Notice that $1 \cdot \bar{1} = \bar{1}, 2 \cdot \bar{1} = \bar{1}, 3 \cdot \bar{1} = \bar{1}$, and so on. Further, $1 \cdot \bar{3} = \bar{3}, 2 \cdot \bar{3} = \bar{1}, 3 \cdot \bar{3} = \bar{3}, 4 \cdot \bar{3} = \bar{1}$, and so on. The results for $\bar{5}$ and $\bar{7}$ are similar to those for $\bar{3}$.

7 The group is cyclic because it has a generator. A generator is i, since $1 \cdot i = i$, $2 \cdot i = i \cdot i = -1$, $3 \cdot i = -1 \cdot i = -i$, and $4 \cdot i = -i \cdot i = 1$.

9 If $x \in \mathfrak{R}$ is a generator of the group, then there exist integers m and n such that $m \cdot x = 2$, with $m \neq 0$, and $n \cdot x = \sqrt{2}$. Now $m \cdot x = 2$, or $x = \frac{2}{m}$, implies x is rational because it is the quotient of two integers, 2 and m. But if x is rational, then $n \cdot x$ is rational because it is equal to the product of the integer n and the rational number x. However, since $n \cdot x = \sqrt{2}$, it would follow that $\sqrt{2}$ is rational, which is not the case. Hence, we have a contradiction, and must conclude that there does not exist an element x in $\mathfrak{R}$ that generates $(\mathfrak{R}, +)$. Thus, $(\mathfrak{R}, +)$ is not cyclic.

17 *Definition* 35/2: If $(G, \star)$ is a group, n is an integer greater than or equal to 0, e is the identity of $(G, \star)$, and $a \in G$, then the integral powers of a are defined as follows:
1) $a^n = e$ for $n = 0$; that is, $a^0 = e$.
2) $a^n = a$ for $n = 1$; that is, $a^1 = a$.
3) $a^{n+1} = a^n \star a$ for $n \geqq 1$.

The group elements e, a, and $a^n \star a$ are the zero, first, and $(n + 1)$st *powers* of a, respectively.

Definition 36/2: If $(G, \star)$ is a group, $a \in G$, a' is the inverse of a, and n is a positive integer, then $a^{-n} = (a')^n$.

Theorem 34/2: If $(G, \star)$ is a group, n is a negative integer, and a' is the inverse of $a \in G$, then $(a')^n = a^{-n}$.

Theorem 35/2: If $(G, \star)$ is a group, $a \in G$, and $n = -1$, then $a^{n+1} = a^n \star a$.

Theorem 36/2: If $(G, \star)$ is a group, $a \in G$, and $n < -1$, then $a^{n+1} = a^n \star a$.

Theorem 37/2: If $(G, \star)$ is a group, $a \in G$, and m and n are integers, then $a^{m+n} = a^m \star a^n$.

Theorem 38/2: If $(G, \star)$ is a group, $a \in G$, and m and n are integers, then $a^{mn} = (a^m)^n$.

Definition 37/2: If $(G, \star)$ is a group, then $(G, \star)$ is *cyclic* if and only if there exists an $a \in G$ such that, for each $b \in G$, $a^n = b$ for some integer n. The element a is called a *generator* of $(G, \star)$.

18 Let $(G, \star)$ be a cyclic group with generator a and let $b, c \in G$. Then there exist integers m and n such that $m \cdot a = b$ and $n \cdot a = c$. Now

$$b \star c = (m \cdot a) \star (n \cdot a) = (m + n) \cdot a = (n + m) \cdot a = (n \cdot a) \star (m \cdot a) = c \star b.$$

Hence, $(G, \star)$ is commutative.

149-151 **6** Step 1: b is replaced by $t \cdot a$, and c is replaced by $s \cdot a$. Operation $\star$ is well defined.
Step 2: Theorem 37/2

Step 3: Definition of function f
Step 4: $b = t \cdot a$ and $c = s \cdot a$; addition is well defined.
Step 5: Definition of function f

7 Consider the mapping from I into E_I given by

$$f = \{(x, y) \mid x \in I \text{ and } y = 2x + 2\}.$$

Suppose that $(a, b) \in f$ and $(a, c) \in f$. Then $b = 2a + 2$ and $c = 2a + 2$. Hence, $b = c$, and it follows that f is a function. Now suppose that $(a, c) \in f$ and $(b, c) \in f$. Then $c = 2a + 2$ and $c = 2b + 2$. Thus, $2a + 2 = 2b + 2$, or $a = b$. Hence, f is a one-to-one function. If $b \in E_I$, there exists $c \in I$ such that $b = 2c$. Now let $a = c - 1$, then $(a)f = (c - 1)f = 2(c - 1) + 2 = 2c = b$. Hence, function f maps I *onto* E_I. Finally we show that the one-to-one function f is not an isomorphism by showing that it does not preserve the group operations. Since $(x)f = 2x + 2$ and $(y)f = 2y + 2$ for $x, y \in I$, we have $(x)f + (y)f = 2x + 2 + 2y + 2 = 2(x + y) + 4$. But because $(x + y)f = 2(x + y) + 2$, we have $(x)f + (y)f \neq (x + y)f$.

12 To prove that $(e_G)f = e_H$, we must show that for each $h \in H$,

$$h \circ (e_G)f = (e_G)f \circ h = h.$$

Since f is an isomorphism, it follows that for each $h \in H$, there exists an $a \in G$ such that $(a)f = h$. We have

$$h = (a)f = (a \star e_G)f = (a)f \circ (e_G)f = h \circ (e_G)f;$$
$$h = (a)f = (e_G \star a)f = (e_G)f \circ (a)f = (e_G)f \circ h.$$

Therefore, $(e_G)f = e_H$.

14 By definition of an inverse element, $(x)f \circ \big((x)f\big)' = e_H$. Also, $(x)f \circ (x')f = (x \star x')f = (e_G)f$. By exercise 12, $(e_G)f = e_H$. Hence, $(x)f \circ (x')f = e_H = (x)f \circ \big((x)f\big)'$. Thus, $(x')f = \big((x)f\big)'$.

16 The groups described in parts a and b are isomorphic to each other. The correspondence

$$\bar{1} \leftrightarrow \bar{0},\ \bar{5} \leftrightarrow \bar{1},\ \bar{8} \leftrightarrow \bar{3}, \text{ and } \overline{12} \leftrightarrow \bar{2}$$

establishes an isomorphism. The group given in part c is not isomorphic to the others because no mapping can be established that preserves group operations. Notice that the groups in a and b are cyclic, but the group in part c is not.

24a Let $(G, \star)$ be a group and let f be a mapping from G into G such that $(x)f = x$ for each $x \in G$. Mapping f, called the identity mapping, is a one-to-one function that is onto G. Function f also preserves the operation of G since

$$(x)f \star (y)f = x \star y$$
$$= (x \star y)f.$$

Hence, f is an automorphism.

24b If $(b, c) \in f$ and $(b, d) \in f$, then by definition of f, $c = a \star b \star a'$ and $d = a \star b \star a'$. Thus, $c = d$, and f is a function. If (b, d) and $(c, d) \in f$, then $d = a \star b \star a'$ and $d = a \star c \star a'$. So, $a \star b \star a' = a \star c \star a'$, which implies that $b = c$. Hence, f is one-to-one. Now let z be an arbitrary element of G. The element $a' \star z \star a$, which is an element of G because operation ☆ is closed in (G, ☆), has z as its image under function f. This is so because

$$\begin{aligned}(a' \star z \star a)\mathrm{f} &= a \star (a' \star z \star a) \star a' \\ &= (a \star a') \star z \star (a \star a') \\ &= e \star z \star e \\ &= z.\end{aligned}$$

Therefore, since an arbitrary element z of G is the image of the element $a' \star z \star a$ of G, function f is *onto* G. To show that f preserves the operation of (G, ☆), let x and y be arbitrary elements of G. Then

$$\begin{aligned}(x)\mathrm{f} \star (y)\mathrm{f} &= (a \star x \star a') \star (a \star y \star a') \\ &= (a \star x) \star (a' \star a) \star (y \star a') \\ &= (a \star x) \star e \star (y \star a') \\ &= a \star x \star y \star a'.\end{aligned}$$

Also, $(x \star y)\mathrm{f} = a \star x \star y \star a'$. Hence, $(x)\mathrm{f} \star (y)\mathrm{f} = (x \star y)\mathrm{f}$, and f preserves the operation of (G, ☆). Thus, f is an automorphism.

159-160 **1** The element $(\bar{2}, \bar{1})$ is another generator of $(I/3 \times I/2, +)$. $1 \cdot (\bar{2}, \bar{1}) = (\bar{2}, \bar{1})$, $2 \cdot (\bar{2}, \bar{1}) = (\bar{1}, \bar{0})$, $3 \cdot (\bar{2}, \bar{1}) = (\bar{0}, \bar{1})$, $4 \cdot (\bar{2}, \bar{1}) = (\bar{2}, \bar{0})$, $5 \cdot (\bar{2}, \bar{1}) = (\bar{1}, \bar{1})$, and $6 \cdot (\bar{2}, \bar{1}) = (\bar{0}, \bar{0})$.

13 *Theorem*: If (G, ☆), (H, ∘), and (K, □) are groups with (a, b, c), $(d, e, f) \in G \times H \times K$ and the operation △ is defined by

$$(a, b, c) \triangle (d, e, f) = (a \star d, b \circ e, c \,\square\, f),$$

then the system $(G \times H \times K, \triangle)$ is a group.
Proof: Let $G \times H \times K = G \times (H \times K) = (G \times H) \times K$ (the set operation of forming the cross product is associative). By Theorem 41/2, $(H \times K, \triangledown)$, with operation ▽ appropriately defined, is a group. Again, by Theorem 41/2, $\big(G \times (H \times K), \triangle\big) = (G \times H \times K, \triangle)$ is a group.

16 The elements of $I/6 \times I/3$ are $(\bar{0}, \bar{0})$, $(\bar{0}, \bar{1})$, $(\bar{0}, \bar{2})$, $(\bar{1}, \bar{0})$, $(\bar{1}, \bar{1})$, $(\bar{1}, \bar{2})$, $(\bar{2}, \bar{0})$, $(\bar{2}, \bar{1})$, $(\bar{2}, \bar{2})$, $(\bar{3}, \bar{0})$, $(\bar{3}, \bar{1})$, $(\bar{3}, \bar{2})$, $(\bar{4}, \bar{0})$, $(\bar{4}, \bar{1})$, $(\bar{4}, \bar{2})$, $(\bar{5}, \bar{0})$, $(\bar{5}, \bar{1})$, $(\bar{5}, \bar{2})$. The group is not cyclic. The group is not isomorphic to $(I/18, \oplus_{18})$. Yes, $\big(\{(\bar{0}, \bar{0}), (\bar{1}, \bar{0}), (\bar{2}, \bar{0}), (\bar{3}, \bar{0}), (\bar{4}, \bar{0}), (\bar{5}, \bar{0})\}, +\big)$ is isomorphic to $(I/6, \oplus_6)$. Yes, $\big(\{(\bar{0}, \bar{0}), (\bar{0}, \bar{1}), (\bar{0}, \bar{2})\}, +\big)$ is isomorphic to $(I/3, \oplus_3)$. There is no subgroup isomorphic to $(I/9, \oplus_9)$. Yes, the subgroup $\big(\{(\bar{0}, \bar{0}), (\bar{3}, \bar{0})\}, +\big)$ is isomorphic to $(I/2, \oplus_2)$.

17 The elements of $I/2 \times I/9$ are $(\bar{0}, \bar{0})$, $(\bar{0}, \bar{1})$, $(\bar{0}, \bar{2})$, $(\bar{0}, \bar{3})$, $(\bar{0}, \bar{4})$, $(\bar{0}, \bar{5})$, $(\bar{0}, \bar{6})$, $(\bar{0}, \bar{7})$, $(\bar{0}, \bar{8})$, $(\bar{1}, \bar{0})$, $(\bar{1}, \bar{1})$, $(\bar{1}, \bar{2})$, $(\bar{1}, \bar{3})$, $(\bar{1}, \bar{4})$, $(\bar{1}, \bar{5})$, $(\bar{1}, \bar{6})$, $(\bar{1}, \bar{7})$, $(\bar{1}, \bar{8})$. G is cyclic, and $(\bar{1}, \bar{1})$ is a generator. G is isomorphic to $(I/18, \oplus_{18})$. Yes, the subgroup $\big(\{(\bar{0}, \bar{0}), (\bar{1}, \bar{0})\}, +\big)$ is isomorphic to $(I/2, \oplus_2)$. Yes, $\big(\{(\bar{0}, \bar{0}), (\bar{0}, \bar{1}), (\bar{0}, \bar{2}), (\bar{0}, \bar{3}), (\bar{0}, \bar{4}), (\bar{0}, \bar{5}), (\bar{0}, \bar{6}), (\bar{0}, \bar{7}), (\bar{0}, \bar{8})\}, +\big)$ is isomorphic to $(I/9, \oplus_9)$. Yes, $\big(\{(\bar{0}, \bar{0}), (\bar{0}, \bar{3}), (\bar{0}, \bar{6})\}, +\big)$ is isomorphic to $(I/3, \oplus_3)$. Yes, $\big(\{(\bar{0}, \bar{0}), (\bar{0}, \bar{3}), (\bar{0}, \bar{6}), (\bar{1}, \bar{0}), (\bar{1}, \bar{3}), (\bar{1}, \bar{6})\}, +\big)$ is isomorphic to $(I/6, \oplus_6)$.

164-167 **2** The order of $(\bar{0}, \bar{0})$ is 0; the order of $(\bar{2}, \bar{0})$ is 2; the order of $(\bar{0}, \bar{1})$ and $(\bar{0}, \bar{2})$ is 3; the order of $(\bar{1}, \bar{0})$ and $(\bar{3}, \bar{0})$ is 4; the order of $(\bar{2}, \bar{1})$ and $(\bar{2}, \bar{2})$ is 6; and the order of $(\bar{1}, \bar{1})$, $(\bar{3}, \bar{1})$, $(\bar{1}, \bar{2})$, and $(\bar{3}, \bar{2})$ is 12.

7 $G = (\{(\bar{0}, \bar{0}), (\bar{0}, \bar{1}), (\bar{0}, \bar{2}), (\bar{0}, \bar{3}), (\bar{0}, \bar{4}), (\bar{0}, \bar{5}), (\bar{1}, \bar{0}), (\bar{1}, \bar{1}), (\bar{1}, \bar{2}), (\bar{1}, \bar{3}), (\bar{1}, \bar{4}), (\bar{1}, \bar{5})\}, +)$.

$(\{(\bar{0}, \bar{0}), (\bar{1}, \bar{0})\}, +) \cong (I/2, \oplus_2)$.

$(\{(\bar{0}, \bar{0}), (\bar{0}, \bar{1}), (\bar{0}, \bar{2}), (\bar{0}, \bar{3}), (\bar{0}, \bar{4}), (\bar{0}, \bar{5})\}, +) \cong (I/6, \oplus_6)$. It is not possible to establish an isomorphism by using corresponding subgroups because two elements, $(\bar{1}, \bar{0})$ and $(\bar{0}, \bar{3})$, would be mapped onto $\bar{6}$, and the mapping would not be one-to-one. No, the two groups are not isomorphic because $(I/12, \oplus_{12})$ has elements of order 12, but G does not.

8 Yes. The function f described below is an isomorphism between these two groups.

$(\bar{0}, \bar{0}, \bar{0})f = (\bar{0}, \bar{0})$. $\quad (\bar{0}, \bar{1}, \bar{2})f = (\bar{0}, \bar{1})$.
$(\bar{1}, \bar{0}, \bar{0})f = (\bar{1}, \bar{0})$. $\quad (\bar{1}, \bar{0}, \bar{1})f = (\bar{1}, \bar{2})$.
$(\bar{0}, \bar{0}, \bar{1})f = (\bar{0}, \bar{2})$. $\quad (\bar{1}, \bar{0}, \bar{2})f = (\bar{1}, \bar{4})$.
$(\bar{0}, \bar{0}, \bar{2})f = (\bar{0}, \bar{4})$. $\quad (\bar{1}, \bar{1}, \bar{0})f = (\bar{1}, \bar{3})$.
$(\bar{0}, \bar{1}, \bar{0})f = (\bar{0}, \bar{3})$. $\quad (\bar{1}, \bar{1}, \bar{1})f = (\bar{1}, \bar{5})$.
$(\bar{0}, \bar{1}, \bar{1})f = (\bar{0}, \bar{5})$. $\quad (\bar{1}, \bar{1}, \bar{2})f = (\bar{1}, \bar{1})$.

11 Function f described below is an isomorphism between $(I/3 \times I/6, +)$ and $(I/2 \times I/3 \times I/3, +)$. Let $\bar{a} \in I/3$; then

$(\bar{a}, \bar{0})f = (\bar{0}, \bar{0}, \bar{a})$. $\quad (\bar{a}, \bar{3})f = (\bar{1}, \bar{0}, \bar{a})$.
$(\bar{a}, \bar{1})f = (\bar{1}, \bar{2}, \bar{a})$. $\quad (\bar{a}, \bar{4})f = (\bar{0}, \bar{2}, \bar{a})$.
$(\bar{a}, \bar{2})f = (\bar{0}, \bar{1}, \bar{a})$. $\quad (\bar{a}, \bar{5})f = (\bar{1}, \bar{1}, \bar{a})$.

Notice that each of these conditions actually describes the effect of function f upon three different elements of each group.

14 Function f described below is an isomorphism between $(I/2 \times I/2 \times I/2 \times I/3, +)$ and $(I/2 \times I/2 \times I/6, +)$. Let $\bar{a}, \bar{b} \in I/2$; then

$(\bar{a}, \bar{b}, \bar{0}, \bar{0})f = (\bar{a}, \bar{b}, \bar{0})$. $\quad (\bar{a}, \bar{b}, \bar{1}, \bar{0})f = (\bar{a}, \bar{b}, \bar{3})$.
$(\bar{a}, \bar{b}, \bar{1}, \bar{1})f = (\bar{a}, \bar{b}, \bar{1})$. $\quad (\bar{a}, \bar{b}, \bar{0}, \bar{1})f = (\bar{a}, \bar{b}, \bar{4})$.
$(\bar{a}, \bar{b}, \bar{0}, \bar{2})f = (\bar{a}, \bar{b}, \bar{2})$. $\quad (\bar{a}, \bar{b}, \bar{1}, \bar{2})f = (\bar{a}, \bar{b}, \bar{5})$.

Notice that each of these conditions actually describes the effect of function f upon four different elements of each group.

18 Three groups may be so constructed. They are $(I/24, \oplus_{24})$, $(I/2 \times I/2 \times I/6, +)$, and $(I/4 \times I/6, +)$.

20 The order of $(\bar{0}, \bar{0})$ and of $\bar{0}$ is 0; the order of $(\bar{0}, \bar{1})$ and of $\bar{4}$ is 3; the order of $(\bar{0}, \bar{2})$ and of $\bar{8}$ is 3; the order of $(\bar{1}, \bar{0})$ and of $\bar{9}$ is 4; the order of $(\bar{1}, \bar{1})$ and of $\bar{1}$ is 12; the order of $(\bar{1}, \bar{2})$ and of $\bar{5}$ is 12; the order of $(\bar{2}, \bar{0})$ and of $\bar{6}$ is 2; the order of $(\bar{2}, \bar{1})$ and of $\overline{10}$ is 6; the order of $(\bar{2}, \bar{2})$ and of $\bar{2}$ is 6; the order of $(\bar{3}, \bar{0})$ and of $\bar{3}$ is 4; the order of $(\bar{3}, \bar{1})$ and of $\bar{7}$ is 12; and the order of $(\bar{3}, \bar{2})$ and of $\overline{11}$ is 12.

23 By definition of the order of an element, the order of (x, y) is equal to the least integer p such that $p \cdot (x, y) = (e_G, e_H)$. That is, the "product" of p and (x, y) must be equal to the identity of $(G \times H, +)$, which is the element (e_G, e_H). Let $(p \cdot x, p \cdot y)$ denote $p \cdot (x, y)$. It follows from exercises 21 and 22 that $p \cdot x = e_G$ if and only if $p = km$, with $k \in I$. Similarly, $p \cdot y = e_H$ if and only if $p = ln$, with $l \in I$. Hence, $(p \cdot x, p \cdot y) = (e_G, e_H)$ if and only if $p = km$ and $p = ln$; that is, if and only if p is a multiple of both m and n. Therefore, by the definition of the order of an element, the order p of (x, y) is the *least* common multiple of m and n.

25 The element $\bar{1}$ of $I/20$ has order 20. The element $(\bar{1}, \bar{1})$ of $I/2 \times I/10$ has order 10. No, since an isomorphism preserves the order of elements, and $I/2 \times I/10$ has no element of order 20.

40 The element $(\bar{1}, \bar{1}, \bar{1})$ of $I/2 \times I/2 \times I/9$ has order 18. The element $(\bar{1}, \bar{1}, \bar{1})$ of $I/3 \times I/3 \times I/4$ has order 12. The two groups could *not* be isomorphic because the second one has no element of order 18.

42 The element $(\bar{1}, \bar{1}, \bar{1}, \bar{1})$ of $I/2 \times I/2 \times I/3 \times I/3$ has order 6. The element $(\bar{1}, \bar{1}, \bar{1})$ of $I/2 \times I/2 \times I/9$ has order 18. The two groups could *not* be isomorphic because the first one has no element of order 18.

179-181 **3a** It is not possible for A and B to be equal since entry $a_{22} = 0$ and entry $b_{22} = -5$.

4 (3a) $A \cdot B = \begin{pmatrix} 1+2y & x-10 \\ -1 & -x \end{pmatrix}$. $B \cdot A = \begin{pmatrix} 1-x & 2 \\ y+5 & 2y \end{pmatrix}$.

(3b) $A \cdot B = \begin{pmatrix} 1+2y & x-10 \\ -1+zy & -x-5z \end{pmatrix}$.

$B \cdot A = \begin{pmatrix} 1-x & 2+xz \\ y+5 & 2y-5z \end{pmatrix}$.

(3c) $A \cdot B = \begin{pmatrix} -3x-6+6z-3yz & 12-6y \\ -12-3xz & 6-6x \end{pmatrix}$.

$B \cdot A = \begin{pmatrix} -3x-6 & -6+3y \\ 3xz+12z+24 & 6z-3zy+6-6x \end{pmatrix}$.

(3d) $A \cdot B = \begin{pmatrix} -6x+3+5z & 3z \\ -3y-5x-10 & 3-3x \end{pmatrix}$.

$B \cdot A = \begin{pmatrix} -6x+3 & -3z \\ 10x+3y+10 & 5z+3-3x \end{pmatrix}$.

5 (3a) It is not possible since the entry in column 1 of row 2 is -1, and $-1 \neq 0$.

(3b) If $A \cdot B = \begin{pmatrix} 1 & 0 \\ 0 & 1 \end{pmatrix}$, then $1+2y = 1$, $x-10 = 0$, $-1+zy = 0$, and $-x-5z = 1$. This is not possible since $1+2y = 1$ implies that $y = 0$, and $-1+zy = 0$ implies that $y \neq 0$.

(3c) If $A \cdot B = \begin{pmatrix} 1 & 0 \\ 0 & 1 \end{pmatrix}$, then $-3x-6+6z-3yz = 1$, $12-6y = 0$, $-12-3xz = 0$, and $6-6x = 1$. From $12-6y = 0$, we have $y = 2$; from $6-6x = 1$, we have $x = \frac{5}{6}$; and from $-12-3xz = 0$, we have $z = -4\frac{4}{5}$. These values do not satisfy $-3x-6+6z-3yz = 1$; therefore, it is not possible to find replacements for x, y, and z such that $A \cdot B = \begin{pmatrix} 1 & 0 \\ 0 & 1 \end{pmatrix}$.

(3d) If $A \cdot B = \begin{pmatrix} 1 & 0 \\ 0 & 1 \end{pmatrix}$, then $-6x + 3 + 5z = 1$, $3z = 0$, $-3y - 5x - 10 = 0$, and $3 - 3x = 1$. From $3z = 0$, we have $z = 0$; from $3 - 3x = 1$, we have $x = \frac{2}{3}$; from $-3y - 5x - 10 = 0$, we have $y = -\frac{40}{9}$. These values do not satisfy $-6x + 3 + 5z = 1$; therefore, it is not possible for $A \cdot B$ to equal $\begin{pmatrix} 1 & 0 \\ 0 & 1 \end{pmatrix}$.

7 $A + B = \begin{pmatrix} a_{11} & a_{12} \\ a_{21} & a_{22} \end{pmatrix} + \begin{pmatrix} b_{11} & b_{12} \\ b_{21} & b_{22} \end{pmatrix}$, with $A, B \in E_{2 \times 2}$.

By definition of matrix addition,

$$\begin{pmatrix} a_{11} & a_{12} \\ a_{21} & a_{22} \end{pmatrix} + \begin{pmatrix} b_{11} & b_{12} \\ b_{21} & b_{22} \end{pmatrix} = \begin{pmatrix} a_{11} + b_{11} & a_{12} + b_{12} \\ a_{21} + b_{21} & a_{22} + b_{22} \end{pmatrix}.$$

By the commutative property of addition of integers,

$$\begin{pmatrix} a_{11} + b_{11} & a_{12} + b_{12} \\ a_{21} + b_{21} & a_{22} + b_{22} \end{pmatrix} = \begin{pmatrix} b_{11} + a_{11} & b_{12} + a_{12} \\ b_{21} + a_{21} & b_{22} + a_{22} \end{pmatrix} = B + A.$$

Hence, $A + B = B + A$ for each $A, B \in E_{2 \times 2}$.

12b This system is not a ring since the associative property is not satisfied for subtraction, and the distributive property is not satisfied.

12i This system is a ring.

12o This system is not a ring since multiplication is not closed.

12p This system is a ring.

13 Let $A = \begin{pmatrix} a_{11} & a_{12} \\ a_{21} & a_{22} \end{pmatrix}$ and $B = \begin{pmatrix} b_{11} & b_{12} \\ b_{21} & b_{22} \end{pmatrix}$ be elements of $I_{2 \times 2}$.

By exercise 5, section 19/2, we need only show that $A + (-B)$ is in $I_{2 \times 2}$ to show that $I_{2 \times 2}$ is a commutative subgroup of $M_{2 \times 2}$ under matrix addition.

$$A + (-B) = \begin{pmatrix} a_{11} + (-b_{11}) & a_{12} + (-b_{12}) \\ a_{21} + (-b_{21}) & a_{22} + (-b_{22}) \end{pmatrix},$$

which is an element of $I_{2 \times 2}$ since I is closed under addition and has an inverse property. Thus, properties 1 through 5 of a ring are satisfied. The closure and associative properties of multiplication in $I_{2 \times 2}$ follow from the corresponding properties of integers and the closure property of addition of integers. The distributive property follows from the corresponding property of $(M_{2 \times 2}, +, \cdot)$.

19 $(\mathcal{I}, +, \cdot)$ is a ring. The properties are verified as follows: Let f, g, and $h \in \mathcal{I}$.

1) Since the domain and range of f and g are in the set of integers, closure of addition follows from closure of addition of integers.

2) By the associative property of addition of integers, for each $x \in \mathrm{I}$,

$$\begin{aligned}(x)\big((f+g)+h\big) &= (x)(f+g)+(x)h \\ &= \big((x)f+(x)g\big)+(x)h \\ &= (x)f+\big((x)g+(x)h\big) \\ &= (x)f+(x)(g+h) \\ &= (x)\big(f+(g+h)\big).\end{aligned}$$

Thus, by the definition of equality of functions, $(f+g)+h = f+(g+h)$.

3) The additive identity is the function $(x)f = 0$ for all $x \in \mathrm{I}$, which is an element of $\mathcal{I}$ by definition. Thus, if $(x)f = 0$, then, for all $g \in \mathcal{I}$, $(x)(f+g) = (x)f + (x)g = (x)g = (x)g + (x)f = (x)(g+f)$.

4) Let $f \in \mathcal{I}$, and define the additive inverse of f as $(x)g = -\big((x)f\big)$ for each $x \in \mathrm{I}$. Function $g \in \mathcal{I}$ because every integer has an additive inverse. Then

$$\begin{aligned}(x)(f+g) &= (x)f+(x)g \\ &= (x)f+\big(-[(x)f]\big) \\ &= 0. \\ (x)(g+f) &= (x)g+(x)f \\ &= -\big((x)f\big)+(x)f \\ &= 0.\end{aligned}$$

5) The commutative property of addition follows from the corresponding property of addition of integers.

6) The closure property of multiplication follows from closure of multiplication of integers.

7) Associativity of multiplication follows from the corresponding property of integers.

8) The distributive property follows from the corresponding property of $(\mathrm{I}, +, \cdot)$. Thus,

$$\begin{aligned}(x)\big(f\cdot(g+h)\big) &= (x)f\cdot\big((x)(g+h)\big) \\ &= (x)f\cdot\big((x)g+(x)h\big) \\ &= \big((x)f\cdot(x)g\big)+\big((x)f\cdot(x)h\big) \\ &= (x)(f\cdot g)+(x)(f\cdot h) \\ &= (x)(f\cdot g+f\cdot h).\end{aligned}$$

Also,

$$\begin{aligned}(x)\big((f+g)\cdot h\big) &= (x)(f+g)\cdot(x)h \\ &= \big((x)f+(x)g\big)\cdot(x)h \\ &= \big((x)f\cdot(x)h\big)+\big((x)g\cdot(x)h\big) \\ &= (x)(f\cdot h)+(x)(g\cdot h) \\ &= (x)(f\cdot h+g\cdot h).\end{aligned}$$

187-188 **1** All the rings except $(\{6x \mid x \in \mathrm{I}\}, +, \cdot)$ satisfy the multiplicative-identity property. All the rings except $(\mathrm{I}/4_{2\times 2}, +, \cdot)$ and $(\mathrm{I}/5_{2\times 2}, +, \cdot)$ satisfy the commutative property of multiplication.

2a $(\mathrm{I}_{2\times 2}, +, \cdot)$ has multiplicative identity $\begin{pmatrix}1 & 0\\ 0 & 1\end{pmatrix}$, but it is not a commutative ring.

2e $(\mathcal{S}, +, \cdot)$ is a commutative ring since $A \cap B = B \cap A$ for all $A, B \in \mathcal{S}$. It is also a ring with identity. Set S is the identity since, for each $A \in \mathcal{S}$, $S \cap A = A \cap S = A$.

2f $(\mathcal{I}, +, \cdot)$ is a commutative ring with identity. The commutative property of multiplication follows from the fact that multiplication of integers is commutative. The multiplicative identity is the function $(x)\mathrm{f} = 1$ for all $x \in \mathrm{I}$.

3 $\bar{a} \odot_n (\bar{b} \oplus_n \bar{c}) = \overline{a(b + c) - q_1 n} = \bar{r}_1$, where $0 \leqq r_1 < n$ and $q_1 \in \mathrm{I}$. $(\bar{a} \odot_n \bar{b}) \oplus_n (\bar{a} \odot_n \bar{c}) = \overline{ab + ac - q_2 n} = \bar{r}_2$, where $0 \leqq r_2 < n$ and $q_2 \in \mathrm{I}$. Now

$$\begin{aligned} r_1 - r_2 &= \big(a(b + c) - q_1 n\big) - (ab + ac - q_2 n) \\ &= (q_2 - q_1)n. \end{aligned}$$

Since $r_1 - r_2 < n$ and $r_2 - r_1 < n$, it follows that $q_2 - q_1 = 0$. Thus, $r_1 - r_2 = 0n = 0$. Hence, $r_1 = r_2$, and $\bar{r}_1 = \bar{r}_2$. Thus,

$$\bar{a} \odot_n (\bar{b} \oplus_n \bar{c}) = (\bar{a} \odot_n \bar{b}) \oplus_n (\bar{a} \odot_n \bar{c}).$$

The proof that $(\bar{a} \oplus_n \bar{b}) \odot_n \bar{c} = (\bar{a} \odot_n \bar{c}) \oplus_n (\bar{b} \odot_n \bar{c})$ is essentially the same.

6 By the commutative properties of addition and multiplication of integers, we have

$$\begin{aligned} (x, a) \cdot (y, b) &= (xy + bx + ay, ab) \\ &= (yx + ay + bx, ba) \\ &= (y, b) \cdot (x, a). \end{aligned}$$

Thus, $(\mathrm{E_I} \times \mathrm{I}, +, \cdot)$ is a commutative ring. The identity element is $(0, 1)$ since

$$\begin{aligned} (0, 1) \cdot (x, a) &= (0 + 0 + x, a) \\ &= (x, a) \\ &= (x, a) \cdot (0, 1). \end{aligned}$$

8 $(\mathrm{E_I} \times \{0\}, +, \cdot)$ is commutative since it is contained in $(\mathrm{E_I} \times \mathrm{I}, +, \cdot)$, which is commutative. If this ring had a multiplicative identity, it would be $(0, 1)$. Since $(0, 1) \notin \mathrm{E_I} \times \{0\}$, the ring does not have a multiplicative identity.

10 First we show that f is a function. Let $(x, 0), (y, 0) \in \mathrm{f}$ such that $x = y$. Then $(x, 0) = (y, 0)$; so f is a function. Now let $(y, 0) \in \mathrm{E_I} \times \{0\}$, then $(y)\mathrm{f} = (y, 0)$; hence, function f is onto. Function f is one-to-one since, if $(x)\mathrm{f} = (y)\mathrm{f}$, then $(x, 0) = (y, 0)$, or $x = y$. Function f preserves addition in the two rings since

$$(x + y)\mathrm{f} = (x + y, 0) = (x, 0) + (y, 0) = (x)\mathrm{f} + (y)\mathrm{f}.$$

Function f also preserves multiplication in the two rings since

$$(x \cdot y)\mathrm{f} = (x \cdot y, 0) = (x, 0) \cdot (y, 0) = (x)\mathrm{f} \cdot (y)\mathrm{f}.$$

Thus, f is an isomorphism from $(\mathrm{E_I}, +, \cdot)$ onto $(\mathrm{E_I} \times \{0\}, +, \cdot)$.

192

5 The following steps establish this property of rings.

$a(b - c) = a\big(b + (-c)\big)$	Definition 48/3
$= ab + a(-c)$	Distributive property of $(\mathrm{S}, +, \cdot)$
$= ab + \big(-(ac)\big)$	Theorem 47/3
$= ab - ac.$	Definition 48/3

10 Since (S, +, •) is closed under addition, $a + a \in S$. Hence, by the assumption given in this exercise, we have

$$\begin{aligned} a + a &= (a + a) \cdot (a + a) \\ &= ((a + a) \cdot a) + ((a + a) \cdot a) \\ &= (a \cdot a + a \cdot a) + (a \cdot a + a \cdot a) \\ &= (a + a) + (a + a). \end{aligned}$$

Hence, $a + a = 0$.

12 Assume that $1 = 0$. By hypothesis, S contains another element $x \neq 1$. By Definition 45/3, $1 \cdot x = x$. By Theorem 45/3, $0 \cdot x = 0$. But, by assumption, $1 = 0$; so, $x = 1 \cdot x = 0 \cdot x = 0$. Hence, $x = 0$, which contradicts the hypothesis that $x \neq 1$. Thus, we reject the assumption that $1 = 0$.

197-198

2 Since $\{a + 0\sqrt{2} \mid a \in I\}$ is a nonempty subset of $I(\sqrt{2})$, by Theorem 49/3, we need only show that the difference and the product of any two elements of the subset are also elements of the subset. For each $a + 0\sqrt{2}$, $b + 0\sqrt{2} \in \{a + 0\sqrt{2} \mid a \in I\}$, $(a + 0\sqrt{2}) - (b + 0\sqrt{2}) = a - b + 0\sqrt{2}$. Since the integers are closed under subtraction, $a - b + 0\sqrt{2} \in \{a + 0\sqrt{2} \mid a \in I\}$. $(a + 0\sqrt{2}) \cdot (b + 0\sqrt{2}) = ab + 0\sqrt{2}$. Since the integers are closed under multiplication, $ab + 0\sqrt{2} \in \{a + 0\sqrt{2} \mid a \in I\}$.

6 Let S denote the nonempty subset, $\{A \mid A \in M_{2 \times 2}, a_{21} = 0$, and $a_{11}, a_{12}, a_{22} \in I\}$, of $I_{2 \times 2}$. Also let

$A = \begin{pmatrix} a_{11} & a_{12} \\ 0 & a_{22} \end{pmatrix}$ and $B = \begin{pmatrix} b_{11} & b_{12} \\ 0 & b_{22} \end{pmatrix}$ be elements of S. Then

$A - B = \begin{pmatrix} a_{11} - b_{11} & a_{12} - b_{12} \\ 0 & a_{22} - b_{22} \end{pmatrix} \in S$, because the integers are closed under subtraction. Also, $A \cdot B = \begin{pmatrix} a_{11}b_{11} & a_{11}b_{12} + a_{12}b_{22} \\ 0 & a_{22}b_{22} \end{pmatrix} \in S$, because the integers are closed under addition and multiplication. Hence, (S, +, •) is a subring of $(I_{2 \times 2}, +, \cdot)$ by Theorem 49/3.

9 From exercise 20 on page 181, we know that the containing system $(\mathcal{I}, +, \circ)$ is not a ring since it does not satisfy part 2 of the distributive property. Since a subring is necessarily a ring, $(\mathcal{T}, +, \circ)$ cannot be a subring.

10c $(\{\bar{0}\}, \oplus_6, \odot_6)$, $(\{\bar{0}, \bar{3}\}, \oplus_6, \odot_6)$, $(\{\bar{0}, \bar{2}, \bar{4}\}, \oplus_6, \odot_6)$, and $(I/6, \oplus_6, \odot_6)$

12a This set forms a subring of $(\mathcal{I}, +, \cdot)$. Let $f, g \in \{f \mid (0)f = 0\}$. Then $(0)(f - g) = (0)(f + (-g)) = (0)f + (0)(-g) = 0 + (-0) = 0$. $0(f \cdot g) = (0)f \cdot (0)g = 0 \cdot 0 = 0$. Since $f - g$ and $f \cdot g$ are both elements of $\{f \mid (0)f = 0\}$, the set forms a subring.

14 Let $\frac{m}{n}, \frac{p}{q} \in R_2$. Then $\frac{m}{n} - \frac{p}{q} = \frac{mq - np}{nq} \in R_2$. This is so because nq, which is the product of integers that do not have 2 as a factor, does not have 2 as a factor. Similarly, $\frac{m}{n} \cdot \frac{p}{q} = \frac{mp}{nq} \in R_2$. Hence, by Theorem 49/3, $(R_2, +, \cdot)$ is a subring of (R, +, •).

16 $(R_6, +, \cdot)$ is not a subring of $(R, +, \cdot)$ because R_6 is not closed under either subtraction or multiplication. For example, $\frac{1}{2}$ and $\frac{1}{3}$ are elements of R_6 because 6 is not a factor of either 2 or 3; however, $\frac{1}{2} - \frac{1}{3} = \frac{1}{6}$ is *not* an element of R_6.

19 Let $\frac{a}{2^n}, \frac{b}{2^m} \in A_2$. Then $\frac{a}{2^n} - \frac{b}{2^m} = \frac{a \cdot 2^m - b \cdot 2^n}{2^{n+m}} \in A_2$. This is so because the integers are closed under addition, multiplication, and subtraction, and, hence, 2^m, 2^n, $a \cdot 2^m$, $b \cdot 2^n$, $a \cdot 2^m - b \cdot 2^n$, and $n + m$ are integers. Similarly,

$$\frac{a}{2^n} \cdot \frac{b}{2^m} = \frac{ab}{2^{n+m}} \in A_2.$$

Thus, by Theorem 49/3, $(A_2, +, \cdot)$ is a subring of $(R, +, \cdot)$.

200-201 **3** The ring of integers is not closed under multiplication by the elements of $G(i)$. For example, $2 \in I$ and $i \in G(i)$, but $2 \cdot i = 2i \notin I$. Hence, conditions 2 and 3 of Definition 51/3 are not satisfied.

4 Set A is the set of all 2×2 real matrices with each entry a_{ij} equal to $8k$, where $k \in I$. The subring $(A, +, \cdot)$ is *not* an ideal of $(M_{2 \times 2}, +, \cdot)$ since A is not closed under multiplication by elements of $M_{2 \times 2}$. For example, the product

$$\begin{pmatrix} \frac{1}{3} & 0 \\ 0 & 0 \end{pmatrix} \cdot \begin{pmatrix} 8 & 8 \\ 8 & 8 \end{pmatrix} = \begin{pmatrix} \frac{8}{3} & \frac{8}{3} \\ 0 & 0 \end{pmatrix}$$

is not an element of A. The system is an ideal of $(I_{2 \times 2}, +, \cdot)$. First of all, A is a subset of $I_{2 \times 2}$ since the entries in each element of A are integers of the form $8k$. To show that $(A, +, \cdot)$ is an ideal of $(I_{2 \times 2}, +, \cdot)$, we must show that the difference of any two elements of A is an element of A and that A is closed under multiplication by the elements of $I_{2 \times 2}$. Thus, if $a, b, c, d, e, f, g, h \in I$, then

$$\begin{pmatrix} 8a & 8b \\ 8c & 8d \end{pmatrix} - \begin{pmatrix} 8e & 8f \\ 8g & 8h \end{pmatrix} = \begin{pmatrix} 8(a-e) & 8(b-f) \\ 8(c-g) & 8(d-h) \end{pmatrix}.$$

This difference is an element of A since the integers are closed under subtraction and multiplication.

If $\begin{pmatrix} w & x \\ y & z \end{pmatrix}$ is an arbitrary element of $I_{2 \times 2}$, then

$$\begin{pmatrix} w & x \\ y & z \end{pmatrix} \cdot \begin{pmatrix} 8a & 8b \\ 8c & 8d \end{pmatrix} = \begin{pmatrix} 8aw + 8cx & 8bw + 8dx \\ 8ay + 8cz & 8by + 8dz \end{pmatrix}.$$

This product is an element of set A since each entry is of the form $8k$, where $k \in I$. Similarly,

$$\begin{pmatrix} 8a & 8b \\ 8c & 8d \end{pmatrix} \cdot \begin{pmatrix} w & x \\ y & z \end{pmatrix} \in A.$$

Thus, $(A, +, \cdot)$ is an ideal of $(I_{2 \times 2}, +, \cdot)$.

8e This system is not an ideal, although it does satisfy the three conditions of Definition 51/3. For example, the set $\mathcal{T}$ is closed under subtraction, since, if f, g $\in \mathcal{T}$, with $(x)f = k$ and $(x)g = j$, where k and j are fixed integers, then $(x)(f - g) = (x)f - (x)g = k - j$, which is a fixed integer. Hence, $f - g \in \mathcal{T}$. For composition of functions, let $f \in \mathcal{T}$ and $g \in \mathcal{T}$. Then $(x)(f \circ g) = ((x)f)g = (k)g = j$, where j is a fixed integer.

Also, $(x)(g \circ f) = ((x)g)f = k$. However, the system $(\mathcal{I}, +, \circ)$ is not a ring, and since an ideal must be a ring, $(\mathcal{T}, +, \circ)$ is not an ideal.

8g R_3 is the set of all rational numbers $\frac{m}{n}$, where 3 is not a factor of n. $(R_3, +, \cdot)$ is not an ideal of $(R, +, \cdot)$ because R_3 is not closed under multiplication by elements of R. For example, $\frac{1}{3} \in R$ and $\frac{1}{4} \in R_3$, but $\frac{1}{3} \cdot \frac{1}{4} = \frac{1}{12} \notin R_3$.

8j A_2 is the set of all rational numbers $\frac{a}{2^n}$, where $a, n \in I$. $(A_2, +, \cdot)$ is not an ideal of $(R, +, \cdot)$ because A_2 is not closed under multiplication by elements of R. For example, $\frac{1}{3} \in R$ and $\frac{1}{2} \in A_2$, but $\frac{1}{3} \cdot \frac{1}{2} = \frac{1}{6} \notin A_2$.

14 This subring is not an ideal since A is not closed under multiplication by elements of $M_{2 \times 2}$. For example,

$$\begin{pmatrix} 1 & 1 \\ 1 & 1 \end{pmatrix} \cdot \begin{pmatrix} 1 & 0 \\ 0 & 0 \end{pmatrix} = \begin{pmatrix} 1 & 0 \\ 1 & 0 \end{pmatrix} \notin A.$$

15 To prove that $(A \cap B, +, \cdot)$ is an ideal of $(S, +, \cdot)$, it is necessary to show that $A \cap B$ is closed under subtraction and to show that $A \cap B$ is closed under multiplication by elements of S. Let $x, y \in A \cap B$ and let $r \in S$.

$x \in A$ and $y \in A$.	Definition of intersection of sets
$x - y \in A$.	$(A, +, \cdot)$ is an ideal and, hence, A is closed under subtraction.
$x \in B$ and $y \in B$.	Definition of intersection of sets
$x - y \in B$.	$(B, +, \cdot)$ is an ideal and, hence, B is closed under subtraction.
$x - y \in A \cap B$.	Definition of intersection of sets

Hence, $A \cap B$ is closed under subtraction.

$x \in A \cap B$ and $r \in S$.	Given
$r \cdot x \in A$ and $r \cdot x \in B$.	Sets A and B are closed under multiplication by elements of S because $(A, +, \cdot)$ and $(B, +, \cdot)$ are ideals of $(S, +, \cdot)$.
$r \cdot x \in A \cap B$.	Definition of intersection of sets
Finally,	
$x \in A \cap B$ and $r \in S$.	Given
$x \cdot r \in A$ and $x \cdot r \in B$.	A and B are closed under multiplication by elements of S.
$x \cdot r \in A \cap B$.	Definition of intersection of sets

Thus, $(A \cap B, +, \cdot)$ is an ideal of $(S, +, \cdot)$.

16a $A \cap B = (I_{6x}, +, \cdot)$ since 6 is the least common multiple of 2 and 3.

16b $A \cap B = (I_{12x}, +, \cdot)$.

18a $I_{4x} + I_{6x} = I_{2x}$. This follows because every element of $I_{4x} + I_{6x}$ is of the form $4x + 6y$, or $2(2x + 3y)$, where $x, y \in I$.

18b $I_{3x} + I_{15x} = I_{3x}$ since every element of I_{15x} is contained in I_{3x}.

19 To show that (A + B, +, •) is an ideal of (S, +, •), it is necessary to show that A + B is closed under subtraction and that A + B is closed under multiplication by elements of S. Let $x, y \in$ A + B and let $r \in$ S.

$x = a_1 + b_1, y = a_2 + b_2$, where $a_1, a_2 \in$ A and $b_1, b_2 \in$ B.	Definition of ideal sum
$x - y = (a_1 + b_1) - (a_2 + b_2)$	$x = a_1 + b_1$ and $y = a_2 + b_2$.
$= (a_1 - a_2) + (b_1 - b_2)$.	Commutative and associative properties of addition in (A, +, •) and (B, +, •)
$(a_1 - a_2) \in$ A and $(b_1 - b_2) \in$ B.	(A, +, •) and (B, +, •) are ideals and, thus, closed under subtraction.
$x - y \in$ A + B.	Definition of ideal sum
$r \cdot x = r \cdot (a_1 + b_1)$	$x = a_1 + b_1$.
$= r \cdot a_1 + r \cdot b_1$.	Distributive properties of ideals (A, +, •) and (B, +, •)
$r \cdot a_1 \in$ A and $r \cdot b_1 \in$ B.	Ideals (A, +, •) and (B, +, •) are closed under multiplication by elements of S.
$r \cdot a_1 + r \cdot b_1 \in$ A + B.	Definition of ideal sum
$x \cdot r = (a_1 + b_1) \cdot r$	$x = a_1 + b_1$.
$= a_1 \cdot r + b_1 \cdot r$.	Distributive properties
$a_1 \cdot r \in$ A and $b_1 \cdot r \in$ B.	Ideals (A, +, •) and (B, +, •) are closed under multiplication by elements of S.
$a_1 \cdot r + b_1 \cdot r \in$ A + B.	Definition of ideal sum

Hence, (A + B, +, •) is an ideal of (S, +, •) because it satisfies the three conditions of Definition 51/3.

207 **4a** This function is not a homomorphism because operations are not preserved. For example, (3)f + (2)f = 14 + 9 = 23, but (3 + 2)f = 30; so (3)f + (2)f ≠ (3 + 2)f.

4d This function is not a homomorphism because operations are not preserved. For example, (−1)f + (0)f = −2 + (−2) = −4, but (−1 + 0)f = −2; hence, (−1)f + (0)f ≠ (−1 + 0)f.

5a Let $a, b \in$ S. Since the homomorphism is a mapping onto S, there exist $x, y \in$ T such that (x)f $= a$ and (y)f $= b$ for $a, b \in$ S. Homomorphism f preserves multiplication; therefore, (x)f $\cdot$ (y)f $= a \cdot b = (x \cdot y)$f. Also, (y)f $\cdot$ (x)f $= b \cdot a = (y \cdot x)$f. But (T, +, •) is commutative, so $x \cdot y = y \cdot x$; hence $(x \cdot y)$f $= (y \cdot x)$f. Thus, $a \cdot b = b \cdot a$.

5d Since f is a homomorphism, f preserves multiplication; therefore, $(a \cdot a^{-1})$f $= (a)$f $\cdot$ (a^{-1})f. Now $(a \cdot a^{-1})$f $= (1_T)$f. By part b of this exercise, (1_T)f is the multiplicative identity of S, say, 1_S. Thus,

$$\begin{aligned}(a)\text{f} \cdot (a^{-1})\text{f} &= (a \cdot a^{-1})\text{f} \\ &= (1_T)\text{f} \\ &= 1_S.\end{aligned}$$

Similarly,

$$\begin{aligned}(a^{-1})\text{f} \cdot (a)\text{f} &= (a^{-1} \cdot a)\text{f} \\ &= (1_{\text{T}})\text{f} \\ &= 1_{\text{S}}.\end{aligned}$$

Since $(a)\text{f} \cdot (a^{-1})\text{f} = 1_{\text{S}} = (a^{-1})\text{f} \cdot (a)\text{f}$, $(a^{-1})\text{f}$ is the multiplicative inverse of $(a)\text{f}$.

8 Function f, described in exercise 6, is the only homomorphism from I/4 onto I/2.

9 This function is not a homomorphism because it does not preserve multiplication. For,

$$(a + b\sqrt{2})\text{f} \cdot (c + d\sqrt{2})\text{f} = a \cdot c,$$

but

$$\big((a + b\sqrt{2}) \cdot (c + d\sqrt{2})\big)\text{f} = \big(ac + 2bd + (bc + ad)\sqrt{2}\big)\text{f} = ac + 2bd.$$

Thus, the product of the images does not equal the image of the product whenever bd is different from 0.

215-217

3a $\bar{7} + \bar{7}x + \bar{1}x^2 + \bar{3}x^3$

3c $\bar{4} + \bar{2}x + \bar{6}x^2 + \bar{3}x^3 + \bar{7}x^4 + \bar{3}x^5$

4a $\bar{3} + \bar{5} \cdot \bar{0} + \bar{1} \cdot \bar{0}^2 = \bar{3}.$

4c $\bar{4} + \bar{2} \cdot \bar{3} + \bar{3} \cdot \bar{3}^3 = \bar{3}.$

6a $(\bar{3} + \bar{5}x + \bar{1}x^2) + (\bar{a} + \bar{b}x + \bar{c}x^2) = \bar{0} + \bar{0}x + \bar{0}x^2.$
Hence, $\bar{a} + \bar{b}x + \bar{c}x^2 = \bar{5} + \bar{3}x + \bar{7}x^2.$

8b
$$\left[\begin{pmatrix}1 & 1\\0 & 1\end{pmatrix} + \begin{pmatrix}2 & 0\\2 & 0\end{pmatrix}x + \begin{pmatrix}0 & 1\\-1 & 0\end{pmatrix}x^2\right] + \left[\begin{pmatrix}1 & 2\\-2 & 1\end{pmatrix} + \begin{pmatrix}2 & 4\\0 & 0\end{pmatrix}x^3\right] =$$
$$\begin{pmatrix}2 & 3\\-2 & 2\end{pmatrix} + \begin{pmatrix}2 & 0\\2 & 0\end{pmatrix}x + \begin{pmatrix}0 & 1\\-1 & 0\end{pmatrix}x^2 + \begin{pmatrix}2 & 4\\0 & 0\end{pmatrix}x^3.$$

9a
$$\begin{aligned}\big(\text{f}_{\text{R}}(x)\big)\text{f}_c &= \begin{pmatrix}1 & 1\\0 & 1\end{pmatrix} + \begin{pmatrix}2 & 0\\2 & 0\end{pmatrix}\begin{pmatrix}1 & 0\\1 & 1\end{pmatrix} + \begin{pmatrix}0 & 1\\-1 & 0\end{pmatrix}\begin{pmatrix}1 & 0\\1 & 1\end{pmatrix}^2 \\ &= \begin{pmatrix}1 & 1\\0 & 1\end{pmatrix} + \begin{pmatrix}2 & 0\\2 & 0\end{pmatrix} + \begin{pmatrix}2 & 1\\-1 & 0\end{pmatrix} = \begin{pmatrix}5 & 2\\1 & 1\end{pmatrix}.\end{aligned}$$

18a This subset of I[x] does form a subring under addition and multiplication. Since a constant term a_0 that is different from 0 will not be introduced either by subtraction or multiplication of any two elements of the set, the difference and the product of any two elements in the set are again in the set. Thus, by Theorem 49/3, the subset does form a subring.

19 There are four subrings of $(\text{I}/6[x], \oplus_6, \odot_6)$. They are the sets of all polynomials whose coefficients are in the following sets: $\{\bar{0}, \bar{3}\}$, $\{\bar{0}, \bar{2}, \bar{4}\}$, $\{\bar{0}, \bar{1}, \bar{2}, \bar{3}, \bar{4}, \bar{5}\}$, and $\{\bar{0}\}$.

22 Let $\text{p}(x), \text{q}(x) \in \text{T}[x]$, which means that the coefficients of $\text{p}(x)$ and $\text{q}(x)$ are in set T. Because $(\text{T}, +, \cdot)$ is a subring of $(\text{S}, +, \cdot)$, the difference of any two elements of T is an element of T. Hence, the coefficients of $\text{p}(x) - \text{q}(x)$ are elements of T. This means that $\big(\text{p}(x) - \text{q}(x)\big) \in \text{T}[x]$.

Similarly, because the sum and product of any two elements of T are elements of T, the coefficients of $p(x) \cdot q(x)$ are elements of T. Thus, $\big(p(x) \cdot q(x)\big) \in T[x]$. Because $T[x]$ is closed under subtraction and multiplication, $(T[x], +, \cdot)$ is a subring of $(S[x], +, \cdot)$.

222-223 **2** If $x \cdot x = x$, then $x \cdot x = x \cdot 1$ since an integral domain has a multiplicative identity property. If $x \neq 0$, then we can use the cancellation property of multiplication for an integral domain to obtain $x = 1$. If $x = 0$, then the conclusion follows. Hence, $x = 0$ or $x = 1$.

3a The ring $(R, +, \cdot)$ is an integral domain. For each $a, b \in R$, $a \cdot b = b \cdot a$. $1 \in R$, and $a \cdot 1 = 1 \cdot a = a$. $a \cdot b = 0$ implies that $a = 0$ or $b = 0$.

3f From exercise 20, page 181, the set is not a ring and hence not an integral domain. Note that property 11 also does not hold. Let $(x)f = 1$ and let $(x)g = x - 1$ for each $x \in I$. Then $(x)(f \circ g) = \big((x)f\big)g = (1)g = 0$. Neither f nor g is the zero function, but $(x)(f \circ g) = 0$ for all $x \in I$, which means that $f \circ g$ is the zero function.

4b This ring is not an integral domain because matrix multiplication is not commutative.

5c This ring is an integral domain since it is a commutative ring with identity and has no zero divisors.

5d This system is not a ring (see the answer on page 281 to exercise 16, page 198). Therefore, it is not an integral domain.

5j This ring is an integral domain.

234-236 **3b** Matrix multiplication is not commutative in $(I/8_{2 \times 2}, +, \cdot)$.
For example,

$$\begin{pmatrix} \bar{1} & \bar{1} \\ \bar{1} & \bar{1} \end{pmatrix} \cdot \begin{pmatrix} \bar{2} & \bar{0} \\ \bar{0} & \bar{0} \end{pmatrix} = \begin{pmatrix} \bar{2} & \bar{0} \\ \bar{2} & \bar{0} \end{pmatrix},$$

but

$$\begin{pmatrix} \bar{2} & \bar{0} \\ \bar{0} & \bar{0} \end{pmatrix} \cdot \begin{pmatrix} \bar{1} & \bar{1} \\ \bar{1} & \bar{1} \end{pmatrix} = \begin{pmatrix} \bar{2} & \bar{2} \\ \bar{0} & \bar{0} \end{pmatrix}.$$

Nor does the multiplicative-inverse property hold.

3d The multiplicative-inverse property is not satisfied. For example, $\frac{2}{5} \in R_2$, but the inverse $\frac{5}{2} \notin R_2$.

3e The set is not closed under multiplication. For example, $(0 + \sqrt[4]{5}) \cdot (0 + \sqrt[4]{5}) = \sqrt[4]{25} = \sqrt{5} \notin \{a + b\sqrt[4]{5} \mid a, b \in R\}$.

3f The multiplicative-inverse property does not hold. For example, $\bar{0} + \bar{1}\sqrt{2}$, which is not the additive identity of the system, does not have an inverse.

4d This system is not a field because multiplication is not closed.

4l This system is a field. In exercise 5j, page 223, it was established that the system is an integral domain. Since every nonzero element $a + b\sqrt[4]{9}$ has a multiplicative inverse $\frac{a}{a^2 - 3b^2} - \frac{b}{a^2 - 3b^2}\sqrt[4]{9}$, it follows that the system is a field.

8 $x = x \cdot 1$ — 1 is the multiplicative identity.
$= x \cdot (a \cdot a^{-1})$ — Given that $a \cdot a^{-1} = 1$
$= (x \cdot a) \cdot a^{-1}$ — Associative property of multiplication
$= 1 \cdot a^{-1}$ — Given that $x \cdot a = 1$
$= a^{-1}$. — 1 is the multiplicative identity.

11 The cosets are:

$$S \oplus_{12} \bar{0} = \{\bar{0}, \bar{6}\} = A. \qquad S \oplus_{12} \bar{3} = \{\bar{3}, \bar{9}\} = D.$$
$$S \oplus_{12} \bar{1} = \{\bar{1}, \bar{7}\} = B. \qquad S \oplus_{12} \bar{4} = \{\bar{4}, \overline{10}\} = E.$$
$$S \oplus_{12} \bar{2} = \{\bar{2}, \bar{8}\} = C. \qquad S \oplus_{12} \bar{5} = \{\bar{5}, \overline{11}\} = F.$$

This system is neither an integral domain nor a field since it has divisors of the additive identity, which is coset A. For example, $C \cdot D = A$, but neither C nor D is equal to A.

242-243 **1b** Elements $\bar{1}$, $\bar{3}$, $\bar{5}$, and $\bar{7}$ have order 8. Elements $\bar{2}$ and $\bar{6}$ have order 4. Element $\bar{4}$ has order 2.

1g Every element has order 0 since there does not exist a positive integer n such that $n \cdot a = 0$ for any nonzero element in the set.

2a This system is not an integral domain because it has divisors of zero. It follows immediately that the system is not a field.

3 The order of each of these elements is 3.

8a $Q_3 = \{\frac{a}{b} \mid a, b \in I/3 \text{ and } b \neq \bar{0}\}$. Thus, the elements of Q_3 are $\frac{\bar{0}}{\bar{1}}, \frac{\bar{1}}{\bar{1}}, \frac{\bar{2}}{\bar{1}}$. $(Q_3, +, \cdot)$ is a field. It follows that it is also an integral domain and a ring.

9a The characteristic of $(I/5, \oplus_5, \odot_5)$ is 5 since $5 \cdot \bar{a} = \bar{0}$ for each $a \in I/5$.

9g The characteristic of this field is 7.

10 Assume that $m \in I^+$, $m < n$, and $m \times b = 0$, with $b \neq 0$. Then

$$\begin{aligned}(m \times a) \cdot b &= m \times (a \cdot b)\\ &= m \times (b \cdot a)\\ &= (m \times b) \cdot a\\ &= 0 \cdot a\\ &= 0.\end{aligned}$$

Since $b \neq 0$, it follows that $m \times a = 0$. But n is given as the additive order of a, which means that n is the *least* positive integer such that $n \times a = 0$. Hence, $m < n$ and $m \times a = 0$ result in a contradiction; so, $m \times b \neq 0$.

249-250 **1** Since $(S, +, \cdot)$ and $(T, +, \cdot)$ are subfields of field F, $S \subseteq F$ and $T \subseteq F$. Thus, $S \cap T \subseteq F$. Now let $a, b \in S \cap T$; it follows that $a, b \in S$ and $a, b \in T$. Since $(S, +, \cdot)$ is a subfield of F, S is closed under subtraction; that is, $a - b \in S$. Similarly, $a - b \in T$. Hence, $a - b \in S \cap T$, and $S \cap T$ is closed under subtraction.

Now let $a, b \in S \cap T$, with $b \neq 0$. Then $a, b \in S$ and $a, b \in T$. Since $(S, +, \cdot)$ and $(T, +, \cdot)$ are subfields, it follows that $a \cdot b^{-1} \in S$ and $a \cdot b^{-1} \in T$. So, $a \cdot b^{-1} \in S \cap T$, and $S \cap T$ is closed under multiplication by inverses.

It follows from Theorem 64/4 that $(S \cap T, +, \cdot)$ is a subfield of F.

3 Since (T, +, •) is a subfield of (F, +, •), it follows that $S \subseteq T$. This is so because (S, +, •) is the intersection of all subfields of F, so its elements must be contained in T. It is thus not possible that $T \subset S$.

6 That $(\frac{n}{m} \times e)f = \frac{n}{m}$ is a one-to-one function is established as follows: Let $\frac{n}{m}$ and $\frac{q}{p}$ be elements in the range of f. $\frac{n}{m} = \frac{q}{p}$ if and only if $\frac{n}{m} - \frac{q}{p} = 0$. $\frac{n}{m} - \frac{q}{p} = 0$ if and only if $(\frac{n}{m} - \frac{q}{p}) \times e = 0$. $(\frac{n}{m} - \frac{q}{p}) \times e = 0$ if and only if $(\frac{n}{m} \times e) - (\frac{q}{p} \times e) = 0$. $(\frac{n}{m} \times e) - (\frac{q}{p} \times e) = 0$ if and only if $\frac{n}{m} \times e = \frac{q}{p} \times e$. Hence, $\frac{n}{m} = \frac{q}{p}$ if and only if $\frac{n}{m} \times e = \frac{q}{p} \times e$. This means that each element $\frac{n}{m} \times e$ in the domain of f has exactly one image in the range of f and that each element in the range is the image of exactly one element in the domain. Thus, f is a one-to-one function. Function f is also an onto function, because each $\frac{n}{m} \in R$ is the image of the element $\frac{n}{m} \times e$ in the domain of f.

The fact that f is an isomorphism is established as follows: Let $\frac{n}{m}, \frac{q}{p} \in R$. Then

$$\begin{aligned}(\tfrac{n}{m} \times e)f + (\tfrac{q}{p} \times e)f &= \tfrac{n}{m} + \tfrac{q}{p} \\ &= \big((\tfrac{n}{m} + \tfrac{q}{p}) \times e\big)f \\ &= \big((\tfrac{n}{m} \times e) + (\tfrac{q}{p} \times e)\big)f.\end{aligned}$$

Hence, f preserves addition. Also,

$$\begin{aligned}(\tfrac{n}{m} \times e)f \cdot (\tfrac{q}{p} \times e)f &= \tfrac{n}{m} \cdot \tfrac{q}{p} \\ &= \big((\tfrac{n}{m} \cdot \tfrac{q}{p}) \times e\big)f \\ &= \big((\tfrac{n}{m} \times e) \cdot (\tfrac{q}{p} \times e)\big)f.\end{aligned}$$

Hence, f preserves multiplication. Therefore, function f is an isomorphism.

9b This set does not form a subfield because the multiplicative-inverse property is not satisfied.

9d This set forms a subfield.

9l This set does not form a subfield since the set is not closed under multiplication.

257-258

3 Suppose that $\sqrt{3} = \frac{a}{b}$, where a and b are relatively prime integers. Then $3 = \frac{a^2}{b^2}$, or $3b^2 = a^2$. Hence, 3 is a divisor of a^2, or $a \cdot a$. If 3 is a divisor of $a \cdot a$, then 3 is a divisor of a. That is, $a = 3 \cdot c$, where $c \in I$. Since $a = 3 \cdot c$, $a^2 = 9c^2$. Thus, $3b^2 = 9c^2$, or $b^2 = 3c^2$. This implies that 3 is a divisor of b^2, and, hence, a divisor of b. Thus, we have that 3 is a divisor of both a and b. But this contradicts the assumption that a and b are relatively prime. Therefore, it is not the case that $\sqrt{3} = \frac{a}{b}$, where a and b are relatively prime integers; so $\sqrt{3}$ is not rational.

5b $1 + \sqrt{2}$ is algebraic, where $p(x) = x^2 - 2x - 1$. That is, $p(1 + \sqrt{2}) = (1 + \sqrt{2})^2 - 2(1 + \sqrt{2}) - 1 = 0$.

8c $R(\sqrt[3]{5}) = \{a + b\sqrt[3]{5} + c\sqrt[3]{25} \mid a, b, c \in R\}$.

9a These extensions are identical. $R(\sqrt{5}) = \{a + b\sqrt{5} \mid a, b \in R\}$. $R(1 + \sqrt{5}) = \{c + d(1 + \sqrt{5}) \mid c, d \in R\}$. But $c + d(1 + \sqrt{5}) = c + d + d\sqrt{5} = (c + d) + d\sqrt{5}$. Since $c + d \in R$, it follows that $R(1 + \sqrt{5}) \subseteq R(\sqrt{5})$. Also, because $R(\sqrt{5}) \subseteq R(1 + \sqrt{5})$, the two extensions are the same.

9b These extensions are not identical. $R(1+\sqrt{3}) = R(\sqrt{3})$ by an argument similar to the one given in answering 9a on the preceding page. $\sqrt[4]{3} \in R(\sqrt[4]{3})$, but $\sqrt[4]{3} \notin R(\sqrt{3})$. Hence, $R(1+\sqrt{3}) \neq R(\sqrt[4]{3})$.

10 $\{x \mid x = a + b\sqrt{5}, a, b \in R, \text{ and } b \neq 0\}$. In other words, the extension of R by any element of $R(\sqrt{5})$, except the rational elements, is equal to the extension by $\sqrt{5}$.

13 Since $1 + 0\sqrt[3]{2} + 0\sqrt[3]{4}$ is the multiplicative identity of $R(\sqrt[3]{2})$, it is necessary to determine replacements for a, b, and c such that
$(1+\sqrt[3]{2}+\sqrt[3]{4}) \cdot (a+b\sqrt[3]{2}+c\sqrt[3]{4}) = 1 + 0\sqrt[3]{2} + 0\sqrt[3]{4}.$
$(1+\sqrt[3]{2}+\sqrt[3]{4}) \cdot (a+b\sqrt[3]{2}+c\sqrt[3]{4} = (a+2b+2c)+$
$(a+b+2c)\sqrt[3]{2}+(a+b+c)\sqrt[3]{4}.$

Hence,

$$a + 2b + 2c = 1,$$
$$a + b + 2c = 0,$$
$$a + b + c = 0.$$

So, $c = 0$, $b = 1$, and $a = -1$. Therefore, the inverse of $1+\sqrt[3]{2}+\sqrt[3]{4}$ is $-1+\sqrt[3]{2}$.

17 Yes, $\sqrt{2} \in R(\sqrt{2}) \cup R(\sqrt{3})$ since $\sqrt{2} \in R(\sqrt{2})$.
Yes, $\sqrt{3} \in R(\sqrt{2}) \cup R(\sqrt{3})$ because $\sqrt{3} \in R(\sqrt{3})$. $\sqrt{2}$ and $\sqrt{3} \in R(\sqrt{2}) \cup R(\sqrt{3})$; however, $\sqrt{2} \cdot \sqrt{3} = \sqrt{6} \notin R(\sqrt{2}) \cup R(\sqrt{3})$. Therefore, $R(\sqrt{2}) \cup R(\sqrt{3})$ is not closed under multiplication and, hence, is not a field.

22 Yes, c is algebraic over $(I/5, \oplus_5, \odot_5)$ since it is a solution of the given polynomial $\bar{1}c^2 - \bar{2} = \bar{0}$; that is, $c = \sqrt{\bar{2}}$. No. $c \notin I/5$. The simple field extension is $(\{\bar{a} + \bar{b}\sqrt{\bar{2}} \mid \bar{a}, \bar{b} \in I/5\}, \oplus_5, \odot_5)$.

Definitions and theorems

This list contains the definitions, theorems, and the corollary to a theorem that are presented in the book.

Definition 1/1 If A and B are sets, then A and B are *equal* (denoted by A = B) if and only if each element of A is an element of B and each element of B is an element of A. [p. 11]

Definition 2/1 If A and B are sets, then A is a *subset* of B if and only if each element of A is an element of B. In other words, A is a subset of B if and only if $x \in A$ implies $x \in B$. That A is a subset of B is denoted by the expression $A \subseteq B$. [p. 14]

Definition 3/1 If A and B are sets, then A is a *proper subset* of B if and only if A is a subset of B and B contains at least one element not in A. The fact that A is a proper subset of B can be denoted by $A \subset B$. The symbol $\not\subset$ is used to represent "is not a proper subset of." [p. 14]

Theorem 1/1 If S is a set containing n elements, where n is a nonnegative integer, and $\mathcal{S}$ is the set of subsets of S, then the number of subsets of S, denoted by $N(\mathcal{S})$, is 2^n. [p. 16]

Definition 4/1 For any two sets A and B, the *Cartesian product* of A and B, denoted by $A \times B$, is the set of all ordered pairs (a, b), where a is an element of A and b is an element of B. Symbolically, $A \times B = \{(a, b) \mid a \in A \text{ and } b \in B\}$. [p. 18]

Definition 5/1 If A and B are sets, then R is a *relation* in $A \times B$ if and only if R is a subset of $A \times B$. Symbolically, R is a relation in $A \times B$ if and only if $R \subseteq A \times B$. If A = B, then R is a relation *on* A. [p. 25]

Definition 6/1 If R is a relation in $A \times B$, then the *domain* of R is the subset of all elements $a \in A$ such that there exists an $(a, b) \in R$. Similarly, the *range* of R is the subset of all elements $b \in B$ such that there exists an $(a, b) \in R$. Symbolically, if $R \subseteq A \times B$, then the domain of R is $\{a \mid a \in A \text{ and there exists } y \in B \text{ with } (a, y) \in R\}$; the range of R is $\{b \mid b \in B \text{ and there exists } x \in A \text{ with } (x, b) \in R\}$. [p. 29]

Definition 7/1 If R is a relation in $A \times B$, then R is a *function* if and only if, for each x in the domain of R, there exists exactly one y in the range of R such that $(x, y) \in R$. [p. 33]

Definition 8/1 If F is a function containing elements (a, c) and (b, c) such that $a \neq b$, then F is *many-to-one*. [p. 34]

Definition 9/1 If F is a function and if $(a, c), (b, c) \in F$ implies that $a = b$, then F is a *one-to-one function*. [p. 35]

Definition 10/1 If A and B are sets and F is a function whose domain is $A \times A$ and whose range is included in B, then F is a *binary operation*. [p. 38]

Definition 11/1 If S is a set, $\mathbb{S}$ is the collection of subsets of S, and A and B are elements of $\mathbb{S}$, then the *union* of sets A and B is the set of elements in A *or* in B. Symbolically, the union of A and B is $A \cup B = \{x \mid x \in A \text{ or } x \in B\}$. [p. 39]

Definition 12/1 If S is a set, $\mathbb{S}$ is the collection of subsets of S, and A and B are elements of $\mathbb{S}$, then the *intersection* of A and B is the set of elements that are in both A and B. Symbolically, the intersection of A and B is $A \cap B = \{x \mid x \in A \text{ and } x \in B\}$. [p. 42]

Definition 13/1 Let A, B, and D be sets and let f be a function whose domain is a subset of A and whose range is a subset of B. Further, let g be a function whose domain includes the range of f and whose range is a subset of D. Then the *composition* of f and g, $f \circ g$, is the function defined by $(x)f \circ g = ((x)f)g$, where x is any element of A that is in the domain of f. [p. 45]

Theorem 2/1 Let A, B, and D be sets and let f be a function whose domain is included in A and whose range is included in B. Let g be a function whose domain includes the range of f and whose range is included in D. Then the domain of $f \circ g$ is the domain of f, and $f \circ g$ is a function in $A \times D$. [pp. 47-48]

Definition 14/1 Let $R = \{\frac{a}{b} \mid a, b \in I \text{ and } b \neq 0\}$ and $\frac{a}{b}, \frac{c}{d} \in R$. Then $\frac{a}{b}$ is equivalent to $\frac{c}{d}$, denoted by $\frac{a}{b} \sim \frac{c}{d}$ if and only if $ad = bc$. [p. 50]

Theorem 3/1 If $\frac{a}{b}$, $\frac{c}{d}$, and $\frac{e}{f} \in R$, then the following properties hold:
1) $\frac{a}{b} \sim \frac{a}{b}$.
2) If $\frac{a}{b} \sim \frac{c}{d}$, then $\frac{c}{d} \sim \frac{a}{b}$.
3) If $\frac{a}{b} \sim \frac{c}{d}$ and $\frac{c}{d} \sim \frac{e}{f}$, then $\frac{a}{b} \sim \frac{e}{f}$. [p. 50]

Definition 15/1 A relation R on a set A is an equivalence relation if and only if the relation has the following properties:
1) Reflexive: For each $a \in A$, $(a, a) \in R$.
2) Symmetric: If $(a, b) \in R$, then $(b, a) \in R$.
3) Transitive: If $(a, b) \in R$ and $(b, c) \in R$, then $(a, c) \in R$. [p. 51]

Theorem 4/1 Let A and B be sets in which equality on set B is an equivalence relation and let f be a function from A into B. Let R be the relation defined by $(x_1, x_2) \in R$ if and only if $(x_1)f = (x_2)f$. Then the relation R is an equivalence relation. [p. 52]

Definition 16/1 Let $a, b \in I$ and let $a = qn + r$, $b = q_1n + r_1$, with $0 \leqq r < n$ and $0 \leqq r_1 < n$, with $n, q, q_1, r, r_1 \in I$, and with $n > 0$. Then a relation R_n in $I \times I$ is defined in the following way: $(a, b) \in R_n$ if and only if $r = r_1$. If $(a, b) \in R_n$, then we say that a is *congruent* to b modulo n. Symbolically, $a \equiv b \bmod n$ if and only if $(a, b) \in R_n$. [p. 55]

Theorem 5/1 The relation "congruent modulo n" on the set of integers, denoted by R_n, is an equivalence relation. [p. 56]

Theorem 6/1 Let S be a set and R an equivalence relation on S. Let S_a denote the set of elements of S that are related to a; that is, let $S_a = \{x \mid x \in S \text{ and } (a, x) \in R\}$. Then the set $\mathcal{P}$ of subsets S_a, where $a \in S$, is called a *partition* of S and has the following properties:
1) Any pair of distinct subsets in $\mathcal{P}$ are disjoint.
2) The union of the subsets in $\mathcal{P}$ is S. [p. 57]

Theorem 7/1 Let $\mathcal{P}$ be a collection of subsets of S such that any two distinct subsets in $\mathcal{P}$ are disjoint and the union of the subsets in $\mathcal{P}$ is S. Let a relation R on S be defined by $(a, b) \in R$ if and only if a and b are in the same subset of $\mathcal{P}$. Then R is an equivalence relation on S. [pp. 57-58]

Definition 17/2 Let f be a function whose domain is $A \times A$ and whose range is set B. Then f is said to be *closed* if and only if set B is included in set A. Symbolically, the operation $A \times A \xrightarrow{f} B$ is closed if and only if $B \subseteq A$. [p. 62]

Theorem 8/2 The set of even counting numbers E_C is closed under addition. [p. 63]

Theorem 9/2 The set of odd counting numbers O_C is closed under multiplication. [p. 63]

Definition 18/2 The set of even integers E_I extended by $\sqrt{2}$, designated by $E_I(\sqrt{2})$, is the subset of all real numbers of the form $a + b\sqrt{2}$, where $a, b \in E_I$. Symbolically, $E_I(\sqrt{2}) = \{a + b\sqrt{2} \mid a, b \in E_I\}$. [p. 63]

Theorem 10/2 The set $E_I(\sqrt{2})$ is closed under the operation of addition. [p. 64]

Definition 19/2 The set of integers extended by i, denoted by $G(i)$, is the set of all complex numbers of the form $a + bi$, where $a, b \in I$ and $i^2 = -1$. Symbolically, $G(i) = \{a + bi \mid a, b \in I \text{ and } i^2 = -1\}$. [p. 65]

Theorem 11/2 The set $G(i)$ is closed under the operation of addition. [p. 65]

Theorem 12/2 The set $G(i)$ is closed under the operation of multiplication. [p. 66]

Definition 20/2 Let I/n denote the set of equivalence classes of the integers modulo n, with $n \in I$ and $n > 0$; that is, let $I/n = \{\bar{0}, \bar{1}, \ldots, \overline{n-1}\}$. If $\bar{a}, \bar{b} \in I/n$, with $0 \leqq a < n$ and $0 \leqq b < n$, then the *sum* of $\bar{a}$ and $\bar{b}$, denoted by $\bar{a} \oplus_n \bar{b}$, is $\bar{r}$, where $a + b = qn + r$, $0 \leqq r < n$, and $q, r \in I$. [p. 66]

Theorem 13/2 The set of integers modulo n, I/n, is closed under the operation of modular addition. [p. 67]

Definition 21/2 Let I/n denote the set of equivalence classes of the integers modulo n, with $n \in I$ and $n > 0$; that is, let $I/n = \{\bar{0}, \bar{1}, \bar{2}, \ldots, \overline{n-1}\}$. If $\bar{a}, \bar{b} \in I/n$, with $0 \leqq a < n$ and $0 \leqq b < n$, then the *product* of $\bar{a}$ and $\bar{b}$, denoted by $\bar{a} \odot_n \bar{b}$, is $\bar{r}$, where $a \cdot b = qn + r$, $0 \leqq r < n$, and $q, r \in I$. [p. 67]

Theorem 14/2 The set I/n is closed under modular multiplication. [p. 68]

Definition 22/2 If ☆ is a closed binary operation from $S \times S$, then ☆ is *associative* if and only if, for each $x, y, z \in S$, $(x ☆ y) ☆ z = x ☆ (y ☆ z)$. [p. 72]

Definition 23/2 Let f and g be functions with the same domain A and with ranges included in a set B. Then $f = g$ if and only if, for each $x \in A$, $(x)f = (x)g$. [p. 73]

Theorem 15/2 Let A be a set of elements and let $\mathcal{F}$ be the set of functions with domain A and range a subset of A. Then set $\mathcal{F}$ under the operation of composition, denoted by $\circ$, is associative. In function notation, $(f \circ g) \circ h = f \circ (g \circ h)$, for all functions $f, g, h \in \mathcal{F}$. [p. 73]

Definition 24/2 If S is a set and ☆ is a closed binary operation on S that satisfies the associative property, then the system (S, ☆) is a *semi-group*. [p. 74]

Definition 25/2 If C is the set of counting numbers, then for each $a, b \in C$, operation ☆ is defined as $a ☆ b = a + b + ab$. [p. 74]

Theorem 16/2 If $a, b \in C$ and the operation ☆ is defined as $a ☆ b = a + b + ab$, then (C, ☆) is a semi-group. [p. 74]

Theorem 17/2 The system $(I/n, \oplus_n)$ is a semi-group. [p. 75]

Definition 26/2 If (S, ☆) is a semi-group, then (S, ☆) is a *semi-group with identity* if and only if there exists an element $e \in S$ such that $e ☆ a = a ☆ e = a$ for each $a \in S$. [p. 78]

Theorem 18/2 If S is a set and $\mathbb{S}$ is the set of subsets of S, then the system $(\mathbb{S}, \cup)$ is a semi-group with identity. [p. 78]

Theorem 19/2 If S is a set and $\mathbb{S}$ is the set of subsets of S, then the system $(\mathbb{S}, \cap)$ is a semi-group with identity. [p. 78]

Theorem 20/2 Let multiplication modulo n, denoted by $\odot_n$, on the set $I/n = \{\bar{0}, \bar{1}, \bar{2}, \ldots, \overline{n-1}\}$ be defined by $\bar{a} \odot_n \bar{b} = \bar{r}$, with $a \cdot b = qn + r$, $0 \leqq r < n$, $0 \leqq a < n$, and $0 \leqq b < n$. Then the system $(I/n, \odot_n)$ is a semi-group with identity. [p. 79]

Definition 27/2 The element e_l of a semi-group (S, ☆) is a *left identity* if and only if, for each $a \in S$, $e_l ☆ a = a$. The element e_r of a semi-group (S, ☆) is a *right identity* if and only if, for each $a \in S$, $a ☆ e_r = a$. [p. 80]

Definition 28/2 Let (S, ☆) be a semi-group with an identity element denoted by e. Then the system (S, ☆) has an *inverse property* if and only if, for each $a \in S$, there exists an element of S, denoted by a', such that $a' ☆ a = a ☆ a' = e$. The element a' is an inverse of a and a is an inverse of a'. [p. 83]

Theorem 21/2 The semi-group $(\mathbb{S}, \cup)$, consisting of the set of all subsets $\mathbb{S}$ of a nonempty set S under the operation of union, does not satisfy the inverse property. [p. 84]

Theorem 22/2 The semi-group $(\mathbb{S}, \cap)$, consisting of the set of all subsets $\mathbb{S}$ of a nonempty set S under the operation of intersection, does not satisfy the inverse property. [p. 84]

Theorem 23/2 The system of integers modulo n under the operation $\oplus_n$, $(I/n, \oplus_n)$, is a semi-group with identity that satisfies the inverse property. [p. 84]

Definition 29/2 Let G be a nonempty set and let ☆ be a binary operation with domain G × G. Then the mathematical system (G, ☆) is a *group* if and only if the following four properties are satisfied:

Closure 1 For each $a, b \in G$, $a ☆ b \in G$.

Associative 2 For each $a, b, c \in G$, $(a ☆ b) ☆ c = a ☆ (b ☆ c)$.

Identity 3 There exists an element $e \in G$ such that, for each $a \in G$, $e ☆ a = a ☆ e = a$.

Inverse 4 For each $a \in G$, there exists an element $a' \in G$ such that $a' ☆ a = a ☆ a' = e$. [p. 88]

Theorem 24/2 If (G, ☆) is a group, with $a, b \in G$, then there exist unique elements $x, y \in G$ such that

1) $a ☆ x = b$, and

2) $y ☆ a = b$.

Furthermore, if a' is an inverse of a, then $x = a' ☆ b$ and $y = b ☆ a'$. [p. 92]

Theorem 25/2 If (G, ☆) is a group, with $a, b \in$ G, and a' and b' are inverses of the elements a and b, respectively, then an inverse of $a \star b$ is $b' \star a'$. Symbolically, $(a \star b)' = b' \star a'$. [p. 93]

Theorem 26/2 If $S_n = \{1, 2, \ldots, n\}$, G_n is the set of all permutations from S_n onto S_n, and ∘ is the operation of composition of functions in G_n, then the mathematical system $(G_n, \circ)$ is a group. [p. 102]

Definition 30/2 If $S_n = \{1, 2, \ldots, n\}$ and if G_n is the set of all permutations from S_n onto S_n, with ∘ the operation of composition of permutations, then the group $(G_n, \circ)$ is the *symmetric group on* S_n. [p. 104]

Definition 31/2 If $(G_n, \circ)$ is a symmetric group and T is a subset of G_n such that (T, ∘) is a group, then (T, ∘) is a *permutation group.* [p. 104]

Definition 32/2 If (G, ☆) is a group, then (G, ☆) is a *commutative group* if and only if, for each $a, b \in$ G, $a \star b = b \star a$. [p. 111]

Theorem 27/2 If S_n is the set $\{1, 2, \ldots, n\}$ with $n \geqq 3$, and G_n is the set of all permutations on S_n, then the symmetric group $(G_n, \circ)$ is noncommutative. [p. 112]

Definition 33/2 If S is a nonempty subset of G, then (S, ☆) is a *subgroup* of (G, ☆) if and only if (S, ☆) is a group. The subgroups (G, ☆) and ($\{e\}$, ☆) are called *trivial subgroups* of (G, ☆). [p. 119]

Theorem 28/2 If S is a nonempty subset of G and the identity of (G, ☆) is e, then (S, ☆) is a subgroup of (G, ☆) if it has the following two properties:
1) *Closure:* For each $a, b \in$ S, $a \star b \in$ S.
2) *Inverse:* For each $a \in$ S, there exists an $a' \in$ S such that $a' \star a = a \star a' = e$.
[p. 119]

Theorem 29/2 If $I_{nx} = \{nx \mid n \in C \text{ and } x \in I\} = \{\ldots, -2n, -n, 0, n, 2n, \ldots\}$, then I_{nx} under the operation of addition is a subgroup of the integers under addition. Symbolically, $(I_{nx}, +)$ is a subgroup of (I, +). [p. 120]

Theorem 30/2 If (S, +) is a nontrivial subgroup of the integers under addition, then there exists a counting number n such that S is the set of all integral multiples of n, I_{nx}. [p. 121]

Theorem 31/2 If (H, ☆) and (K, ☆) are subgroups of (G, ☆), then (H ∩ K, ☆) is a subgroup of (G, ☆). [p. 125]

Theorem 32/2 If $\mathbb{S}$ is a set of subgroups of (G, ☆), then the intersection of the elements of $\mathbb{S}$ under the operation ☆ is a subgroup of (G, ☆). [p. 126]

Definition 34/2 If a and b are counting numbers and the multiples of a and b are denoted by $M_a = \{a, 2a, 3a, 4a, \ldots\}$ and $M_b = \{b, 2b, 3b, 4b, \ldots\}$, then the *least common multiple* of a and b is the least member of $M_a \cap M_b$, which is the set of all common multiples of a and b. The least common multiple of a and b will be denoted by l.c.m. (a, b) or by $[a, b]$. [p. 127]

Theorem 33/2 If $(I_{ax}, +)$ and $(I_{bx}, +)$ are subgroups of (I, +), then their intersection is the subgroup determined by the least common multiple of the counting numbers a and b. In symbols, $I_{ax} \cap I_{bx} = I_{[a,b]x}$. [p. 127]

Definition 35/2 If (G, ☆) is a group, n is an integer greater than or equal to 0, e is the identity of (G, ☆), and $a \in G$, then the product of n and a is as follows:
1) $n \cdot a = e$, for $n = 0$; that is, $0 \cdot a = e$.
2) $n \cdot a = a$, for $n = 1$; that is, $1 \cdot a = a$.
3) $(n + 1) \cdot a = (n \cdot a) ☆ a$, for $n \geqq 1$.
The group elements e, a, and $(n \cdot a) ☆ a$ are called the *products* of 0 and a, of 1 and a, and of $(n + 1)$ and a, respectively. [p. 133]

Definition 36/2 If (G, ☆) is a group, $a \in G$, a' is the inverse of a, and n is a positive integer, then $-n \cdot a = n \cdot a'$. [p. 134]

Theorem 34/2 If (G, ☆) is a group, n is a negative integer, and a' is the inverse of $a \in G$, then $n \cdot a' = -n \cdot a$. [p. 135]

Theorem 35/2 If (G, ☆) is a group, $a \in G$, and $n = -1$, then $(n + 1) \cdot a = (n \cdot a) ☆ a$. [p. 135]

Theorem 36/2 If (G, ☆) is a group, $a \in G$, $n \in I$, and $n < -1$, then $(n + 1) \cdot a = (n \cdot a) ☆ a$. [p. 135]

Theorem 37/2 If (G, ☆) is a group, $a \in G$, and m and n are integers, then $(m + n) \cdot a = (m \cdot a) ☆ (n \cdot a)$. [p. 136]

Theorem 38/2 If (G, ☆) is a group, $a \in G$, and m and n are integers, then $(m \cdot n) \cdot a = m \cdot (n \cdot a)$. [p. 137]

Definition 37/2 If (G, ☆) is a group, then (G, ☆) is *cyclic* if and only if there exists an $a \in G$ such that, for each $b \in G$, $n \cdot a = b$ for some integer n. The element a is called a *generator* of (G, ☆). [p. 137]

Definition 38/2 If (G, ☆) and (H, ∘) are groups, then (G, ☆) is *isomorphic* to (H, ∘) if and only if there exists a one-to-one function f from G onto H that preserves the group operations. In symbols, if f represents a one-to-one function from G onto H, then (G, ☆) ≅ (H, ∘) if and only if, for each $g_1, g_2 \in G$, $(g_1 ☆ g_2)f = (g_1)f \circ (g_2)f$. [p. 143]

Theorem 39/2 Let (G, ☆) be a finite cyclic group and let a be any element of G such that a is a generator of G. Then there exists a least positive integer n such that $n \cdot a = e$ and (G, ☆) is isomorphic to the group of integers modulo n under modular addition. Symbolically, if (G, ☆) is cyclic with generator a such that $n \cdot a = e$ (and n is the least such integer), then (G, ☆) ≅ $(I/n, \oplus_n)$. [p. 145]

Theorem 40/2 If (G, ☆) is an infinite cyclic group and a is a generator of the group, then (G, ☆) is isomorphic to the group of integers under addition, (I, +). [p. 147]

Theorem 41/2 If (G, ☆) and (H, ∘) are groups, with $(a, b), (c, d) \in G \times H$ and the operation △ is defined by $(a, b) \triangle (c, d) = (a ☆ c, b \circ d)$, then the system $(G \times H, \triangle)$ is a group. [p. 156]

Theorem 42/2 If (G, ☆) and (H, ∘) are groups, the operation △ in the system $(G \times H, \triangle)$ is defined as the group operation on corresponding components, and $\overline{G}$ is the set of elements $\{(g, \phi) \mid g \in G\}$ with ϕ the identity of (H, ∘), then
1) $(\overline{G}, \triangle)$ is a subgroup of $(G \times H, \triangle)$.
2) $(\overline{G}, \triangle)$ is isomorphic to (G, ☆). [p. 158]

Definition 39/2 If (G, ☆) is a group whose identity is e, $a \in G$, and there exists a positive integer n such that $n \cdot a = e$, then the least such positive integer n is the *order* of a. Symbolically, $o(a) = n$. [p. 161]

Theorem 43/2 If (G, ☆) and (H, ∘) are isomorphic under the mapping f and if $a \in G$, $b \in H$ are such that $(a)f = b$, then $o(a) = o(b)$. [p. 162]

Definition 40/3 Suppose that S is a set and that + and • are two binary operations defined on S; that is, + is a function from S × S into S and • is a function from S × S into S. Then (S, +, •) is a *ring* if and only if (S, +) is a commutative group and the following properties also hold:

Closure for • **6** For each $a, b \in S$, $a \cdot b \in S$.

Associativity for • **7** For each $a, b, c \in S$, $(a \cdot b) \cdot c = a \cdot (b \cdot c)$.

Distributive **8** For each $a, b, c \in S$,
1) $a \cdot (b + c) = (a \cdot b) + (a \cdot c)$ and
2) $(a + b) \cdot c = (a \cdot c) + (b \cdot c)$. [p. 171]

Definition 41/3 Let $M_{2 \times 2}$ be the set of all *arrays* A of the form

$$A = \begin{pmatrix} a_{11} & a_{12} \\ a_{21} & a_{22} \end{pmatrix},$$

where a_{11}, a_{12}, a_{21}, and a_{22} are real numbers. An element of the set $M_{2 \times 2}$ is a *2 × 2 real matrix*. The numbers that occur in the matrix are the *entries* of the matrix. In a 2 × 2 matrix, the real numbers a_{i1} and a_{i2} are the entries in the ith row for $i = 1, 2$; and the real numbers a_{1j} and a_{2j} are the entries in the jth column for $j = 1, 2$. [p. 173]

Definition 42/3 If A and B are elements of $M_{2 \times 2}$, then the *sum* of A and B is the 2 × 2 real matrix whose entry in the ijth position is the sum of the entries in the ijth position of A and in the ijth position of B. That is, if $A = \begin{pmatrix} a_{11} & a_{12} \\ a_{21} & a_{22} \end{pmatrix}$ and $B = \begin{pmatrix} b_{11} & b_{12} \\ b_{21} & b_{22} \end{pmatrix}$, then

$$A + B = \begin{pmatrix} a_{11} & a_{12} \\ a_{21} & a_{22} \end{pmatrix} + \begin{pmatrix} b_{11} & b_{12} \\ b_{21} & b_{22} \end{pmatrix} = \begin{pmatrix} a_{11} + b_{11} & a_{12} + b_{12} \\ a_{21} + b_{21} & a_{22} + b_{22} \end{pmatrix}.$$

[p. 174]

Definition 43/3 If $A = \begin{pmatrix} a_{11} & a_{12} \\ a_{21} & a_{22} \end{pmatrix}$ and $B = \begin{pmatrix} b_{11} & b_{12} \\ b_{21} & b_{22} \end{pmatrix}$ are 2 × 2 real matrices, then the *product* of A and B, denoted by A • B, is as follows:

$$A \cdot B = \begin{pmatrix} a_{11} & a_{12} \\ a_{21} & a_{22} \end{pmatrix} \cdot \begin{pmatrix} b_{11} & b_{12} \\ b_{21} & b_{22} \end{pmatrix} = \begin{pmatrix} a_{11}b_{11} + a_{12}b_{21} & a_{11}b_{12} + a_{12}b_{22} \\ a_{21}b_{11} + a_{22}b_{21} & a_{21}b_{12} + a_{22}b_{22} \end{pmatrix}.$$

[p. 175]

Definition 44/3 If A is a 2 × 2 real matrix, then A is a 2 × 2 *even matrix* if and only if each entry of A is an even integer. We denote the set of 2 × 2 even matrices by $E_{2 \times 2}$. Symbolically, if $A \in M_{2 \times 2}$, then $A \in E_{2 \times 2}$ if and only if each entry a_{ij} in A is an element of E_I for each $i = 1, 2$ and each $j = 1, 2$. [p. 176]

Theorem 44/3 The mathematical system ($E_{2 \times 2}$, +, •) is a ring. [p. 176]

Definition 45/3 If (S, +, •) is a ring, then S is a *ring with identity* if and only if there exists an element e in S such that, for each $a \in S$,

Identity for • **9** $e \cdot a = a \cdot e = a$. [p. 181]

Definition 46/3 If (S, +, •) is a ring, then S is a *commutative ring* if and only if, for each $a, b \in S$,

Commutativity for • 10 $a \cdot b = b \cdot a$. [p. 182]

Definition 47/3 If (T, +, •) and (S, ⊕, ⊙) are rings, then (T, +, •) and (S, ⊕, ⊙) are *isomorphic* if and only if there exists a one-to-one function f from set T onto set S such that, for each $a, b \in T$,
1) $(a + b)f = (a)f \oplus (b)f$ and
2) $(a \cdot b)f = (a)f \odot (b)f$. [p. 187]

Theorem 45/3 If (S, +, •) is a ring whose additive identity is denoted by 0, then, for each $a \in S$, $a \cdot 0 = 0 = 0 \cdot a$. [p. 189]

Theorem 46/3 If (S, +, •) is a ring and $a_1, a_2, b_1, b_2 \in S$, then

$$(a_1 + a_2) \cdot (b_1 + b_2) = (a_1b_1 + a_1b_2) + (a_2b_1 + a_2b_2).$$ [p. 190]

Definition 48/3 If (S, +, •) is a ring and $a, b \in S$, then the *difference* of a and b, denoted by $a - b$, is the sum of a and the additive inverse of b. Symbolically, for each $a, b \in S$, $a - b = a + (-b)$. [p. 190]

Theorem 47/3 If (S, +, •) is a ring and $a, b \in S$, then
1) $(-a)b = -(ab)$,
2) $a(-b) = -(ab)$,
3) $(-a)b = a(-b)$. [p. 190]

Theorem 48/3 If (S, +, •) is a ring and x and y are elements of S whose additive inverses are $-x$ and $-y$, respectively, then $(-x)(-y) = xy$. [p. 191]

Definition 49/3 If (S, +, •) is a ring with additive identity 0, $a \in S$, and n is a nonnegative integer, then the product of n and a is as follows:
1) $n \cdot a = 0$, for $n = 0$; that is, $0 \cdot a = 0$.
2) $n \cdot a = a$, for $n = 1$; that is, $1 \cdot a = a$.
3) $(n + 1) \cdot a = (n \cdot a) + a$, for $n \geqq 1$. [p. 191]

Definition 50/3 If (S, +, •) is a ring and T is a nonempty subset of S, then the system (T, +, •) is a *subring* of (S, +, •) if and only if (T, +, •) is a ring. If (T, +, •) is a subring of (S, +, •), then (S, +, •) is the *containing ring*. [p. 193]

Theorem 49/3 If (S, +, •) is a ring and T is a nonempty subset of S, then (T, +, •) is a subring of (S, +, •) if and only if, for each $a, b \in T$,
1) the difference $a - b \in T$, and
2) the product $ab \in T$. [p. 193]

Theorem 50/3 If (I, +, •) is the ring of integers and S is a subset of I, then the subsystem (S, +, •) is a subring of (I, +, •) if and only if there exists a positive integer n such that $S = \{nx \mid x \in I\}$. [p. 196]

Definition 51/3 Let (S, +, •) be a ring and let T be a nonempty subset of S. Then the system (T, +, •) is an *ideal* of (S, +, •) if and only if for each $a, b \in T$ and for each $s \in S$, each of the following is true:
1) the difference $a - b \in T$,
2) the product $s \cdot a \in T$, and
3) the product $a \cdot s \in T$. [p. 198]

Theorem 51/3 The subring (I, +, •) is not an ideal of the ring (R, +, •). [p. 200]

Definition 52/3 Let $(T, +, \cdot)$ and $(S, \oplus, \odot)$ be rings and let f be a function from T onto S. Then f is a *homomorphism* from T onto S if and only if, for each $t_1, t_2 \in T$,
1) $(t_1 + t_2)f = (t_1)f \oplus (t_2)f$ and
2) $(t_1 \cdot t_2)f = (t_1)f \odot (t_2)f$. [p. 205]

Theorem 52/3 If $(T, +, \cdot)$ and $(S, \oplus, \odot)$ are rings with additive identities 0_T and 0_S, respectively, and if f is a homomorphism from T onto S, then $(0_T)f = 0_S$. [p. 205]

Theorem 53/3 Let $(T, +, \cdot)$ and $(S, \oplus, \odot)$ be rings, and let f be a homomorphism from T onto S. If $t \in T$ and if $-t$ denotes the additive inverse of t, then the image of the additive inverse is the additive inverse of the image. That is, $(-t)f = -\big((t)f\big)$. [p. 206]

Theorem 54/3 Let $(T, +, \cdot)$ and $(S, \oplus, \odot)$ be rings; let f be a homomorphism from T onto S; and let K be $\{t \mid t \in T \text{ and } (t)f = 0_S\}$, where 0_S is the additive identity of the ring S. Then the system $(K, +, \cdot)$ is an ideal of $(T, +, \cdot)$. [p. 206]

Definition 53/3 If $(S, +, \cdot)$ is a commutative ring with identity and $S[x]$ denotes the set of all expressions of the form

$$a_0x^0 + a_1x^1 + a_2x^2 + \ldots + a_nx^n$$

where $a_0, a_1, a_2, \ldots, a_n \in S$, and n is a nonnegative integer, then the elements of $S[x]$ are *polynomials* in x. [p. 208]

Definition 54/3 Let $S[x]$ be the set of all polynomials with coefficients in $(S, +, \cdot)$, a commutative ring with identity. If

$$f(x) = a_0 + a_1x + a_2x^2 + \ldots + a_nx^n$$

and

$$g(x) = b_0 + b_1x + b_2x^2 + \ldots + b_mx^m$$

are polynomials in the set $S[x]$, where $m \geqq n$, then the *sum* of $f(x)$ and $g(x)$ is as follows:

$$f(x) + g(x) = (a_0 + b_0) + (a_1 + b_1)x + (a_2 + b_2)x^2 + \ldots + (a_n + b_n)x^n + b_{n+1}x^{n+1} + \ldots + b_mx^m.$$

The *product* of the polynomials $f(x)$ and $g(x)$ is as follows:

$$f(x) \cdot g(x) = (a_0b_0) + (a_1b_0 + a_0b_1)x + (a_2b_0 + a_1b_1 + a_0b_2)x^2 + \ldots + (a_ib_0 + a_{i-1}b_1 + \ldots + a_0b_i)x^i + \ldots + (a_nb_0 + \ldots + a_0b_n)x^n + \ldots + (a_nb_m)x^{n+m}.$$ [p. 209]

Theorem 55/3 If $(S, +, \cdot)$ is a commutative ring with identity and $S[x]$ is the set of all polynomials in x with coefficients in the ring S, then $(S[x], +, \cdot)$ is a commutative ring with identity. [p. 211]

Definition 55/3 If $(S, +, \cdot)$ is a commutative ring with identity and $S[x]$ is the set of polynomials with coefficients in S, then, for each $c \in S$, f_c is the function given by

$$p(x) \xrightarrow{f_c} p(c), \text{ or}$$
$$\big(p(x)\big)f_c = p(c)$$

for each $p(x) \in S[x]$. [p. 212]

Theorem 56/3 If $(S, +, \cdot)$ is a commutative ring with identity and f_c is the function from the ring $S[x]$ onto the ring S given by $p(x) \xrightarrow{f_c} p(c)$ for a given $c \in S$, then f_c satisfies

$$p(x) + q(x) \xrightarrow{f_c} p(c) + q(c), \text{ and}$$
$$p(x) \cdot q(x) \xrightarrow{f_c} p(c) \cdot q(c).$$ [p. 213]

Definition 56/3 If (S, +, •) is a commutative ring with identity, then (S, +, •) is an *integral domain* if and only if S contains no divisors of zero. Symbolically, (S, +, •) is an integral domain if and only if for each $x, y \in S$,

11 $x \cdot y = 0$ implies that $x = 0$ or $y = 0$. [p. 219]

Theorem 57/3 If $n \in I$, $n > 1$, then the commutative ring with identity, $(I/n, \oplus_n, \odot_n)$, is an integral domain if and only if n is prime. [p. 220]

Definition 57/3 If (S, +, •) is a commutative ring with identity, then (S, +, •) is an integral domain if and only if the multiplicative cancellation property holds. Symbolically, if $x, y, a \in S$, with $a \neq 0$, then (S, +, •) is an integral domain if and only if

11a $xa = ya$ implies that $x = y$. [p. 221]

Theorem 58/3 If (S, +, •) is a commutative ring with identity, then (S, +, •) has no zero divisors if and only if (S, +, •) has the cancellation property for multiplication. [p. 221]

Definition 58/4 Let (S, +, •) be an integral domain whose multiplicative identity is denoted by 1 and whose additive identity is denoted by 0. Then (S, +, •) is a *field* if and only if, for each $a \in S$ with $a \neq 0$, there exists an element $a^{-1} \in S$ such that

Multiplicative inverse 12 $a^{-1} \cdot a = a \cdot a^{-1} = 1$.

The element a^{-1} is the *inverse* of a; the element a is the *inverse* of a^{-1}. [pp. 230-231]

Theorem 59/4 If (S, +, •) is a commutative ring with identity that satisfies the multiplicative-inverse property, then (S, +, •) is a field. [p. 231]

Theorem 60/4 If (S, +, •) is a finite integral domain, then (S, +, •) is a field. [p. 233]

Corollary 60/4 The system $(I/n, \oplus_n, \odot_n)$ forms a field if and only if n is prime. [p. 234]

Theorem 61/4 If (S, +, •) is a field, then the additive order of all nonzero elements is the same. [p. 238]

Definition 59/4 If (S, +, •) is a field and if there exists a positive integer k such that $k \cdot a = 0$ for each nonzero element a of S, then the least such integer n is the *characteristic* of the field. If no such positive integer n exists, then the characteristic of the field is 0. [p. 239]

Theorem 62/4 If (S, +, •) is a field with a positive integral characteristic n, then n is a prime integer. [p. 239]

Definition 60/4 If (S, +, •) is a field with multiplicative identity e, then $\{n \times e \mid n \in I\}$ is the set generated by e. [p. 240]

Theorem 63/4 If (S, +, •) is a field with multiplicative identity e, then the additive subgroup generated by e is classified as follows:

1) If the characteristic of (S, +, •) is p, where p is a prime number, then the additive subgroup $(\{n \times e \mid n \in I\}, +)$ is isomorphic to the group of integers modulo p under addition.
2) If the characteristic of (S, +, •) is 0, then the additive subgroup $(\{n \times e \mid n \in I\}, +)$ is isomorphic to the group of integers under addition.

[p. 240]

Definition 61/4 If (S, +, •) is a field and $T \subseteq S$, then the mathematical system (T, +, •) is a *subfield* of (S, +, •) if and only if (T, +, •) is a field. [p. 244]

Theorem 64/4 If $(S, +, \cdot)$ is a field and T is a nonempty subset of S, then $(T, +, \cdot)$ is a subfield of $(S, +, \cdot)$ if and only if the following conditions hold:
1) For each $a, b \in T$, $a - b \in T$.
2) For each $a, b \in T$, with $b \neq 0$, $ab^{-1} \in T$. [p. 244]

Theorem 65/4 If $(S, +, \cdot)$ is a field and K is a collection of subfields of $(S, +, \cdot)$, then the intersection of all the subfields in set K is a subfield of $(S, +, \cdot)$. [p. 246]

Definition 62/4 If $(S, +, \cdot)$ is a field and if $(P, +, \cdot)$ is the subfield that is the intersection of all subfields of $(S, +, \cdot)$, then $(P, +, \cdot)$ is called the *prime subfield* of $(S, +, \cdot)$. [p. 246]

Theorem 66/4 If $(S, +, \cdot)$ is a field and has characteristic p, where p is a prime integer, then the prime subfield P of the field S is

$$(\{n \times e \mid 1 \leqq n \leqq p\}, +, \cdot).$$

This prime subfield is isomorphic to the field of integers modulo p. [p. 246]

Theorem 67/4 If $(S, +, \cdot)$ is a field whose characteristic is 0, then the prime subfield P is isomorphic to the field of rational numbers. [p. 249]

Definition 63/4 If $(S, +, \cdot)$ is a field, $(T, +, \cdot)$ is a subfield of $(S, +, \cdot)$, and $c \in S$, then the smallest subfield of S that contains both T and c, denoted by $(T(c), +, \cdot)$ is the *simple extension* of the field T by the element c. [p. 253]

Definition 64/4 If $(S, +, \cdot)$ is a field, $(T, +, \cdot)$ is a subfield of S, and $c \in S$, then c is *algebraic* over T if and only if there exists a polynomial

$$p(x) = a_0 + a_1x^1 + a_2x^2 + \ldots + a_nx^n,$$

with $a_0, a_1, a_2, \ldots, a_n \in T$ such that

$$p(c) = a_0 + a_1c^1 + a_2c^2 + \ldots + a_nc^n = 0.$$

If no such polynomial exists, the element c is called *nonalgebraic* (or *transcendental*) over T. [p. 254]

Theorem 68/4 The simple, proper extension $(R(\sqrt{3}), +, \cdot)$ of $(R, +, \cdot)$ by $\sqrt{3}$ is the subfield $(\{a + b\sqrt{3} \mid a, b \in R\}, +, \cdot)$. [p. 255]

Theorem 69/4 If $(S, +, \cdot)$ is a field and if $(T, +, \cdot)$ is a subfield of S with $c \in S$ such that c is algebraic over T, then the simple field extension $T(c)$ consists of all polynomial expressions of the form

$$a_0 + a_1c^1 + a_2c^2 + \ldots + a_nc^n,$$

with $a_0, a_1, a_2, \ldots, a_n \in T$. [p. 256]

Theorem 70/4 Suppose that $(S, +, \cdot)$ is a field, that $(T, +, \cdot)$ is a subfield of S, and that $d \in S$ such that d is transcendental over the field T. Then the simple transcendental extension, denoted by $T(d)$, consists of the field of all rational expressions

$$\frac{a_0 + a_1d^1 + \ldots + a_nd^n}{b_0 + b_1d^1 + \ldots + b_md^m}$$

with $a_0, a_1, \ldots, a_n \in T$ and $b_0, b_1, \ldots, b_m \in T$. [p. 256]

Index

Definitions are indicated by boldface numerals.

Absolute value, 26, 31
Addition
associative property, 71, 72
closure under, 63-67, 177
of counting numbers, 36, 38, 71, 72
of even counting numbers, 63
functions that preserve, 202-203
of Gaussian integers, 65
of integers extended by real or complex number, 64, 65
of integers modulo n, **66**-67, 69-**70**, 75-76, 84-85, 86-87
of inverses, 244, 245
of odd counting numbers, 61
of polynomials, **209**-210
of 2 × 2 matrices, 174, 177-178
Additive identity, 87
of even matrices, 177-178
of field, 230
of homomorphisms of rings, 205, 206
of rings, 177, 182, 189
of subring, 194
Additive inverse
of even matrix, 178
of field, 232
of group, 87
of homomorphism, 206
of ring, 172, 182
of subgroup, 120
for subtraction in ring, 190
Additive order of elements, 236-238
in field, **238**
Additive subgroup, 240
Algebraic numbers, **254**-256
in simple extension of rational numbers, 254-256
Answers, 261-288
Arrays, matrix as element of set, 173
Associative property
of binary operations, 70-76, **72**
of composition of functions, 72-**73**
of composition of permutations, 98, 102
of field operations, 232
of group operation, 88-89, 102-103
of ring operations, 171-172, 177, 178, 182
of subring operations, 194
Automorphism, 151

Binary operations, 36-48, **38**, 71
see also individual operations
associative property, 70-76, **72**
cancellation property, 221-222, 233
closure of, 60-70, **62**
commutative property, **111**-113
distributive property, 171, 172
equivalent properties, 221
as functions, 36-48, 60-63
functions that preserve, 143-144, 147, 149, 162, 186-187, 202-207, 213-215, 240-241, 248-249
for Gaussian integers, 65-66, **228**-229
identity property, 77-81, **78**
inverse property, 82-85, **83**
notation for, 39, 42, 45, 66, 67, 68, 158
of polynomial rings, **209**-210, 213-214

Cancellation law
left, 95
right, 95
Cancellation property, for integral domains, 221-222, 233
Cartesian product(s), 18-21, 36-37, 71
commutative group constructed from, 153, 163
of groups, 151-160
as rings, 187
Cartesian sets
infinite, relation in, 25-26
number of elements in, 21
Center of group, 124
Centroid of triangle, 97
Chapter reviews, 59, 167-168, 224-225, 258-259
cumulative, 168-169, 225-226, 259-260
Characteristic of field, 236-242, **239**
of integers modulo p, 246
of prime subfield, 246, 249
of rational numbers, 247
of real numbers, 251
Class, *see* Set
Classification
of cyclic groups, 140-151
of fields, 240-241
of finite commutative groups, 140-147, 151-167
Classification theorems, 122, 145-149, 240-241
Closure, of binary operations, 60-70
Closure property, **62**-63
of composition of permutations, 98, 102
of field operations, 232, 244-245
of group operation, 86, 88-89, 102-103
of ring operations, 171-172, 177-178, 182, 206
of subfield operations, 244, 245, 247
of subgroup operation, 118-119, 120, 125, 129
of subring operations, 193, 194, 196
Coefficients of polynomials, 208, 209
Gaussian integers as, 216
ith term of product, 210
rational, 229
Collection, *see* Set
Commutative group(s), **111**-117
center of, 124
classification theorems, 122
constructed from Cartesian products, 153, 163
finite, construction of, 160-164
forming rings, 171, 178
2 × 2 even matrices as, 178
Commutative property, 111
in classification of groups, 113
of field operations, 232
of group operation, 111-117, 122, 124
of ring operations, 172, 182-183, 185
of subring operations, 194
Commutative ring(s), **182**-183, 185

contained in commutative rings, 186
contained in noncommutative rings, 186, 188-189
distinguished from integral domain, 218, 219, 221
as field, **231**
with identity, 182, 185, 208-214, 218-219, 231
Complement of a set, 33-34
Complex numbers
Gaussian integers, **65**-66
subset of, 87-88
Composition of functions, 44-48, **45**
associative property of, 72-74, **73**
as closed operation, 69, 72-73
inverse property of, 85
notation for, 45
for ordered pairs of Cartesian product, 94
permutations under, 96-105, 112
Congruence, 55-56
symbol, 55
Constants, 208
Containing ring, 186, 193
Correspondence, one-to-one, *see* Isomorphism
Coset, right, **123**-124
Counting numbers
addition, 61, 63, 71
binary operations involving, 36-39
division, 61
even, 11, 38, 63
integral multiples of, as group, 120-122
least common multiple, **127**
multiplication, 63, 71
odd, 11, 38, 61
set notation, 11, 12
subtraction, 61
Cyclic groups, 131-140, **137**
classification of, 140-151
finite, 145-147
generator of, 137-138
infinite, 147-149

Definitions, 289-299
Denominator, rationalizing, 252
Disjoint sets, 57
Distributive property
of field operations, 232
of ring operations, 171, 172, 178-179, 182, 189-190
of subring operations, 194
Division
of counting numbers, 61
of integers, 37
Divisors of zero, 219
systems with, 218-220

Domain(s)
integral, *see* Integral domains
of a relation, 27-29

Element(s)
additive order of, 236-238
field, additive order of, **238**-239
field, algebraic and nonalgebraic, 254, 256
group, generator of cyclic group, 137-138
group, multiplication by integer, 132-134
identity, 77-81, 98, 102, 103
image of, 30, 45-46, 206
inverse, 82-84, 93-94
one-to-one correspondence in groups, 140, 141, 142
order of, under isomorphism, 161-162
right coset as set of, 123
ring, elementary operations on, 189-191
of a set, 10
Empty set, 12, 15
in Cartesian product, 21
as identity element, 78, 81
as intersection of equivalence classes, 57
as proper subset, 15
subset of, 15
symbols for, 12
Equality
of polynomials, 208-209
relation of, 24, 49
of sets, 11, 14
Equilateral triangle
group of motions of, 102
reflections about angle bisectors in plane, 100, 101
rotations in a plane, 97, 99, 101
Equivalence classes
integers modulo *n*, 56-58, 66-67, 69-70, 145
integers modulo *p*, 241
integers modulo 3, 203
Equivalence relation, 49-53
integers modulo *n* as, 54-58
of 2 × 2 matrix, 173
Equivalent to, symbol, 50
Even integers
extension of, **63**-65
notation for, 12
ring of, 172, 176-179, 183, 184
ring of 2 × 2 matrices, as ideal, 199
as subgroup, 118, 120
as subring, 194
2 × 2 matrices, as subring, 195

Even matrices (2 × 2), 176-179, 184
zero divisors of, 218-219
Exponential notation, 133-134

Field(s), **231**
additive order of elements, **238**-239
characteristic of, 236-242, **239**, 246, 247, 251
finite, 233-234
integers modulo *n* as, 234
intermediate, 251-253
properties, 227-235
simple extensions, 251-258, **253**
subgroup generated by multiplicative identity, **240**-241
4-tuple, ordered, 164
Full cycle, of symmetric group, 110
Function(s), 31-35
binary operations as, 36-48, 60-63
closed, binary operation as, **62**-63
identity, 47
many-to-one, 34-35, 203, 205, 213
many-to-one, preserving operations, 202-207, **205**, 213-215
notations for, 33
one-to-one, 34-**35**, **144**
one-to-one, permutation as, **97**
one-to-one, preserving operations, 143-144, 147, 149, 162, 186-187, 240-241, 248-249
onto, 149, 172, 212-213
real-valued, 46
relation as, 32-34

Gauss, C. F., 65
Gaussian integers, **65**-66
as coefficients in polynomial ring, 216-217
Generator
of additive subgroup of field, 240-241
of cyclic group, 137-138
Group(s), 70, **88**, **95**
Cartesian product of, 151-160
center of, 124
classification of, 122, 140-147, 151-167
commutative, **111**-117, 122, 160-164, 171, 178
construction of, 152-158, 160-164
cyclic, 131-140, **137**, 140-151

Groups (*continued*)
independence of properties of, 91
isomorphic, 143-145, 151, 154, 163, 187
of motions of equilateral triangle, 102
of motions of a square, 108
noncommutative, 96-103, 111, 112-113
permutation, 96-110, **104**
permutations as elements of, 98, 101-103, 111
product of elements and negative integers, 133-**134**
product of elements and nonnegative integers, 132-134, **133**
properties of, 86-96, **88**, 102-103
subgroups of, 117-124, 240-241
symmetric, 96-110, **104**, 112-113

Homomorphisms, 202-208, **205**, 213-215
additive identity of, 205
additive inverse of, 206

Ideal(s), **198**-202
in homomorphisms, 206, 207
of polynomial ring, 214
subrings as, 199-200
Ideal sums, 201
Identity element
additive, 87, 177-178, 182, 189, 194, 205, 206, 230
empty set as, 78, 81
left, **80**
multiplicative, 181-183, 185, 186, 230, 240-241
right, **80**
in set of permutations under composition, 98, 102, 103
symbol for, 78
Identity function, 47
Identity property
of field operations, 230, 232
of group operation, 89-90, 102-103
of ring operations, 172, 181-183, 185, 208-216
semi-groups with, 77-81, **78**
of subfield operations, 245
of subring operations, 194
Image, 30, 45-46, 206
Indeterminate, x as, 211
Index of subgroup, **123**
Infinite cyclic groups, 147-149
Integers
even, *see* Even integers
Gaussian, **65**-66, 216-217
as group, 113-115
groups isomorphic to, 144-149
intersection of subgroups, 126-127
least positive, as field characteristic, 239
multiplication of ring elements by, 191
negative and nonnegative, 14
nontrivial subgroups, 120-122
odd, *see* Odd integers
ordered pairs of, 19
prime, as field characteristic, 239-240
product of group elements and negative, 133-**134**
product of group elements and nonnegative, 132-134, **133**
rings of, 171, 185
set notation, 11, 13-14
subgroups of, 118, 120-121
as subring of ring of rational numbers, 194, 200
subrings of, 194-196
trivial subgroups, 119
Integers modulo n, 54-58
addition, **66**-67, 69-**70**, 75-76, 84-85, 86-87
Cartesian products of, 152-158, 162-163
as commutative ring with identity, 185
equivalence classes for, 56-58, 145
as finite commutative group, 160, 163
as finite field, 234
group properties, 86-87
as integral domain, 218, 219-221
multiplication, **67**-68, **70**, 79
Integers modulo p
subfield isomorphic to, 246, 247-248
subgroup isomorphic to, 240, 241
Integral domains, 217-224, **219**
characteristic of, 239
distinguishing properties, 218-219, 221-222
finite, as fields, 233-234
with multiplicative inverses, 228-230
Integral multiples
of fixed counting number, 120-122
of fixed integer n, 196, 199
Integral multiplication of group elements, 132-137
Intermediate fields, 251-253
Intersection
of equivalence classes modulo n, 57
notation for, 42
of sets, **42**-43, 126-127
of subfields, as subfield, 246, 253, 255
of subgroups, 124-128
Invariant property, 162
Inverse element(s)
additive, 87, 178, 182, 206, 232
under group operation, 93-94
of homomorphism, 206
multiplicative, 88, 245
Inverse property, 82-85, **83**
of field operations, 228-233, **230**, 251-252
of group operation, 90-91, 102, 103-104
of group of permutations, 98, 102
of integral domain operations, 233-234
of ring operations, 172, 182, 190
of subfield operations, 244-245, 247-248
of subgroup, 119, 120, 125-126, 129
of subring operations, 194
Irrational numbers
algebraic, **254**-256
transcendental, **254**-256
Isomorphism
of additive subgroup, 240-241
of group onto itself, 151
of groups, 143-145, 152, 187
of groups constructed from Cartesian products, 154, 156, 163
notation, 143, 144
order of elements in, 161-162
of prime subfields, 246, 248-249
of rings, 186-**187**, 202

Least common multiple, **127**
"Less than" relation, 22-23, 24, 50

Many-to-one functions, 34-35, 203, 205, 213
preserving operations, 202-207, **205**, 213-215
Mapping, 141, 142
see also Homomorphism, Isomorphism
many-to-one, 202
one-to-one, 99, 100, 202
onto, 145, 146, 202-206, 212
Matrices, 2 × 2, 173-179, **174**
even, 176-179, 184, 195, 199, 218
identity property, 179, 183
notation for, 173

ring of, as ideal, 199
subrings of, 195
sum of two even, 177-178
Members of a set, 10
Modular addition, **66**-67, 69-**70**, 75-76, 84-85, 86-87
Modulus, prime
for field, 234
for integral domain, 220-221
Motions
of equilateral triangle, 102
of a square, 108
Multiplication
cancellation property, 221-222, 233
of counting numbers, 36-37, 38, 63, 71
functions that preserve, 202, 204
of Gaussian integers, 65-66, **228**-229
of group elements by negative integers, 133-134
of group elements by nonnegative integers, 132-134
of integers modulo *n*, **67**-68, **70**
integral, of group elements, 132-137
by inverses, 244-245
modular, **67**-68, **70**
of polynomials, **209**-210
of 2 × 2 matrices, 174-176
Multiplicative identity
of fields, 230, 240-241
generating subgroup of field, **240**-241
of rings, 181-183, 185
rings without, contained in rings with, 186
Multiplicative inverse, 88
of field, 229-233, 251-252
of integral domains, 233-234
of subfields, 244-245, 247-248

Nonalgebraic numbers, **254**
Noncommutative groups, 111, 112-113
Noncommutative ring with identity, 215-216
Nontrivial subgroups, 120-121
Normal subgroups, 124
Null set, *see* Empty set
Numbers, *see* Complex numbers, Counting numbers, Integers, Rational numbers, Real numbers, etc.

Odd integers
under addition, 118
notation for, 12
as subsystem, 194
One-to-one correspondence, 140-142
see also Isomorphism
preserving operation of group, 141-**143**
One-to-one function, 34-36, 44, **144**
preserving group operations, 143-144, 147, 149
Order
additive, of elements, 236-238
of elements under isomorphism, 161-162
of exponents in polynomial, 209
Ordered 4-tuples, finite commutative group constructed from, 164
Ordered pairs, 18-21
components of, 18
equality of, 89
of integers modulo *n*, 152-153, 155, 162-163
and points in the plane, 18-19
Ordered triples, finite commutative group constructed from, 161, 163

Partition, 57
Permutation(s), 44-45
composition of, 97-98, 99-105
as elements of group, 98, 101-103, 111
full cycle of, 110
identity element for, 103
notation for, 98-99
Permutation groups, 96-110, **104**
isomorphisms of, 150
of motions of a square, 108
noncommutativity in, 112-113
of rotations of square, 104-108
of rotations of triangle, 97
Plane
coordinate axes determining, 18-19
real, 18, 25
Polynomial(s), **208**
coefficients of, 208, 209, 210, 216, 229
constant, 209, 213, 229-230
equality of, 208-209
as integral domain, 229
notation for, 208
as simple field extensions, 254, 256
zeros of, 211
Polynomial ring(s), 208-217
ideal of, 214
as integral domain, 223
noncommutative, with identity, 215
Powers of group elements, 133
Prime integer, as characteristic of field, 239-240
Prime modulus
for field, 234
for integral domain, 220-221
Prime subfield, 244, **246**-249
Product(s)
Cartesian, 18-21, 36-37, 151-160, 162-163, 187
of group element and negative integer, 133-**134**
of group element and nonnegative integer, 132-134, **133**
of matrices, 174-176, 199
of polynomials, **209**-210
relations between, in rings, 190
of two negative real numbers, 191
Properties, *see also* specific properties
cancellation, 221-222, 233
characteristic, 236-242, **239**, 246, 247, 251
divisors of zero, 218-219
of a field, 227-235
of a group, 86-96, **88**, 102-103
of integral domains, 218-219, 221-222
of integral multiplication, 136-137
invariant, 162
isomorphic, 152
necessary for a subgroup, 118-119
of rings, 171-172, 177-179, 181-185, 211
of subfields, 244-245, 246-248
of subrings, 193-194, 196
well-ordering, 121

Quotient, of ordered pair, 37

Range of a relation, 27-30
Rational numbers
intermediate field of, 251-253
polynomials over the, 209
prime subfield isomorphic to field of, 249, 251
set of, 14
set notation, 14
as simple algebraic extension of field, 254-256
as simple extension of field, 254
subring of ring of, 194, 200
Rationalizing denominator, 252
Real numbers
algebraic, 254-256
ordered pairs of, and points in the plane, 18-19
product of two negative, 191

Real numbers (*continued*)
rational numbers as prime subfield of, 251
set of, 14
set notation, 14
subsets forming rings, 171-172, 185
subsystems of, 111
transcendental, 254-256
Reflections in a plane
of square, 106-107
of triangle, 100
Reflexive property, 50-52
of congruence modulo *n*, 56
Relation, **25**
of congruence modulo *n*, 55-56
domain of, 27-29
of equality, 24, 49
equivalence, 49-53
function as, 32-34
in infinite Cartesian sets, 25-26
of "less than," 22-23
of "less than or equal to," 24, 50
notation for, 22
range of, 27-30
single-valuedness of, 33-34, 37, 148, 149
using concept of absolute value, 26
Right coset of subgroup, **123**-124
Ring(s), 170-181, **171**
commutative, **182**-183, 185
commutative, contained in commutative rings, 186
commutative, contained in noncommutative rings, 186, 188-189
commutative, with identity, 181-**182**, 185, 208-215, 218-219, 231
containing, of subring, 193
as field, 231
ideal of, **198**-202, 214
with identity, **181**-185, 208-215
as integral domain, 217-224
isomorphism for, 186-**187**, 202
noncommutative, with identity, 215-216
polynomial, 208-217
properties of, 171-172, 181-185, 189-192
subsystems of, 192-198
Rotations
of square, 104-105, 106
of triangle, 97, 106

Semi-groups, **74**-85
with identity, 77-81, **78**, 83-85
with inverse, 82-85, **83**
left and right identities, **80**
Set(s)
Cartesian, 18-21, 25-26
complement of, 33-34
empty, 12, 15, 21, 57, 78, 81
equality of, 11, 14
finite, 12
forming rings, 171-181
infinite, 12
intersection of, **42**-43, 126-127
notation, 10-13, 14
number of subsets of, 15-17
pairwise disjoint, 57
partition of, 57
right coset, 123
standard description of, 11, 40
subsets of, 13-17
tabulation of, 10-11
union of, 39-41
Simple extensions of fields, 251-256, **253**
Single-valued relation, 33, 34, 37, 148, 149
Square
group of motions of, 108
reflections in a plane, 106-108
rotations in a plane, 104-107
Subfields, **244**-250
intersection of, as subfield, 246, 253, 255
isomorphic, 246, 248-249
prime, 244, **246**-249
properties of, 244-245, 246-248
smallest of, 246, 249, 253, 255
trivial, 246
Subgroups, 117-124
additive, generated by multiplicative identity of field, **240**-241
index of, **123**
intersection of, 124-128
isomorphic, 154, 158, 240-241
necessary properties for, 118-119
nontrivial, 120-121
normal, 124
right coset of, **123**-124
trivial, **119**
union of, 128-129
"Subgroup-union," **131**
Subrings, 192-198, **193**
distinguished from ideals, 198-199
as ideals, 199-200
as integral domains, 223
properties of, 193-194
Subset(s), **13-14**
of algebraic and transcendental numbers, 254-256
complement of, 33-34
as domain and range of a relation, 29
of empty set, 15
improper, 15
notation, 14, 15, 33
number of, 15-17
in a partition, 57
proper, 14
of a set, 13-17, 78-79, 84
of symmetric groups, 104
Subtraction
closure under, 193, 244, 245
of counting numbers, 37, 61
Sum
ideal, 201
of matrices, 174
of ordered pair, 36
of polynomials, **209**-210
of two even matrices, 177-178
Symmetric groups, 96-110, **104**
full cycle of, 110
as noncommutative groups, 112-113
subgroups of, 104
Symmetric property, 50-52
of congruence modulo *n*, 56

Terms of polynomial, 208, 209
Theorems, 289-299
classification, 122
classifying cyclic groups, 145-149
classifying fields, 240-241
Transcendental numbers, **254**-256
in simple field extensions, 256
Transitive property, 50-52
of congruence modulo *n*, 56
Triangle, equilateral
group of motions of, 102
reflections in a plane, 100, 101
rotations in a plane, 97, 99, 101
Triples, ordered, 161, 163
Trivial subfield, 246
Trivial subgroups, **119**

Union
of equivalence classes modulo *n*, 57
notation for, 39
of sets, **39**-41
of subgroups, 128-129
"subgroup-union," **131**

Variable, *x* as, 211

Well-ordering property, 121

Zero divisors, 219
and property of field, 231
and property of integral domain, 219-220
Zeros of polynomial, 211

3 4 5 6 7 8 9 10 11 12 13 14 15 16 17 18 19 20 21 22 23 24 25 NR 75 74 73 72 71 70 69